Electron and Nuclear Counters

THEORY and USE

BY

SERGE A. KORFF, M.A., Ph.D.

Professor of Physics
College of Engineering, New York University

WITH CHAPTER ON SCINTILLATION COUNTERS BY

H. KALLMANN, Ph.D.

Professor of Physics
Washington Square College, New York University

SECOND EDITION—SECOND PRINTING

D. VAN NOSTRAND COMPANY, Inc.

PRINCETON, NEW JERSEY

TORONTO   NEW YORK   LONDON

D. VAN NOSTRAND COMPANY, INC.

120 Alexander St., Princeton, New Jersey
257 Fourth Avenue, New York 10, New York
25 Hollinger Rd., Toronto 16, Canada
Macmillan & Co., Ltd., St. Martin's St., London, W.C. 2, England

*All correspondence should be addressed to the
principal office of the company at Princeton, N. J.*

PREFACE

It is the purpose of this book to gather together and summarize the pertinent facts regarding the theory of the discharge mechanism and the practical operation of various types of counters.

In this new edition, in order to make the book more generally useful and to bring it up to date, several new sections were added. These include (a) more data on gas-discharge phenomena, (b) references to recent developments in the field of counters in general as well as new experiments on the discharge mechanism, (c) typical problems and suggested experiments for students, to make the book more useful as a text, (d) a chapter on scintillation counters, and (e) deletion of obsolete electronic circuits.

The book is written on an intermediate level for users of counters, most of whom are persons with scientific training but who do not possess specialized knowledge in the field of counters. It presupposes an acquaintance with the main concepts of atomic physics, such as ionization, recombination, radiation and diffusion, as well as some familiarity with vacuum tube circuits.

In doing work on Geiger and proportional counters, the author has often found it necessary to look up constants, data, and similar material, which at present are scattered through the literature. The collection of these data in the revised edition in a readily usable form is intended to bring within one pair of covers much more material of the type which is used in studying and constructing counters and in evaluating the measurements made with such devices. As an example, the latest neutron cross section data are shown for the guidance and interpretation of neutron counting.

Since the first edition, a great deal of work has been done by many persons in the field covered by this book. It is obviously quite impossible to give detailed consideration to each paper. Hence only brief reference is made to those which seem to the author to have added significantly to our knowledge of the subject. The bibliography has been greatly extended, and many times the original number of references will be found throughout the book. Because of the rapid development of parts of this subject, it is possible only to indicate points of departure, so that those who are interested in going thoroughly into any one phase of the subject shall have (a) some background material showing connections with other branches of the subject, and (b) a list of references from which their studies may diverge in whatever direction interests them. It is, of course, true that an entire book could be written on what is covered in one paragraph; yet such a book would be of interest only to a few specialists.

Chapter 8 on Scintillation Counters is written by one of today's leading authorities on this subject, Professor H. Kallmann. A discussion of the error in counting has been written by Professor Y. Beers as part of Chapter 6.

Finally, for use in teaching, problems and experiments have been added. Since there is today a growing tendency to have courses in "Nuclear instrumentation," it seemed worth while to include problems which had appeared in examinations in such courses and typical experiments which can be adapted to advanced laboratory courses.

SERGE A. KORFF

November 1954

ACKNOWLEDGMENT

In preparing the revised edition, the author has had many stimulating conversations with members of the Physics Department at New York University to whom he wishes to acknowledge his indebtedness. Out of these conversations grew the contributions by Professors Kallmann and Beers cited in the Preface. Also, the author served as Project Director of the Counter Research Project, sponsored by the Office of Naval Research, and in this capacity derived much stimulation from the various members of the Project. The contributions of E. Wantuch, A. Krumbein, A. Laufer, S. Kitchen, J. Heirtzler, and many others are cited in the work. The author is grateful to Professor S. S. Friedland, formerly of the Project and now at the University of Connecticut, whose cooperation enabled some of the more difficult problems connected with neutron counters to be solved. Particular thanks are due to Harold Sherman, currently of the Project, who has read proof on the entire revised edition and who has helped notably in its preparation.

Finally, the author wants to renew his expression of gratitude to those mentioned in the Acknowledgment to the first edition of this book.

CONTENTS

LIST OF SYMBOLS USED

(except as otherwise noted)

A the gas amplification

B a constant

C the electrostatic capacity, usually in microfarads

D the standard deviation

E an electric field, in volts per cm (sometimes represents the energy)

F an area in sq cm

G the efficiency

I the current, usually in amperes

L the Loschmidt number, 2.687×10^{19} molecules per cc in a gas at STP

M the mass of a proton or heavier particle

N Avogadro's number, 6.02×10^{23} atoms per gram atomic weight

Q the charge, usually in microcoulombs

R the resistance, usually in ohms

T the temperature, degrees absolute

U the volume, usually in cc

V the potential in volts

Z the atomic number

Å Ångstrom unit, 10^{-8} cm

a the slope of the curve of ionization cross section as a function of energy

c the velocity of light in vacuo

d a distance

e the charge on the electron, 4.80×10^{-10} esu or 1.60×10^{-19} coulomb (Note: where followed by an exponential, *e* is the base of natural logarithms, 2.7183 . . .)

h Planck's constant, 6.624×10^{-27} erg sec

i a flux or number crossing a sq cm per sec

k the mobility (Note: where followed by *T* it is the Boltzmann constant, 1.37×10^{-16} erg/deg)

l a length

m the mass of the electron in grams, 9.1×10^{-28} gram

n a number

p the pressure of a gas, usually in atmospheres

q the rate of production of ions per cc per sec

r a radius

t a time

v a velocity

ev electron volt (1.6×10^{-12} erg)

kev thousand electron volts

Mev   million electron volts

Bev   billion (10^9) electron volts

α the first Townsend coefficient (Note: also designates the alpha particle)

β the recombination coefficient (Note: where it appears in an energy formula, such as eq. 2–8,

it represents v/c in accordance with usual notation)

ϵ an energy

λ a wavelength

μ the atomic weight

ν a frequency

π 3.14159 . . .

ρ a density, grams per cc

σ a cross section, in sq cm

A letter or number with a bar over it designates an average value.

CHAPTER 1

INTRODUCTION

A. History

Since the early experiments of Rutherford and Geiger, made early in the century, it has been known that a useful device capable of counting individual atomic particles could be made by a combination of two electrodes in a gas. The device will detect the passage of charged particles through the volume between the electrodes and manifest this passage in the form of an electrical impulse. The apparatus will thus count the particles and is therefore called a *counter*. Counters have a wide variety of designs and uses. Almost anything can be made to count. One well known laboratory has an exhibit which consists of a fork and a spoon supported in air with a potential difference between them. This arrangement provides counting action and is a good, if somewhat extreme, illustration of the point that virtually any disposition of electrodes and gases can be used for the purpose. This situation has led to the publication of a great number of quasi-empirical papers, in which the several authors report that the particular combinations of gases and electrodes used will count. Unfortunately, these observations have generally been made in an unsystematic manner, with few controlled conditions, and are hence of little value, and sometimes quite misleading.

The problem of making counters into instruments of precision and of causing them to count quantitatively and accurately and to yield reproducible results is in no way insoluble, providing the basic factors are recognized. A great deal of work by a large number of investigators has been done on the

1

problems pertaining to the construction and operation of these devices, and many theories regarding the functioning of counters have been evolved.

As early as 1908, Rutherford and Geiger [R1] arranged a cylinder and axial wire, applied a potential, and projected particles into the cylinder. They found that "the current through the gas due to the entrance of an alpha particle into the detecting vessel was magnified . . . sufficiently to give a marked deflection to the needle of an electrometer of moderate sensibility." They had devised the first counter, making use of the additional ionization produced by collision, as the electrons produced by the alpha particle traveled toward the central wire, to give an increase in the pulse size by a factor of "several thousand." Cylindrical symmetry in the distribution of the electric field was used from the first, and shortly thereafter Geiger's [G1] point counter, which employed spherical geometry, was developed. For some time, various types of filar electrometers [G2] were used to detect the pulses. These types were superseded as the rapid development of vacuum tubes during the two decades from 1920–1940 made electronic circuits possible which were faster, easier to adjust, readily portable and capable of amplifying the pulses as well as recording them. Counters with large sensitive areas were constructed in 1928 by Geiger and Mueller [G3] and have been generally called Geiger-Mueller counters.

The observation that at certain voltages the counter would detect alpha particles only, while at higher voltages it would detect both alphas and betas, was made in the early experiments. Later developments by Geiger and Klemperer [G4] in 1928 laid the foundation for the modern technique of "proportional counting" in which the difference in the ionization produced by an alpha and a beta particle is made the basis for distinguishing between them. Thus, proportional counters have been known about as long as any counters, although they were not so designated until much later.

The next important forward step resulted in the late 1920's from the recognition of the possibility of using counters in "coincidence" and the development of the techniques for this type of operation by Bothe and Kolhörster [B1], Rossi [R2], and Tuve [T1]. Widespread use of coincidence counters in cosmic ray measurements followed almost at once. Since counters had been shown to be versatile instruments, many investigators became interested in them and several contributed notably to the understanding of the manner in which these devices operated. The main motivation of these experimenters was not a desire to study counters, but the desire to prepare better instruments for their cosmic ray researches. The discovery of coincidence counting ushered in the modern period in the use and study of counters.

B. Present Uses

At the present time, counters are widely used in various branches of research and industry. In research, such devices usually serve to detect and record the number of particles emitted in various experiments involved in the study of nuclear radiation, disintegration and transmutation. These instruments are virtually indispensable in interpreting the data obtained by cyclotrons and Van de Graaff generators in that they enable the number of particles in a given beam, or the numbers produced in a given reaction, to be determined with accuracy. Counters are also used in ascertaining whether a bombardment has given rise to a radioactive product, and to determine the nature, the intensity, and period of the resulting activity. Similarly, they may be used to establish the identity and amount of naturally radioactive material or artificially activated substances. Neutron counters can be built to detect preferentially either fast or slow neutrons, and can therefore be used to measure the intensity of a neutron source, the number of neutrons in any given experimental arrangement, or the number diffusing out, from some apparatus into the surrounding room.

In cosmic radiation, counters constitute perhaps the most important single device for studying the nature and properties of the radiation and the ionizing secondaries which these rays produce. Further, by the use of electronic circuits described in Chapter 7, it is possible to impose on two counters the condition that only discharges nearly coincident in time shall be recorded. Such coincident discharges occur when a penetrating ionizing particle passes through both counters. Thus, we may determine the direction in which particles are traveling as well as the numbers that have traversed a given thickness of matter between the counters. This technique has been highly developed in recent years. It is now possible to analyze quite complex ionizing events, and to study the behavior of the rays and the many secondary processes which attend their passage through matter.

In medicine many uses for counters have also been found. Among these one may cite the detection of minute traces of radioactive substances in biological material, either radium and its decomposition products or artificially activated substances such as are commonly used in biological tracers. These studies may investigate the amount of substance introduced by accident or by design into a biological system, the distribution of the radioactive substance, and may follow the active material through various biological changes and through the parts of the system. Also, counters may detect and measure X-ray dosages and may be used to warn the operating personnel against possible overexposures, an effect of some importance when stray or scattered radiation is present in quantity. Similarly, fast or slow neutron dosages may be measured and counters may be used to ascertain effectiveness of protective procedures.

In industry, again, many uses have developed. These include detection of industrial tracers in which artificially activated substances may be followed through complex chemical and mechanical transformations, the location of lost tubes of radium, the detection of minute radioactive impurities, and the testing of samples of radioactive ores. In the study of petroleum geology, counters have found a use. A counter and a source of radiation may be lowered into an oil well boring, and the counter will measure the different amounts of radiation scattered back to it from the various strata of different materials through which the bore passes. This procedure can be made to reveal the location of hydrocarbon deposits, and the technique is in wide use today.

Neutron counters, being sensitive to neutrons, which in turn are strongly scattered by hydrogen-containing substances, have been used to detect the presence of hydrocarbon accumulations in the ground, or in pipes or other containers. An absolute altimeter has been proposed, in which the scattered neutrons would indicate water nearby, and the technique may be used for locating water.

In short, any industrial use of nuclear physics may be aided by using these instruments in the detecting procedures. It will be recalled that in metallurgy, diffusion phenomena, order-disorder studies, and tracer researches have made use of artificially activated substances. In each case, counters represent a useful detecting technique. Similarly in chemistry, the study of reaction rates, surface properties, molecular structure, low vapor pressures, equilibrium measurements, small solubilities, and catalysis have all been aided by the use of artificially radioactive elements. In each case a counter could be used to detect the activity, both in amount and in nature, and could follow the active substance through various changes and reactions. In geology, in addition to prospecting for radioactive deposits, identification of minerals, and assaying, counters have been employed in connection with artificially activated substances used in sedimentation studies.

It is the purpose of this book to describe the properties and behavior of counters and counting systems, and hence we next turn to a discussion of the electrical phenomena produced by counters.

C. Description of the Phenomena as a Function of Voltage

1. Low Voltage Region. Let us consider any system of the type ordinarily used for counting action, such as a cylindrical cathode and an axial wire anode. It is evident that the main function of the cylinder is to dis-

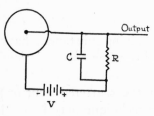

FIG. 1–1. Fundamental counter circuit.

tribute the potential, and to form a volume in which the electric field is defined by the geometry of the electrodes. Suppose the wire of this system is connected to a sensitive device for measuring the voltage changes, or pulses which may appear on it, such as an oscilloscope with high amplification; let us consider the pulse sizes and distributions as the voltage across the counter is raised. Such a counter will then form a part of the fundamental circuit shown in Fig. 1–1, in which the cross section of a counter is depicted, a potential is applied across it, and a resistance R inserted in order that a pulse may be passed to the detecting unit. The condenser C is understood to include all the distributed capacity in the circuit. The recovery of the wire after a pulse has occurred is controlled by the familiar exponential RC time constant and cannot be made shorter than this value but can, of course, exceed this figure if the discharge conditions are suitably varied. We shall assume that curves of the number of counts at various voltages are obtained, while the flux of radiation passing through the counter is kept constant. We shall consider the wire to be positive with respect to the cylinder and shall therefore discuss the collection of negative ions and electrons on the central wire. The operation of the counter in various voltage regions will be described. We shall show how this device functions at low voltages as an ionization chamber. As the voltage is progressively raised, the device becomes in turn a proportional counter and a Geiger counter. We thus have several voltage regions: the low voltage region, the proportional region, and the Geiger region, in which quite different types of phenomena occur, and in which the same counter may be used for quite diverse purposes. We shall consider these in turn.

The word "ionization" is used in physics in two distinct senses. In the narrow sense it means the process of removal of an electron from a neutral atom. We shall use it in its broader sense, to mean any act or process by which a molecule or atom which was neutral acquires a charge, or by which electrons are freed in a gas. We shall also use the word to describe the results of the process, in the sense that we may say that "ionization has been produced in the gas." We are less concerned with the nature of the event causing the ionization, and more interested in the collection of the charges produced and in all the processes which accompany this collection. The reader will recognize that we must therefore discuss electrical discharges in a gas. Since this book cannot also be a treatise on gas discharges, we shall assume some acquaintance with the subject and refer the reader to standard texts for further details. We shall now examine the results which follow when ionization is produced in a counter.

It will be recalled that when ionization is produced, in general an ion-pair, positive and negative, is formed from what was initially a neutral atom. We must consider what happens to both of these fractions as they are drawn, respectively, to the negative and positive electrodes. For the sake of simplicity we shall discuss these two parts separately, but it must always be kept in mind that both are present and that their interactions must be considered.

At zero voltage across the counter, there will be no fluctuations in the potential of the central wire, save those caused by the random arrival of individual ions on the wire. If a small voltage is applied, a field is established in the space between the cathode and anode, and any positive ions formed in this volume tend to drift toward the cylinder, and the negatives toward the wire. As the voltage is first applied on the cylinder, the arrangement becomes in effect an ionization chamber in which any electron's produced in the volume of the counter are swept by the field to the central wire where they are collected. The size of the voltage pulse appearing on the central wire is determined by the number of charges arriving and by the distributed capacity of the central wire and anything attached electrically to it, such as the grid of the tube in the first stage of the amplifier. The wire potential will also be subject to a transient influence if a positive space charge exists. A change in potential, dV, will be produced by the arrival of a charge, dq, on an electrode of capacity C. In terms of the arrival of particles of unit electronic charge equal to 1.60×10^{-19} coulombs, the rise in potential of the central wire will be given by

$$dV = dq/C = 1.60 \times 10^{-7} n/C \qquad (1-1)$$

where n is the number of electrons arriving, dV is the rise in potential in volts, and C is in micromicrofarads. Eq. (1–1) assumes no effect of positive space charge and hence is correct *after* the positives have been collected. The changes in potential of the wire, while the positives are moving out to the cylinder, will be discussed later.

The time rate of change of the voltage is determined by the rapidity with which the ions are collected on the central wire, providing this is small compared to the time constant RC. To know this, we must know the mobility of the charged particles collected, which for negative ions is of the order of 1.2 to 1.4 cm per sec per volt per cm referred to air at standard temperature and pressure. For electrons, the mobilities are much greater and the drift velocity is larger by a factor of 1000 to 10,000. Thus, for example, in a counter of 1-cm radius with 1000 volts between the electrodes and 1 atm. pressure, the collection of negative ions would take place in approximately 10^{-3} sec, whereas electrons will all be collected in a microsecond or less. In an ionizing event, electrons and positive ions are formed. The probability of the attachment of these electrons to neutral molecules to form negative ions will be discussed later. It will suffice here to say that in most cases few negative ions are formed, and we shall therefore mention chiefly electrons here.

At low voltages V_o, the electrons do not create any additional ions by collision during the collection process. The number which arrive on the central wire will therefore be equal to the number which were produced in the initial ionizing event less the number which have disappeared by recombination. The number which disappear by recombination will be small in most counters, since the fields are high and the pressures are low. The size of the pulse which arrives on the central wire is independent of the collecting voltage as long as the field is sufficient to cause ions to move with an appreciable velocity and remains independent of the potential as the voltage is increased up to the point at which secondary electrons are produced by collision in the gas.

The positive ions, in the meantime, travel outward to the cylinder where they are neutralized. Later we shall discuss this process in detail; for the time being, it will suffice to assume that they are collected at the cylinder and thus disappear.

2. The Proportional Region. When the voltage across the counter is raised above that minimum V_p, at which secondary electrons are first formed by collision, the pulse which appears on the wire will then be larger by reason of the additional ions formed by collision. This process, as the potential is slowly raised, will first take place in the immediate neighborhood of the wire where the field is greatest. It will take place as soon as the field, dV/dr, is sufficient so that the incoming electron attains enough energy to produce ionization upon its next impact. The electron loses most of its kinetic energy each time it collides with an atom. Hence, if it is to produce ionization by collision, it must gain an amount of energy sufficient to ionize, i.e., equal to the ionization potential of the gas, in one free path, between collisions. The original electron and the new one thus produced will each be accelerated again by the field and will produce still more ions by collision. This process is cumulative, and an "avalanche" of electrons is thus produced. The phenomenon is frequently called the Townsend avalanche, in honor of J. S. Townsend who, forty years ago, did important pioneer work in this subject. We thus may define r_o, the critical radius, as the radius at which the field is sufficient so that the process of cumulative ionization starts. The lowest voltage at which cumulative ionization is observed is defined as the threshold voltage V_p for proportional counter action.

If there are A ion-pairs formed by collision as each electron travels toward the central wire, then the size of the voltage pulse on the central wire will be given by a modification of eq. (1–1), namely

$$dV = 1.60 \times 10^{-7} An/C \qquad (1-2)$$

The quantity A is defined as the "gas amplification." This number may in actual practice vary between the limits of unity, in the case when the counter acts like an ionization chamber, to about 10^7 at the end of the proportional region. In general, a counter ceases to be in the proportional region when the figure exceeds 10^7, but in many cases a counter cannot be operated in the proportional region when values of A exceed about 10^3. The useful limits on A depend on the type of gas. The theory describing the dependence of A on the gas in the counter, the voltage, the geometry and other factors will be discussed fully in Chapter 3 in the section on proportional counters. As long as A remains a constant, the counter will produce a pulse dV which is proportional to the number of ions n formed in the initial ionizing event.

We have already noted that for a proportional counter A does not ordinarily exceed about 10^7. As the voltage across the counter is still further increased, the value of A appropriate to small pulses will not always remain the same as that for A appropriate to large pulses. Thus, for example, if ten ion-pairs were formed in the counter and A were 10^7, the pulse size would correspond to the arrival of 10^8 particles. If, however, 10^4 ion-pairs should be produced in the counter by an initial ionizing event, say, for example, the passage of an alpha particle through the gas, then application of the same A would give a pulse resulting from the arrival of 10^{11} ion-pairs. This, however, is not generally observed. The size of the pulse is frequently limited to about 10^9 ions, and the effective value of A is therefore about 10^5 in this case. It will thus be seen that at higher voltages the value of A is a function of the pulse size. The voltage region in which A is constant is called the "proportional region." The voltage region in which A depends somewhat on the pulse size is called the region of "limited proportionality." It should be noted that counters may be operated in the region of limited proportionality and may still in this region distinguish between the arrival of a beta ray and an alpha particle since there is a large difference in the total number of ions produced by each of these two entities.

3. The Geiger Region. As the voltage is further raised, the dependence of A upon pulse size becomes more pronounced. The counter will enter a voltage region in which the size of the pulse arriving on the wire is independent of the number of ions formed in the initial ionizing event. This is called the Geiger region and is characterized, when viewed on an oscilloscope screen, by all the pulses appearing to be of the same height.

The minimum voltage at which this condition is realized is called the threshold voltage V_G for Geiger counting action. The absolute size of the pulses observed in the Geiger region is, of course, a function of the voltage applied to the counter and will therefore go through a considerable range as the voltage is changed. In the earliest experiments, counters were operated both in the proportional region and in the Geiger region. The transition between these regions is not abrupt. There is a continuous gradation of pulse size as the voltage is raised.

Referring to eq. (1–2), we may say that, in the proportional region, A is independent of n. In the region of limited proportionality, A depends somewhat upon n, the dependence being more for larger pulses and less for the smaller. In the Geiger region, A becomes an inverse function of n, so that, at any one voltage, the quantity nA is a constant. In the Geiger region it is the quantity nA which increases with the voltage, instead of merely A as in the proportional region. The region of limited proportionality is the region of transition between these two conditions.

To illustrate the above discussion, let us consider the history of a pulse produced by the passage through a counter of a fast cosmic ray which leaves behind it perhaps 30 ion-pairs, and also the pulse due to the passage of an alpha particle through the counter leaving behind it 10^4 ion-pairs. We shall consider what happens to these pulses as the voltage on the counter is raised (see Fig. 1–2). While the device is operating as an ionization chamber, the pulse produced by the cosmic ray and that produced by the alpha particle will each be collected on the central wire and the magnitude of each will be given by eq. (1–1). The pulse sizes will be in the ratio 30:10,000, and this ratio will be independent of the collecting voltage. As the voltage across the counter is raised, the threshold for proportional counting action is reached. The two pulses will then each increase in size since, as the counter enters the proportional region, the gas amplification A will be an increasing function of the voltage. In the proportional region, the pulse observed on the wire due to the alpha particle will still be about 300 times as large as that due to the cosmic ray. This ratio will be maintained until the region of limited proportionality is entered.

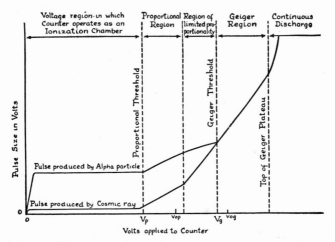

Fig. 1–2. Operating characteristics of a counter in various regions for large and small ionizing events. Top curve shows pulse resulting from passage of alpha particle producing 10,000 ions during its passage through the counter. Bottom curve, pulse resulting from cosmic ray producing 30 ions. The curves merge at the Geiger threshold. Recommended operating voltages: for proportional counting, Vop, near top of proportional region, to get large pulses; Vog, for Geiger counting near Geiger threshold to avoid excessive pulse size and damage to counter.

As this region is first approached, the value of A appropriate to the alpha particle pulse will cease to increase as fast with voltage as does that appropriate to the smaller pulse. At a slightly higher voltage, therefore, the pulse due to the alpha particle will be less than 300 times as large as that due to the cosmic ray. As the voltage is still further raised and the region of limited proportionality is traversed, the ratio of the pulse sizes approaches unity, while the absolute magnitude of each of the pulses still increases as the voltage is raised. The voltage at which the pulse size due to the cosmic ray has become equal to that due to the alpha particle is the Geiger threshold, and above this voltage the ratio of the pulse sizes will be unity. The absolute magnitude of the pulse will increase with voltage throughout the Geiger region. The dependence will be discussed in the section on Geiger counters. Fig. 1–2, originally given by Montgomery and Montgomery [M1], shows the several regions and traces the pulse size in each.

At the end of the Geiger region, the counter goes into what is called a continuous discharge. This discharge is not really continuous, but consists of a large number of multiple pulses. The properties of such a pseudo-continuous discharge are not within the scope of this work and will therefore not be discussed, except to say that a "continuous" discharge constitutes the upper limit of the region of Geiger counting action. Indeed, the growth of multiple pulses is also a gradual phenomenon, and the top limit of the Geiger region is therefore not sharply defined. The curves and complete discussion of this will be given in the appropriate sections. The gas amplification A becomes very large (often $> 10^8$) in a continuous discharge. This statement is not strictly accurate if a continuous discharge is considered from a microscopic viewpoint, but it provides an operationally adequate description.

D. Definition of Terms and Symbols to Be Used

It has long been apparent that it would be most desirable to standardize the terminology used in describing counters. Unfortunately many authors, especially in the early days, used diverse words, occasionally using the same word in two or more quite different senses. A start was made in the first edition of this work. Later, the American Institute of Electrical Engineers and the Institute of Radio Engineers appointed a committee to study the problem of the terminology and testing. The report of the Radiation Counter Tube Subcommittee, of which the present author was privileged to be a member, has

been published in the *Proceedings of the IRE*, Vol. 40, pages
924 to 930, No. 8, August, 1952.   Reprints of the standards,
designated 52 IRE 7.S2 (testing procedures) and 52 IRE 7.S3
(definitions), may be purchased for $0.75 and $0.50 respectively
from the IRE, 1 East 79th Street, New York 21, New York.
The definitions are listed in this book by permission, with due
credit to the committees and to the institutes.   Acknowledgment should be made to all the members of these committees,
who have held long and diligent discussions regarding the
words that most nearly convey the physical meaning, as represented by our present understanding of the processes involved.
The list given on pages 16–20 contains more words than were
defined in the first edition of this book, and the new words
should clearly be credited in their entirety to the committee.
The deliberations and discussions have brought forth many
improvements in the definitions of the words originally listed,
and the present author is grateful for the opportunity to in-
corporate the opinions of many of his colleagues into the
list.

It has been proposed to use the words "radiation counter
tube" to describe what in this work we shall call "counters."
The three words were decided upon in order (a) to identify
the nature of the entities being counted, (b) to distinguish the
devices from mechanical counters, and (c) to suggest that
these devices were in the category of gas-discharge tubes.
Since, however, this book deals with such tubes only, we shall
continue to use the shorter word "counters" in the text.   We
shall also from time to time deviate slightly from the exact
words used below.

Furthermore, the committees have considered a series of
tests and specifications.   It is hoped that eventually it may
be possible to arrive at acceptable figures of merit for tubes,
and to define the properties of counters in such a manner that
exact and meaningful specifications may be drawn up.   A
symbol for a counter, drawn in a manner to conform to stand-

ard vacuum-tube practice, has been proposed. Standard test procedures and test circuits, including this symbol, are also available. The symbol is shown in Fig. 1-3. The present author has not felt it necessary to correct the older drawings in this text to conform to this symbol, but expects to use it in future work.

To recapitulate the situation regarding the name of these tubes, the general name "radiation counter tube" is considered a good compromise at the present time. We shall in this text refer to them simply as "counters." The general class is subdivided into "Geiger counter tubes," or in this text "Geiger counters"; this supplants the older definition, in which a "Geiger counter" meant a point counter, and a "Geiger-Mueller counter" meant a cylindrical counter. A "proportional counter tube," or in this text simply a "proportional counter," supplants the older "Geiger-Klemperer counter."

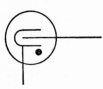

Fig. 1-3. Symbol for radiation counter tube.

Avalanche: A cascade multiplication of ions.

Background Counts: Counts caused by radiation coming from sources other than that measured.

Count (in a Radiation Counter): A single response of the counting system. *Note—See also* Tube Count.

Counting-Rate Versus Voltage Characteristic: Counting rate as a function of applied voltage for a given constant average intensity of radiation.

Dead Time: The time from the start of a counted pulse until an observable succeeding pulse can occur. *Note—See also* Recovery Time.

Efficiency (of a Radiation Counter Tube): The probability that a tube count will take place with a specified particle or quantum incident in a specified manner.

Externally Quenched Counter Tube: A radiation counter tube that requires the use of an external quenching circuit to inhibit reignition.

Gas Amplification: The ratio of the charge collected to the charge liberated by the initial ionizing event. *Note—See also* Standards on Gas-Filled Radiation Counter Tubes: Methods of Testing, section 12.

Gas-Filled Radiation Counter Tube: A gas tube, in a radiation counter, used for the detection of radiation by means of gas ionization.

Geiger-Mueller Counter Tube: A radiation counter tube designed to operate in the Geiger-Mueller region.

Geiger-Mueller Region (of a Radiation Counter Tube): The range of applied voltage in which the charge collected per isolated count is independent of the charge liberated by the initial ionizing event.

Geiger-Mueller Threshold: The lowest applied voltage at which the charge collected per isolated tube count is substantially independent of the nature of the initial ionizing event.

Hysteresis (of a Radiation Counter Tube): The temporary change in the counting rate versus voltage characteristic caused by previous operation.

Initial Ionizing Event: An ionizing event that initiates a tube count.

Ionizing Event: Any interaction by which one or more ions are produced.

Multiple Tube Counts (in Radiation Counter Tubes). Spurious counts induced by previous tube counts.

Normalized Plateau Slope: The slope of the substantially straight portion of the counting rate versus voltage characteristic divided by the quotient of the counting rate by the voltage at the Geiger-Mueller threshold. *Note—See* Fig. 1–4.

Overvoltage: The amount by which the applied voltage exceeds the Geiger-Mueller threshold.

Plateau: The portion of the counting rate versus voltage characteristic in which the counting rate is substantially independent of the applied voltage.

Plateau Length: The range of applied voltage over which the plateau of a radiation counter tube extends.

Predissociation: A process by which a molecule that has absorbed energy dissociates before it has had an opportunity to lose energy by radiation.

Proportional Counter Tube: A radiation counter tube designed to operate in the proportional region.

Proportional Region: The range of applied voltage in which the gas amplification is greater than unity and is independent of the charge liberated by the initial ionizing event. *Note*—The proportional region depends on the type and energy of the radiation.

Quenching (in a Gas-Filled Radiation Counter Tube): The process of terminating a discharge in a radiation counter tube by inhibiting reignition.

Radiation: In nuclear work, the term is extended beyond its usual meaning to include moving nuclear particles, charged or uncharged, and electrons moving with sufficient speed to enter into nuclear processes.

Radiation Counter: An instrument used for detecting or measuring radiation by counting action.

Recovery Time (of a Radiation Counter): The minimum time from the start of a counted pulse to the instant a succeeding pulse can attain a specific percentage of the maximum value of the counted pulse.

Region of Limited Proportionality: The range of applied voltage below the Geiger-Mueller threshold, in which the gas amplification depends upon the charge liberated by the initial ionizing event.

Reignition (of a Radiation Counter Tube): A process by which multiple counts are generated within a counter tube by atoms or molecules excited or ionized in the discharge accompanying a tube count.

Relative Plateau Slope: The average percentage change in the counting rate near the mid-point of the plateau per increment of applied voltage. *Note*—Relative plateau slope is usually expressed as the percentage change in counting rate per 100-volt change in applied voltage. *See* Fig. 1–4.

Resolving Time (of a Radiation Counter): The time from the start of a counted pulse to the instant a succeeding pulse can assume the minimum strength to be detected by the counting circuit. (This quantity pertains to the combination of tube and recording circuit.)

Self-Quenched Counter Tube: A radiation counter tube in which reignition of the discharge is inhibited by internal processes.

Sensitive Volume (of a Radiation Counter Tube): That portion of the tube responding to specific radiation.

Spurious Tube Counts (in Radiation Counter Tubes): Counts in radiation counter tubes other than background counts and those caused by the source measured. *Note*—Spurious

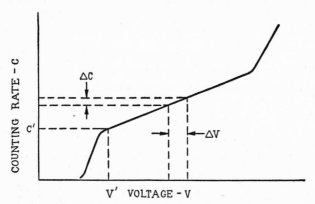

FIG. 1–4. Counting rate-voltage characteristic, in which

$$\text{Relative plateau slope} \quad = 100 \, \frac{\Delta C/C}{\Delta V}$$

$$\text{Normalized plateau slope} = 100 \, \frac{\Delta C/\Delta V}{C'/V'} = \frac{\Delta C/C'}{\Delta V/V'}$$

counts are caused by failure of the quenching process, electrical leakage, and the like. Spurious counts may seriously affect measurement of background counts.

Tube Count: A terminated discharge produced by an ionizing event in a radiation counter tube.

PROBLEMS

1. Rutherford states that an alpha particle from radium C produces about 220,000 ion-pairs along its range in air. Assuming that the entire range ends within the counter, and that the distributed capacity of the collecting electrode is 10 micromicrofarads, find the size of the voltage pulse for ionization chamber operation.

(*Ans.* 3.52 × 10⁻³ volt.)

2. A proportional counter is counting neutrons, and a pulse size of 0.8 volt is observed. Assuming a capacity of 10 micromicrofarads, and that about 50,000 ion-pairs are produced in the gas, find A.

(*Ans.* 1000.)

3. A proportional counter counting alpha particles yields pulses of 4.24 volts each. Assuming the counter is operating at an A of 2×10^3, and that the distributed capacity is 15 micromicrofarads, find the energy required to produce the average ion-pair. Assume the alpha particles are from radium, and have an energy of 4.74 Mev each.

(*Ans.* 23.7 ev each.)

4. A beta particle is projected into a counter, with an energy of 0.5 Mev. Assume that 50 ev are required to produce an ion-pair, that A is 10^4, and that C is 16 micromicrofarads. If the pulse noted on the wire is 0.5 volt, did the electron stop in the counter?

(*Ans.* No.)

5. A gamma ray initiates a count of 25-volt amplitude. Taking C as 16 micromicrofarads, state whether or not the counter is in all probability operating in the Geiger region, and why.

(*Ans.* nA is 2.5×10^9; and since n is probably 1 or at least small, A is so large as to imply Geiger operation.)

CHAPTER 2

IONIZATION CHAMBERS

A. Introduction

In this chapter, we shall discuss the operation of ionization measuring devices in the first or lowest voltage region. In this region the ionization produced in the vessel is directly collected and measured, with no gas amplification. Eq. (1–1) applies, since A is equal to unity. The electrical diagram which applies is that shown in Fig. 1–1. The ionization to be measured takes place inside the vessel. A potential difference applied across the counter causes the ions to be swept toward the electrode and collected on it. The arrival of the ions produces a change dV in the potential of the electrode, as given in eq. (1–1). The problem in the operation of these instruments is therefore that of detecting, measuring and recording the pulse dV thus produced.

There are two distinct types of ionization chambers which accomplish this purpose in quite different manners. In the first instrument the pulses due to the individual particles are detected, while in the second the pulses are allowed to add up, and the integrated total of all the ionization produced in a certain time is determined. In principle the same chamber can perform either function, and which it will perform is determined by the time constant RC of the circuit (Fig. 1–1). If the initial potential of the collecting electrode were V_o, it would have a potential V after a time t given by

$$V = V_o e^{-t/RC} \qquad (2\text{–}1)$$

Thus the return to $1/e$ of its original value for a typical chamber, with resistance R of 10^8 ohms and capacity C of 10^{-11}

21

farads, takes place in 10^{-3} seconds. The collection of the ions must take place in less than this time, since if the charge leaks off the collecting electrode through R as fast as it arrives, the rise in potential is negligible. The collection time depends on the mobility of the ions collected, which in turn depends on the nature and sign of the ions, and the nature and pressure of the gas employed in the vessel as well as the field.

In the integrating types of ionization chambers, the resistance R is high, of the order of 10^{15} ohms or so. For the collecting system cited, the time constant is, therefore, 10^4 sec, and a moderately low collecting field is possible. In this case it is necessary to measure the changes in potential of the electrode at suitable intervals. Thus the former type of chamber measures and counts the individual rays whereas the latter type measures the flux or total radiation. In the former type, the recorded pulse size is proportional to the amount of ionization liberated in each primary ionizing event, whereas in the latter, it is not possible to tell, except with the aid of subsidiary measurements, whether a given amount of ionization is produced by a few large ionizing events or many small ones. The decision as to which of these two to use will therefore depend on the particular problems to be studied. We will consider the counting and integrating types in turn.

B. Counting Chambers

Let us consider the aspects of producing and detecting a pulse dV due to an ionizing event which has taken place in the chamber. Such an ionizing event might be the passage of an alpha particle, a beta particle or a cosmic ray, through the chamber. Since an alpha particle has a range of only a few cm in air, it will, in general, expend its entire range in the gas of the chamber. As alpha particles observed in chambers usually come from contamination (usually radium A), we may assume that the alpha particle produces about 3.5 Mev of

energy in ionization.   Since it requires about 35 volts to produce an ion-pair, a total of 10^5 ions will be formed by the average alpha particle.   Provisionally we will neglect recombination.   Since the electronic charge is 1.6×10^{-19} coulomb, we
have a dQ of 1.6×10^{-14} coulomb, which on a capacity of
10^{-11} farad will produce a pulse dV of 1.6×10^{-3} volt.   A
beta particle will produce a much smaller amount of ionization
and may liberate 10^3 or so ions on its traversal of the chamber,
while a cosmic ray passing along a 10-cm path in atmospheric
air will produce some 300 ions.   If we wish to study cosmic
rays, the problem is to detect pulses of 10^{-3} to 10^{-5} volt amplitude.   In general, it is practical to detect such pulses only if
they take place in a comparatively short time, since most
amplifying systems involve measurements of dV/dt.   The electrical circuits for detecting such pulses will be discussed later.

Let us further assume that the resistance R is 10^{10} ohms, so
that a time of 10^{-1} sec is available.   The collection of charges
produced in the ionizing event must be completed in this time.
Referring to the mobilities mentioned above, if we have a
chamber of 10-cm radius, operating at 1000 volts, with average
fields of about 100 volts per cm, the ionic velocities would be
about 100 cm per sec and ions would travel the dimensions of
the chamber in 10^{-1} sec.

Any ionization chamber will exhibit a certain background,
and it is the statistical fluctuations in this background which
set the fundamental limit to the smallest amount of ionization
detectable in each instrument.   This background is caused by
three types of radiation: (a) alpha particle contamination of
the inside of the chamber, (b) cosmic radiation, and (c) natural
radioactivity of the surroundings.   The alpha particle contamination may be reduced to a low value by painting the inside of the chamber with carbon black or other very pure
organic chemicals such as collodion.   A good chamber will still
have perhaps 10^{-4} alpha particle per square cm per minute.
In some chambers, a gauze has been arranged just inside the
surface of the chamber and charged to a positive potential,

which collects the ionization produced by alpha particles. However, the front surface of such a gauze will itself emit some particles, and it will be impossible to reduce the background to zero. The number emitted in any given counter will, moreover, be constant, and may readily be counted and thus allowed for. The number of alpha particles will not depend on the pressure of the gas in the chamber, except to the extent that the gas is contaminated with radon, which for carefully purified gases is negligible.

The contribution due to cosmic radiation may be reduced to small value by operating the chamber in a deep mine, but as this is often impractical, it is again desirable to determine the number and allow for it. A rough rule is that about 1.5 cosmic rays per minute will cross every square cm of horizontal cross sectional area at or near sea level. The number is larger at higher elevations, being roughly 3 at 5000 feet and 6 at 15,000 feet. If alpha particles or protons are being measured, these will produce a large amount of ionization compared to the individual cosmic rays, and hence can be distinguished by making pulse-size measurements. Such pulse-size measurements will serve to eliminate the effects of beta rays and gamma rays from whatever source and cosmic rays, except in the integrating type of ionization chamber. In the pulse-detecting chambers, the pulse size will increase with the pressure of the gas in the vessel, but of course the number of cosmic rays and contamination rays will remain constant.

The contributions due to the natural contamination from the surroundings external to the chamber can be reduced by making the walls of the chamber thick enough to exclude these radiations. Thus, for example, in the conventional cosmic ray meters, operating under ten cm lead shields, the contribution due to this cause is negligible.

The final limit to the smallest amount of ionization detectable will be that which can just be distinguished from the fluctuations in the background. In Chapter 5 we will discuss in

detail the computation of these quantities. To a first approximation a "square root rule" may be applied. For example, a
chamber exhibiting a background of 10 alpha rays per minute
may be used to measure intensities of as low as 3 alphas per
minute in an observation lasting one minute; and similarly for
the normal cosmic ray and beta ray background at sea level.

The shape and size of the chamber are usually determined by
the nature and number of particles to be detected. Thus, for
example, a chamber designed to count alpha particles may be
made quite small, thus reducing the background due both to
cosmic rays and to contamination. A suitable window through
which the particles to be measured may be projected into the
chamber must be provided. This should be no larger than
necessary, both for reasons of mechanical strength and also because such a window is also transparent to contamination radiation originating nearby. The body of the chamber, or the
sensitive volume, need not be larger than the range of alpha
particles in the gas which it contains. For alpha particles, this
will ordinarily not exceed a few cm. For higher energy protons,
however, the range may be large compared to the dimensions
of the chamber, since, for example, a 10 Mev proton has a
range of about 1 meter of air. Hence, in detecting protons, only
a small fraction of its range will be expended in traversing the
chamber.

Typical arrangements of electrodes in chambers, suitable for
detecting alpha particles or protons, are shown in Fig. 2–1. A
differential chamber may be constructed as shown in Fig. 2–2,
by placing the collecting electrode in the middle of the field,
so that positive ions are collected on one side and negatives on
the other. Then, a particle which passes right through the
chamber will produce substantially equal numbers of particles
on each side of the foil and the resulting pulse will be small,
whereas one stopping in the front part of the chamber will
produce ions of which those of one sign only are collected and
hence produce a large pulse.

A chamber designed to detect slow neutrons will, in general, be larger in size. Such a chamber may be lined with boron or a boron compound and filled with some gas such as argon, or it may be filled with BF_3 and not lined. In either case, the neutron may be captured by the B^{10} nucleus, in which case an alpha particle is given out. It is these alpha particles which are counted. Since the efficiencies, that is, the ratio of the number of neutrons traversing the chamber to the number de-

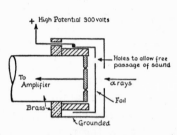

FIG. 2–1. Ionization chamber for counting alpha rays. (W. B. Lewis, *Electrical Counting*, p. 8, 1942)

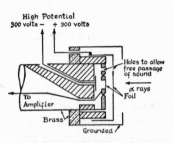

FIG. 2–2. Differential chamber. (W. B. Lewis, *Electrical Counting*, p. 10, 1942)

tected, of such chambers are in general low, it is usual to make the chamber as large as may be convenient in order to secure large counting rates. Such boron-lined or BF_3-filled chambers have been used by various observers and are standard in many laboratories.

Fast neutrons are generally detected by the recoil protons which they can produce. Thus, in constructing ionization chambers to detect fast neutrons, it is usual to dispose some hydrogenous material such as paraffin inside or outside the chamber. Since the range of protons is greater than that of alpha particles, such recoil protons may readily pass through windows which are at the same time strong enough mechanically to sustain pressure differentials and yet not too absorbent. A one or two mil aluminum foil has the stopping-power of a few cm of air; and while it would reduce the range of alpha particles by an amount rendering them undetectable, for protons it presents no serious obstacle. The principal problem encountered with thin aluminum foils is their likelihood of having pinholes. When the pressure differential which they are required to support is negligible, a few coats of lacquer will seal such holes adequately. For higher pressure differences, thicker foils of substances such as nickel-silver are suitable. A 3-mil foil of this material will withstand a pressure of several atmospheres over an area of several square cm, and yet will be the equivalent of only some 50 cm of air; quite enough to exclude alpha particles, but not enough to prevent the admission of a 10 Mev proton. The discussion of the efficiency as a function of the neutron velocity of various types of detectors is given in the section of neutron counting in the chapter on proportional counters.

Ionization chambers are often sensitive to "microphonic" disturbances. These effects are often traceable to the fact that if parts of the chamber move relatively to one another, the capacity of the system changes. If the charge on the collecting electrode is constant, and the capacity varies, the result will be a varying potential or, in other words, a pulse. The changes need not be large. If the capacity of such a system is 10^{-11} farads, and the collecting potential is 300 volts, the charge Q will be 3×10^{-3} microcoulombs. Now if the charge remains constant, and the capacity changes by one part in a million, the voltage pulse will be of the order of 10^{-4} volt. This pulse is of the same order as that produced by an alpha particle. Microphonics may be reduced by increasing the capacity or decreasing the sweeping potentials, but both of these procedures are undesirable since they reduce the pulse size or collection time. Consequently the practical approach to the problem is to construct the chambers with rigidly mounted parts, to provide holes for the equalization of gas pressures inside the chamber, and to mount the chambers on vibration-free supports and surround them with rubber or other sound-absorbing material.

Ionization chambers frequently employ a "guard ring." This ring surrounds part of the collecting electrode, and performs several extremely important functions. A typical arrangement may be seen in Fig. 2–3. The guard ring is often operated at ground potential. Any surface leakage currents across or volume leakage through the insulating material separating the outer shell or case from the collecting electrode, as well as the fluctuations due to the polarization of the dielectric in the high fields will terminate at the guard ring. The poten-

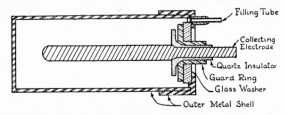

Fig. 2–3.   Ionization chamber showing use of guard ring. The surfaces in contact may be sealed with a thin layer of hot wax.

tial difference between the guard ring and the collecting electrode should be small. In case the guard ring is not operated at ground potential, it should be connected to ground through a large condenser, so that its potential will stay as constant as possible. The second, and perhaps the most important, function of the guard ring is to serve as an electrostatic shield and to prevent any part of the collecting electrode from "seeing" any external point or object, the potential of which is not constant. With alternating current supplied to most laboratories today, any part of the collecting electrode system unshielded from the laboratory room may readily pick up pulses of the order of 10^{-4} volts in amplitude. Thus, for example, an ordinary electric lamp operating on AC can readily be detected at considerable distances due to the pulses which it emits. Therefore the geometry of the collecting electrode, the outside case and the guard ring must always be so disposed that no straight line from any point on the collecting system to any point outside the shell of the chamber can be so drawn that it is not intercepted by the guard ring, even though this line passes through considerable thicknesses of the insulating material separating the electrode from the case.

C. Integrating Types of Ionization Chambers

This type of chamber is characterized by the fact that its time constant RC is long compared to the time for the collection of the ions formed in the primary acts of ionization. As the ions from the various ionizing events are collected, the collecting electrode experiences a progressive change in potential. The potential is measured at suitable intervals, and thus indicates the total charge Q collected during the interval.

One type of integrating ionization chamber is compensated. In this type, a second chamber is provided, connected in parallel with the first, but with potentials reversed. This second chamber is small in volume compared to the first, so that the ionization produced by its background will be small compared to that in the main chamber. It is provided with a source of ionizing radiation of some type, usually some uranium on an adjustable rod, which can be so altered in position that the amount of ionization which it produces in the compensating chamber can be adjusted. The entire arrangement is then so balanced that the ionization received in the main chamber is exactly equal to that produced in the compensating chamber. Hence the potential of the collecting electrode does not vary. This type of device, then, is a null instrument, indicating zero under normal conditions, and showing departures from zero, both increasing and decreasing, as the ionization through the main vessel is made larger or smaller than that in the compensating chamber.

Examples of these ionization chambers are the cosmic ray meters designed by Millikan, Compton and their collaborators. In the Millikan instrument,[M2] a built-in electroscope is employed, which consists of a gold-plated quartz fibre arrangement under torsion. When the electroscope system is charged, the fibre is repelled by, and stands away from, its support. Then, as the central system including the electroscope is charged with respect to the case, any ionization produced in the device is collected on the central system. This arrival of charge partly neutralizes the initial charge on the system, and permits the torsional force to cause the needle (the quartz fibre) to approach the support more closely. The position of the needle is a measure of the charge Q on the system, and the change in its position therefore registers the amount of ionization produced in the vessel. It remains, therefore, only to calibrate the device, so that the position of the needle may be quantitatively related to the ionization produced in the chamber, determine the zero and contributions due to natural contamination in the chamber, and then automatically to photograph the position of the needle. The same clockwork mechanism which drives the photographic film also operates a recharging switch and returns the electroscope system to its fully charged position at any desired interval.

The Compton type of meter [c1] is of the compensating type, using a balance chamber with a uranium source which is adjusted until it balances out the normal cosmic radiation. The fluctuations of the cosmic ray intensity above and below the normal averages will, therefore, show on the collecting system, which is connected to a Lindemann electrometer. As with the Millikan type of meter, the collecting system is automatically recharged at intervals and the readings of the electrometer are automatically recorded photographically. Since the intensity of the ionization in the compensating chamber may be altered by adjusting a shield over the uranium source, the zero is conveniently variable, and the device can be set to indicate the ionization produced by the cosmic rays at various elevations. Similarly the ionization produced by any other radiation reaching the interior of the vessel may be measured.

The limit to the sensitivity of these integrating devices is again imposed by the fluctuations in the background. The absolute value of the background can be determined and allowed for, but the statistical fluctuations in this value constitute the ultimate limiting factor.

Both the instruments described above employ a main vessel in which the ionization is detected, filled with 30 to 50 atm of very pure argon. The amount of ionization measured is the total formed along the paths of all the particles passing through the chamber. In the case of cosmic radiation, the specific ionization of the particles is practically uniform along their paths, and virtually no particles end their range in the gas of the chamber. The total amount of charge Q due to ionization produced per particle is therefore given by

$$Q = ne = slpe \qquad (2\text{-}2)$$

where n is the total number of ions formed, s is the specific ionization in ions/cm/atm for cosmic ray particles in argon, l is the average path length through the chamber, p is the pressure in atmospheres of the argon in the vessel and e is the charge per ion. The chamber is spherical in shape. It can readily be shown that the average path through a sphere is $\frac{2}{3}$ the diameter. Hence, the number of ions i formed per particle, in a sphere of 15 cm diameter, l being thus 10, for a pressure p of 50 atm and a specific ionization of 50 ions per cm per atm is 25,000 ions. The change dQ in charge of the collecting electrode is $2.5 \times 1.6 \times 10^{-15}$ coulombs; and assuming the capacity of the system to be 10^{-11} farads, the change in potential is about 4×10^{-4} volt. Since some 300 cosmic rays per minute will pass through such a vessel at sea level, the potential of the collecting electrode changes at the rate of perhaps 0.1 volt per minute, an easily measurable quantity.

The total amount of ionization, appearing in a chamber of the integrating type, in a given length of time is sometimes re-

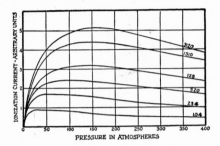

FIG. 2–4. The variation with pressure of the ionization current in air-filled chamber under constant irradiation by gamma rays. Parallel plate electrodes provided uniform collecting fields which are given in volts per centimeter by the numbers attached to each curve. (H. A. Erickson, *Phys. Rev.* **27**, 473 (1908))

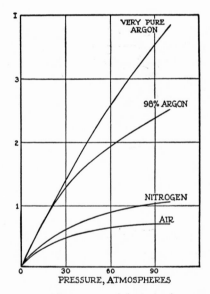

FIG. 2–5. The variation with pressure of the ionization current in various gases, showing the effect of impurities in the case of argon. Ordinate: ionization current in arbitrary units. Abscissae: pressure in atmospheres. (Compton, Wollan, and Bennett, *Rev. Sci. Inst.* **5**, 415 (1934))

ferred to as the ionization current. This conforms to the conventional notation

$$I = dQ/dt \tag{2-3}$$

where the current I in amperes is considered as a time rate of flow of charge Q. From eq. (2–2) it is seen that Q depends on the pressure and it may, therefore, be assumed that in order to have large currents it would be desirable to have high pressures. This is indeed the case at pressures up to that at which the phenomenon of saturation begins to be manifest. At the higher pressures, mobilities become less and the chances of recombination become greater. Fig. 2–4 shows the effects of saturation setting in at various pressures and voltages. At still higher pressures the ionization currents actually decrease due to recombination. Consequently it is not desirable to operate ionization chambers at excessive pressures.

The ionization current also depends on the purity of the gas in the vessel. Fig. 2–5 shows typical curves for the ionization current in argon as the purity of the gas is varied. It will be observed that purity is especially important at high pressures and not especially significant at the lower concentrations.

In the actual operation of ionization chambers and, as we shall see later, also of counters, the background or "zero" of the instrument is made up of two parts, contamination and cosmic rays. The amount of contamination-radiation produced inside the chamber is a constant for a particular instrument, and it can be determined by operating the instrument inside a thick (10-cm) lead shield and in a deep mine, where the cosmic ray background will be much reduced. The purpose of the lead shield is to reduce the background produced by contamination outside but in the vicinity of the chamber. In practice it is found that 10 cm of lead reduces the external contamination-radiation reaching the inside of the instrument to a few percent.

Such a 10-cm lead shield will have but little effect on the cosmic radiation. To exclude cosmic radiation completely is impractical, and to reduce it to a few percent requires considerable thicknesses. Thus, a thousand feet of earth or rock is equivalent to perhaps thirty meters of lead and cuts out most, but not all, of the radiation. A better method of eliminating cosmic radiation, applicable to any counting device, is to use a set of anticoincidence guard counters. The operation of such counters will be discussed later. It will suffice here to say that, by surrounding a detector with such a set, it becomes possible to reduce cosmic ray effects to a low value. This procedure does not apply to integrating chambers which do not readily lend themselves to such an arrangement.

In recent years, a number of chambers illustrating the foregoing principles have been constructed. Thus for example a boron-trifluoride chamber was constructed by Segré and Wiegand [S11] in which the collecting electrode was a steel cylinder with rounded ends. The outer diameter was 5 inches. The gas was present at 75 or 135 cm Hg pressure. The observers found marked increase in the efficiency if the high-pressure filling was operated at collecting voltages around 7000 volts. At lower voltages the electrons move more slowly, and marked electron-capture effects were observed. They also reported that the purity of the BF_3 was important. Another high-pressure chamber was built by Beghian and Halban [B9] in which very pure methane at 35 atmospheres was used. The collection time of the electrons was found to be 0.7 microsecond, and the efficiency was 12% for 2.3-Mev neutrons, the neutrons being detected by the proton-recoil process. The calculations of the effective volume for the cylindrical case are quite complex, and a series of curves has been prepared by Blackman.[B8]

D. The Motion of Ions and Electrons Through Gases

In order to understand the action of ionization detecting devices, we must discuss the motion of electrons and ions in gases, from that point at which they are produced to that at which they are collected. Since an ion or an electron, drifting through a gas under the influence of an electric field, experiences numerous collisions with gas molecules, it generally establishes an average drift velocity, which is defined with the aid of a constant called the "mobility." It is customary to write

$$v = kE/p \qquad (2\text{--}4)$$

where v is the velocity, k the mobility, E the field, and p the pressure. Usually the velocity is expressed in cm per sec, the field in volts per cm, and the pressure in atmospheres. The dimensions of the mobility, therefore, are (cm per sec, per volt per cm) (atm), or cm^2 atm/volt sec. Occasionally authors express the pressure in mm Hg, and the quantity E/p in some papers on gas-discharge phenomena is given in units of volts/cm $\times$ mm Hg. The reader is warned before using such figures that he should look carefully at the units of pressure.

Mobilities of both positive and negative ions in various gases have been studied by Loeb [L1] and others. A list of values is found in Table 2–1. It will be seen that typical positive ions have mobilities of around 1.4 cm/sec in air at STP in unit field (1 volt per cm) and negative ions are a trifle faster around 1.8 cm/sec. The experiments have shown that the concept holds over a considerable range of fields and pressures, and that the constancy of k does not begin to break down until the field becomes large or the pressures low (i.e., large E/p in counters; such high fields exist only in the immediate neighborhood of the wire). In a few gases such as hydrogen, k is larger than it is in air, values of about 6 cm/sec being observed. The values of k are extremely sensitive to the purity of the gas through which the ions are moving. For the mixtures of gases usually employed in counters, approximate values of transit times can be obtained by taking k from Table 2–1.

In a gas, an ion or electron moves an average distance, between collisions, called a "mean free path." The classical

TABLE 2-1. MOBILITIES OF IONS IN GASES

Sign of Charge	Kind of Ion	Kind of Gas	k (cm² atm/volt sec)	Reference
Positive	Alcohol	Alcohol	2.6 at 10-cm pressure	(a)
Positive	Argon	Argon	7.1 at 10-cm pressure	(a)
Positive	Hydrogen	H₂	6.7 per atm	(b)
Positive	Helium	Helium	5.1 per atm	(b)
Positive	Argon	Argon	1.37 per atm	(b)
Positive	Air		1.40 per atm	(b)
Positive	Alcohol		0.34 per atm	(b)
Negative	Air		1.78 per atm	(b)
Negative	Alcohol		0.27 per atm	(b)

(a) H. den Hartog and F. A. Muller, *Physica* **15,** 789 (1949).
(b) Smithsonian Physical Tables.
Note: For slow electrons in very pure gases, such as A or He, the mobility may become very large, 200 and 500 respectively.

mean free path for a sphere moving through a loose aggregate of other spheres of the same diameter is given by the expression:

$$L = 1/n\pi r^2 = 1/n\sigma \qquad (2\text{--}5a)$$

where L is the mean free path in cm, n is the number of obstructing spheres per cc, and r is the radius of each. The spheres are here assumed stationary. Here σ is called the "cross section." It is the geometrical cross-sectional area of each sphere for the particular process—in this case, for a collision. For some other interaction process that is not a simple geometrical collision, the effective cross section of the same atom or molecule may be quite different. Thus, for example, with resonance interactions the effective cross sections can be far greater than the "geometrical" value. If we look through a cubic centimeter from one side in a direction perpendicular to one face so that we see a one square centimeter area, and if this cubic centimeter contains n particles, then $n\sigma$ is the fraction of the total area obscured by the particles which are therein.

In the preceding discussion we have assumed that the atoms in our cubic centimeter were stationary. Since, of course, the molecules are in random motion, with average velocities determined by the temperature, and average energies proportional to kT, where k is Boltzmann's constant and T the absolute temperature, eq. (2–5a) must be modified accordingly. It can be shown that for a Maxwellian distribution of molecular velocities, the free path becomes:

$$L = 1/\sqrt{2}\, n\pi r^2 \qquad (2\text{–}5\text{b})$$

which differs from the previous equation by the factor 1.41 in the denominator. The mean free path equation is used in this form when discussing the motion of positive or negative ions through a gas.

When we come to consider the passage of an electron through a gas, we recognize that (a) the dimensions of the electron are small compared to the gas molecule and (b) the electron is moving much faster, so that the gas molecules are almost stationary in comparison. In this case the equation is

$$L = 4/n\pi r^2 \qquad (2\text{–}5\text{c})$$

i.e., the classical mean free path of the electron is four times that of a gas atom moving in an assembly of like atoms. Typical values are listed in Table 2–2.

Electrons move much faster through gases than do positive or negative ions. Electronic mobilities are greater by factors between 10^3 and 10^4. Unfortunately, values of k are constant only over small ranges of field and pressure, so that simple tables of mobilities cannot be usefully employed. Curves of electron drift velocities have been experimentally determined under a wide variety of differing conditions of fields, pressures, and kind and purity of gases. The values of the mobility are roughly constant within certain limits, but beyond these limits they can suddenly change by large amounts. Thus, for example, in a mixture of 0.95 argon plus 0.05 CO_2, the mobility of electrons is roughly constant, and the velocity is about 4×10^6 cm/sec up to a field of 1 volt

TABLE 2–2. MEAN FREE PATHS, EFFECTIVE COLLISION RADIUS AND MEAN VELOCITY

Gas	l, cm (at STP)	r, cm	$\bar{v}$ (at temperature 300° K) cm/sec
H_2	1.83×10^{-5}	1.36×10^{-8}	$2.0 \ \times 10^5$
He	2.85×10^{-5}	1.10×10^{-8}	$1.4 \ \times 10^5$
A	$1.0 \ \times 10^{-5}$	1.82×10^{-8}	$4.4 \ \times 10^4$
Ne	$1.9 \ \times 10^{-5}$	1.17×10^{-8}	$6.2 \ \times 10^4$
N_2			$5.3 \ \times 10^4$
O_2	0.99×10^{-5}	1.81×10^{-8}	4.95×10^4
Air	0.96×10^{-5}	1.87×10^{-8}	$5.2 \ \times 10^4$
BF_3			$3.4 \ \times 10^4$
$C_2H_5(OH)$			$4.1 \ \times 10^4$
Particle:			
Electron		$2 \ \ \times 10^{-13}$	1.17×10^7
Neutron		$2 \ \ \times 10^{-13}$	$2.8 \ \times 10^5$

Note: 300° K (or +27° C) corresponds to 0.0386 electron volt.
Data on radii from L. B. Loeb, *Kinetic Theory of Gases.*

per cm and a pressure of 4 mm Hg (E/p 0.25 volt per cm $\times$ mm Hg), and the velocity abruptly ceases to rise as the field is raised or the pressure lowered beyond the indicated value.

To the extent that the mobility is roughly constant, and within the limits indicated, observed figures are presented in Table 2–3.

Since the free paths in gases at ordinary pressures are of the order of 10^{-4} cm, a singly charged ion in a field of 1 volt per cm will gain about 10^{-4} ev of energy in advancing one free path. This amount of energy is small compared to its energy owing to normal kinetic motions due to temperature. We recall that

$$\tfrac{1}{2}mv^2 = eV = 3kT/2 \qquad (2\text{-}6)$$

where m is the mass of the particle under discussion, v its velocity, e the charge on the electron, and V the potential difference through which it has dropped, k is Boltzmann's constant, and T the absolute temperature. It follows from

TABLE 2-3.   MOBILITIES OF ELECTRONS IN GASES

Kind of Gas	k (cm²/sec) at Pressure × Volts	Limits E/P	Reference
BF_3	5×10^5 to 2.5×10^6 at 1 cm Hg	5 to 20 v/cm × cm Hg	(a)
Argon-Alcohol	15,700 9 cm A + 1 cm Alcohol		(b)
Alcohol	1630 10 cm		(b)
H_2 and N_2	4×10^5 at 1 mm Hg	2 to 50 v/cm × mm Hg	(c)
He	6×10^5 "	0.2 to 5 "	(c)
Ne	12.5×10^5 "	0.2 to 7 "	(c)
A	2×10^6 "	0.1 to 1 "	(c)
CO_2	1.05×10^6 "	0.5 to 8 "	(c)
BF_3	10^7 "	1 to 9 "	(c)
$0.9\ A + 0.1\ CO_2$	5×10^6 "	0.1 to 1 "	(c)

(a) J. A. Bistline, *Rev. Sci. Instr.* **19**, 842 (1949).
(b) H. den Hartog, F. A. Muller, C. S. W. van Rooden, *Physica* **15**, 581 (1949).
(c) B. Rossi and H. H. Staub, *Ionization Chambers and Counters*, McGraw-Hill (1949).

eq. (2-6) that, at a temperature of 27° C, or 300° absolute, the energy of a molecule in thermal equilibrium is 6.17×10^{-14} erg, or since 1 ev is 1.6×10^{-12} erg, room temperature corresponds to 3.85×10^{-2} ev. Since this figure is two orders of magnitude greater than the gain in energy per free path in unit field, it is evident that diffusion theory will have to be used for an extended discussion. Such a discussion is out of place in this book, and we shall refer the reader interested in greater detail to the treatises listed on p. 292 and elsewhere.

At moderate fields, all the electrons formed in the gas will be collected except those which disappear in transit. Positive and negative charges passing one another may recombine to reconstitute neutral atoms. Recombination usually takes place when a positive and a negative come together without too much kinetic energy. If a positive and a negative charge were allowed to fall toward each other from a great distance, they could acquire large velocities relative to each other and the probability of recombination would be low. If the two charges start from infinity with any appreciable component of initial velocity toward each other, they will describe hyperbolic orbits and return to infinity. For recombination to take place, it is recognized that the particles lose energy by collisions with other molecules, or that recombination takes place in the immediate neighborhood of a third body, such as a wall or other molecule.

If we consider a gas containing N_1 and N_2 positive and negative ions per cc respectively, then we can define the recombination coefficient β by the relation

$$-dN_1/dt = \beta N_1 N_2 = -dN_2/dt$$

or, since usually the numbers of positive and negative ions in a gas are equal,

$$-dN/dt = \beta N^2 \qquad (2\text{--}7)$$

Here it is clear that $-dN/dt$ is the rate at which ions disappear. Values of the recombination coefficient have been measured and have been found to be of the order of 1 to 2×10^{-6} per cc per sec for positive and negative ions in air and other common gases recombining in the absence of any appreciable field. It is evident therefore that the average ion will continue to exist as an ion for a time, or that its average lifetime will be

$$1/t = \beta N \qquad (2\text{--}8)$$

For example, in air at sea level, cosmic rays and natural radioactive contamination produce ionization continuously, and ions recombine continuously. In equilibrium, the rate of production must equal the rate of disappearance, and hence we have

$$+dN/dt = -dN/dt = \beta N^2 = q \qquad (2\text{--}9)$$

and combining with eq. (2–8) we have

$$N = qt \tag{2–10}$$

where q is the rate of production of ions per cc per sec at 1 atm, t the mean life in sec, and N the equilibrium concentration of ions per cc always present. In ordinary air at sea level, the natural causes cited above maintain about 1.6×10^3 ion pairs per cc; and for $\beta = 2 \times 10^{-6}$, the mean life of each ion-pair is 300 sec. Consistent with the foregoing figures is a rate of production q of about 5 ions per cc per sec, more or less evenly divided between ions produced by cosmic rays and produced by the contamination background.

In designing chambers, it is important that the collection time be short compared to the average lifetime, otherwise an appreciable fraction of the ions will be lost by recombination. Consider three examples, a Geiger counter, a chamber at atmospheric pressure, and a high-pressure ionization chamber.

In the counter, the average field is of the order of 1000 volts per cm; the pressure, 0.1 atm. Hence, positive and negative ions would traverse the dimensions of the counter in 10^{-4} sec. Recombination is therefore entirely negligible.

In the chamber at atmospheric pressure, if the chamber is 10 cm in radius, and the field 10 volts per cm, the ion collection time will be roughly 1 sec, and the effects of recombination are still unimportant.

In the high-pressure chamber, at 30 atm, for a 10-cm diameter and a field of 10 volts per cm, the ion transit time will be 30 sec. But in this case, because of the higher pressure, q will be 30 times greater, or 150 ions per cc per sec, and from eq. (2–9) we see that N will be 8.5×10^3 ions per cc. The average lifetime, given by eq. (2–10) or by (2–8), will be 56 sec. Hence, in this case, recombination will be appreciable.

The foregoing discussion has been carried out for positive and negative ions. The recombination of electrons with positive ions is a much less probable event. The values of β

applicable in this case are some four orders of magnitude less. Kenty [K1] and others have measured the recombination coefficient applicable in the case of 0.4-volt electrons and argon ions, and have found a value of 2×10^{-10} cc sec^{-1}. Some other values of β are given in Table 2–4. In all the preceding illustrations, because of this much lower value, if electrons

TABLE 2–4.   RECOMBINATION COEFFICIENT FOR ELECTRON-ION RECOMBINATION

Gas	cc/ions-sec
He	1.7×10^{-8}
Ne	2.03×10^{-7}
A	3×10^{-7}
H_2	2.5×10^{-6}
O_2	2.8×10^{-7}

Data from M. A. Biondi and S. C. Brown, *Phys. Rev.* **76,** 1697 (1949). Coefficient is found to be independent of pressure for monatomic gases but not independent for diatomic gases.

instead of negative ions are collected, recombination is negligible.

In the foregoing discussion we have regarded recombination as a volume phenomenon. Under certain geometrical circumstances, recombination may be much favored. A case called preferential recombination occurs if, immediately after an ion-pair is formed, the components are not separated quickly by the field, or if they are knocked back together by collisions with other atoms. A second circumstance favoring recombination is called "columnar recombination," and occurs when a dense track or column of ions is formed. For example, an alpha particle or a fission fragment passing through a gas produces such a dense column of ionization. It is seen that, although the total number of ions may not be large, they are packed closely together in a small space, and hence very large local values of N may occur. Columnar recombination has been studied by Kanne [K2] and others, who found this effect quite appreciable in the case of heavily ionizing particles. It is evident that the amount of columnar recombination will depend on the orientation of the track in the field, so that the problem becomes quite complex. Kanne pointed out that one way of mathematically expressing this effect was by using higher average values of β.

In much of this discussion we have not dwelt upon the nature of the collisions between the ion or electron and the gas molecules. These collisions can be elastic or inelastic. If the collisions are elastic, only kinetic energy and momentum are transferred from the (projectile) ion to the (target) molecule. For an ion moving through a gas of its own kind, since the mass of the ion and that of the gas molecules are practically equal, on the average one half of the energy of the ion will be transferred to the struck molecule, and the energy transfer can be as large as total transfer. In general, the ion and the molecule will separate along two paths 90° apart in the forward hemisphere. If an ion hits a heavy molecule, for example a helium ion hitting an alcohol molecule, the ion may even be deflected backwards. Since, as we have already pointed out, the gain in energy by the ion per free path is small compared to the mean kinetic temperature velocities, the detailed calculations require diffusion theory. Qualitatively it can be stated that, as a result of elastic collisions, most of the energy derived by the ion from the field will be lost in increasing the thermal agitation in the gas, and the ion will advance quite slowly. The drift velocity should be considered as a "terminal velocity."

As the field is increased, the ion will gain more and more energy per free path and will finally have enough energy to start making inelastic collisions. This process will occur when the electron or ion has attained an amount of energy equal to one of the energy levels in the target atom or molecule. For the monatomic gases this amount of energy is fairly high, but it is somewhat less for diatomic gases and can be much less for polyatomic molecules. This is true because the molecules have many molecular energy levels, in their rotation and vibration as well as electronic band structures; in general, the more complex the molecule, the more of these levels and the lower the lowest level. Thus for an electron striking a helium atom, no inelastic collisions can occur at electron energy below 19.77 volts, but if the same electron strikes an alcohol molecule an inelastic collision can occur at energies below one electron volt. The atoms or molecules excited by this inelastic collision process may dispose of the excess energy either by radiation or by making further inelastic collisions with other molecules. In the latter case the energy finally is converted into heat. If the excited atom should radiate, it may give off one or more quanta. If these quanta have an energy in excess of the photoelectric work function of the surfaces of the container, additional electrons may be liberated. This effect will be considered in detail later.

When finally the ion or electron has acquired an amount of energy equal to or greater than the ionization potential of the target molecule, it may make collisions resulting in ionization, and the processes of cumulative ionization can begin. Indeed, ionization can result from the absorption of several quanta of energy, no one of which is as great as the ionization potential, provided that the absorption acts occur within a time short compared to the radiative lifetime of the several excited states involved. The details of these various processes will be discussed in subsequent chapters when the details of the discharge are considered.

Here, however, we next examine the problem of the initial ionizing event, and of the ability of the primary entity to produce ionization. If the primary entity is a photon, it may produce ionization by the photoelectric effect, either in the gas or in the walls, or by the Compton effect, or by electron-pair production. If the primary entity is an uncharged particle such as a neutron, then it may produce ionization by producing either ionizing disintegrations or recoils.

If the primary entity is a charged particle, it will produce ionization by collision as it passes through the gas. The number of ion-pairs produced by the primary entity per cm advance in a gas is called the "primary specific ionization." Often the ion-pairs produced can themselves again impart further ionization to other atoms struck later so that a total amount of ionization often more than double the "primary" value is produced. The total is normally that which concerns us and is called the "specific ionization" of the entity in question. It is usually expressed in ion-pairs per cm, referred to passage through the gas in question at STP. It is evident that this quantity will be a function of the energy of the primary particle and will thus depend on both its mass and its velocity. The average amount of energy required to form an ion-pair is presented in Table 2–5. It will be seen that these energies are approximately double the ionization potentials, which are listed in Table 4–4. Specific ionization figures are

TABLE 2–5. AVERAGE AMOUNT OF ENERGY REQUIRED TO FORM AN ION-PAIR

Gas	Energy per Ion-Pair (ev)	Reference
H_2	33.0	(a)
He	27.8	(a)
N_2	35.0	(a)
O_2	32.3	(a)
Ne	27.4	(a)
A	25.4	(a)
Kr	22.8	(a)
Xe	20.8	(a)
BF_3	33.8	(b)
Air	32.4	(c)

(a) Rutherford-Chadwick and Ellis, *Radiations from Radioactive Substances*, Cambridge (1930).

(b) J. A. Bistline, *Rev. Sci. Instr.* **19**, 842 (1949).

(c) Value applicable to production of ion-pair by electron with energy above 4 Kev; A. Engel and M. Steenbeck, *Elektrische gasentladungen*, Vol. 1, p. 41.

found in Table 4–1 and are further discussed following eq. (4–3).

For charged particles, the total energy of the particle can eventually be entirely dissipated as ionization, although if the particle has high energy it will usually also lose energy by radiation. Once the particle has slowed down below the energy equal to the ionization potential of the gas through which it is passing, it will no longer be able to produce ionization. Thus it will no longer be able to initiate counts, although the charged particle itself may be collected and, in this act, may start a count. However, this assumes that it has managed to get into the sensitive volume of the counter through whatever envelope the counter may have, with an exceedingly small residual energy; and since this contingency is highly improbable we shall disregard it. But it does not follow that an uncharged entity cannot produce ionization if its energy is below the ionization potential of the gas being traversed. A photon of 4 or 5 volts' energy will have an energy below the ionization potential of most gases. But this photon can produce a photoelectron. Similarly a slow neutron, whose kinetic energy is a small fraction of a volt, can produce, if it enters a nucleus, a disintegration that may liberate fragments with considerable ionizing power.

The specific ionization of various particles with which we shall deal, notably electrons, mesons, protons, and alpha particles, can be thought of in terms of the loss of energy, $-dE/dx$, per unit advance through the gas. We shall first consider the ionization loss by collision processes. This problem has been studied by Bethe and Bloch. The equation,

$$-dE/dx = NZ \frac{8\pi}{3} \left(\frac{e^2}{mc^2} \right)^2 \frac{1}{\beta^2} \left\{ \log \left[\frac{(E - m_0 c^2) E^2 \beta^2}{2 m_0 c^2 I^2 Z^2} \right] \right.$$
$$\left. + \left(\frac{m_0 c^2}{E} \right)^2 \right\} \quad (2\text{–}8)$$

where I is the ionization potential of the gas, N is the number of atoms per cc, and Z the atomic number, has been developed by quantum theory.

The experimental curves have been studied by numerous investigators and can be summarized as in Fig. 2–6. It will be seen that, as the energy increases, the specific ionization drops rapidly until a minimum is reached, and after this min-

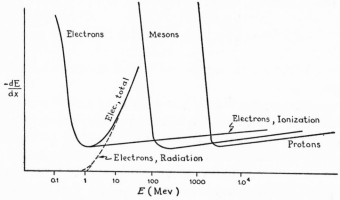

FIG. 2–6. Rate of loss of energy, as a function of the energy of the particle indicated. The curve for electrons has a minimum at around 1 Mev, or $2m_0c^2$, and rises steeply thereafter.

imum the curve again climbs but very slowly. The minimum occurs at around 35 ion-pairs per cm in standard air. All the various particles attain this same value, and hence the ionization by itself is not a sufficient criterion to enable particles to be distinguished from one another, unless something else such as the mass, or the energy, or the velocity is also known.

At energies below that for minimum ionization, the amount of ionization evidently depends inversely on the velocity of the particle; i.e., the longer it stays in the vicinity of the target particle, the greater the probability of interaction. The minimum occurs at about $3m_0c^2$ where m_0 is the relativistic rest-mass of the particle in question. For the electron the minimum occurs at a slightly lower energy since the effects of radiation loss are starting to be appreciable. Thus for protons minimum energy-loss takes place at energies between 2 and 3 Bev.

A particle can also lose energy by radiation, for if a charged particle is suddenly stopped, it will radiate according to classical electrodynamics. Formulae for the rate of loss of energy $-dE$ by radiation in distance dx have also been developed, and the well-known Bethe equation is

$$-dE/dx = \frac{NZ^2}{137}\left(\frac{e^2}{mc^2}\right)^2 E\left(4\log 183Z^{-\frac{1}{3}} + \frac{2}{9}\right) \quad (2\text{–}11)$$

where Z is the atomic number of the gas traversed, and E the energy.

For electrons, this rate of loss of energy becomes significant, i.e., exceeds the rate of loss of energy by ionization at about 8 Mev. The equation implies that other particles would also radiate, but since the mass term is in the denominator, the loss of energy by radiation is not significant for protons until energies of 10^4 Bev have been attained. It is not known today whether the assumptions in deriving eq. (2–11) are still valid at this energy, and radiation from particles heavier than electrons is not often observed. Some discussion of radiation from mesons has appeared in recent months, but as yet no measurements have been published. We can, however, present the curves showing the rate of loss of energy from electrons, on which both the ionization loss and the radiation are presented. Such a curve is given in Fig. 2–6.

Neutrons passing through a gas can produce ionization by the recoil process if the neutron energy is sufficiently high. The energy of neutrons is lost in single, large, and widely spaced events, so that the concept of "energy-loss per cm advance through the gas" has little significance. We shall give the computations for the energy loss of neutrons in Chapter 3 in the discussion of neutron counters. Since a neutron may go for distances up to 100 meters through a gas between ionizing collisions, it is clear that measurements of the average ionization do not provide the ideal method of measuring neutrons, unless the flux of neutrons is exceptionally large.

Quanta passing through a gas can also produce ionization, and since the average free path between ionizing acts is not as large as it is for neutrons, we may discuss it here. Indeed, the flux of quanta is often great enough so that these average energy-loss considerations have experimental meaning. Quanta lose energy by (a) causing the ejection of electrons directly, the photoelectric effect, (b) by Compton encounters, and (c) by producing electron-pairs. We may consider each of these.

In a gas, a photon may cause electrons to be ejected from the gas molecules if the photon energy is equal to or greater than the ionization potential of the gas. Indeed, if the flux of quanta is sufficiently great, so that the probability of a quantum being absorbed by the atom in an excited state is appreciable, the atom may become ionized stepwise by the absorption of several quanta, each of which is itself below the ionization potential so far as energy is concerned. This discussion is further complicated by the existence in certain gases of metastable states, which because of their long lifetime may, in some instances, make considerable difference in the probability of a flux of quanta whose individual energies are below the ionization potential producing ionization. Moreover, it should also be recalled that the same metastable states are subject to "unloading" by collision with foreign gas atoms so that the contributions of these states are important only if the gas is pure; in mixture of gases, the chance of the metastable state contributing appreciably is small. The magnitude of these effects can be readily computed with the aid of data already given, for the mean free time between collisions is the mean free path, eq. (2–5b), divided by the average velocity, eq. (2–6), or

$$t = 1/v = \sqrt{m}/N\pi r^2 \sqrt{6kT} \qquad (2\text{–}12)$$

which, for an average gas at STP, will be around 10^{-9} sec. Since the lifetimes of ordinary excited states are about 10^{-8} sec, stepwise ionization will not often occur, for most of the excited states will lose energy by collision before they have had time to radiate, and the condition for stepwise ionization is that they must have absorbed the second quantum before the inelastic collision has had time to take place. Metastable states have lifetimes against radiative unloading of 10^{-4} sec or even longer, so that at low pressures cumulative effects in gases having such metastable states can be important. Tables of ionization potentials and of the energies of metastable states are given in Chapters 3 and 4.

Quanta incident upon the metallic surface of the electrodes in counters can also produce electrons by the photoelectric effect. The electron is liberated from the metallic electrode if the energy of the incident quantum is equal to or greater than the photoelectric work function of the surface in question. These work functions are ordinarily considerably below the ionization potentials of most gases. Some typical work functions are listed in Table 2–6.

It should be added that the photoelectric efficiencies, i.e., the probabilities that a given quantum of sufficient energy shall actually produce an electron, are low for many surfaces around 10^{-4}, and only for a few carefully prepared surfaces much above 10^{-2}. It should be further added that the photoelectric work function and also the efficiency of a surface are very materially affected by its past history, by the formation of thin oxide or other films, and by its cleaning, heating and other treatment; hence, in practice, considerable variations from the figures in the table will be found.

The Compton effect occurs when a high energy quantum produces a recoiling electron with sufficient energy to ionize. The magnitude of the effect can be computed by writing the equations for the conservation of energy and momentum in the collision between the quantum and the scattered electron.

TABLE 2-6.   PHOTOELECTRIC WORK FUNCTIONS

Surface	Work Function (ev)	Effect of Gas on ϕ, Work Function	
		Increase	Decrease
Ag	4.7–3.85	H_2	O_2, N_2, CN
Au	4.73	H	Air
C	4.82	H_2, CO_2 Air, NH_3	
Cu	4.5–4.1		
Cs	1.9		
Fe	4.7–4.2	O_2, H_2	
Pt	6.3–4.4	H_2, NH_3	O_2
Zn	3.7–3.3		

Data from A. L. Hughes and L. A. DuBridge, *Photoelectric Phenomena*, McGraw-Hill (1932).

The effect is important only at high energies. It is clearly a volume effect, i.e., the probability of a Compton encounter occurring in a counter or ionization chamber is proportional to the volume of the chamber and increases directly as the pressure of the gas in the chamber increases. Electrons may also be scattered out of the walls of the vessel by high energy quanta.

High energy quanta may produce electron-pairs. Such pair production can take place if the energy of the incident quantum is above twice the relativistic rest-energy of the electron, $2m_0c^2$, or around 1 Mev. However, the probability of such pair production at the threshold is small. The probability of pair production increases with increasing photon energy, until, when the quantum energy is large compared to 1 Mev, the "mean free path" for pair production or the average distance a quantum must go before it produces a pair is defined as the "unit length" in radiation theory. It is about

0.4 cm in lead, 35 cm in H_2O, or 275 meters in air. Thus it will be seen that this process also is a volume effect, and that it is not probable that a single high energy quantum will produce many pairs in the gas of the radiation-detecting instrument.

Another mechanism which causes energy-loss in electrons moving through a gas is that of molecular dissociation. The dissociation energies of the majority of two- and three-atom molecules are substantially below the ionization potentials. In some cases the molecules upon impact dissociate into neutral atoms; in others, into ions. Thus, for example, Stueckleberg and Smyth [S18] find that CO_2 dissociates into CO plus O at 5.7 volts, and CO into C and O at 10; N_2 and O_2 dissociate into neutral atoms at 9.1 and 5.6 volts respectively. The various oxides of nitrogen have many complex dissociation products, going into neutral atoms at low energies (for example, N_2O into N_2 plus O at as little as 2 volts) and into ionic fragments at somewhat higher energies. Most of the cases of dissociation accompanied by ionization require as much as 10 to 15 volts, and a few as such as N_2O into NO plus ionized N at 19.1 volts. Since, in a counter, electrons are progressively accelerated, we shall find some dissociation taking place every time that a counter filled with anything except a monatomic gas counts. Some of the decomposition products of the more complex organic molecules will be discussed in Chapter 4, where the problem of quenching is reviewed. (See Chapter 4, Paragraphs B3e.)

THE DYNAMIC CONDENSER OR VIBRATING REED ELECTROMETER

Among the techniques of measurement of small currents and voltages, the dynamic condenser electrometer, also sometimes called the vibrating reed electrometer, has been thoroughly investigated by Palevesky, Swank, and Grenchik [P5] in recent years. This device consists of a condenser, one plate of which is mechanically driven to produce an a-c signal. The small charge to be measured is applied to one plate, altering the signal. Then through a feedback network the original signal is subtracted out, so that shifts of the original signal are compensated; the device thus has very small zero drift. The system which Palevesky and his associates developed has on its lowest range 0 to 10 millivolts ±0.1 millivolt, and higher ranges available by switching; a zero drift of less than 0.1 mv per day; a background current of 10^{-16} ampere, and a noise level of 50-microvolt peak value.

PROBLEMS

Use the data from the tables in the text.

1. Compute the collection time to be expected for positive ions in a chamber with 4-cm spacing of electrodes, an average field of 200 volts per cm, and containing pure argon at 25.3-cm pressure.

(*Ans.* 4830 microseconds.)

2. Compute the collection time for electrons in same chamber.

(*Ans.* 2.52 microseconds.)

3. Show whether recombination is or is not important in the above case.

(*Ans.* Not important.)

4. What potential across a hydrogen-filled chamber with parallel plates 2 cm apart will cause a hydrogen ion to acquire enough energy in one mean free path to ionize a hydrogen molecule, assuming a pressure of 7.6 cm Hg. (Ionization Potentials, see Table 4–4.)

(*Ans.* 154,000 volts.)

5. What is the minimum depth of an ionization chamber required to stop in the gas alpha particles from radon, of range 4.1 cm, assuming it to be filled with 2 atm of argon.

(*Ans.* 1.52 cm.)

6. If an electron produces on the average 100 ion-pairs per cm in argon at 1 atm, find the "range" of a 200-kv electron in a chamber containing argon at 10 atm.

(*Ans.* 8 cm.)

7. Will radiation at wavelength 2537 Å, one of the low-level transitions in mercury, cause photoelectrons to be emitted from copper?

(*Ans.* Yes; 2537 Å = 4.9 ev and ϕ = 4.7 ev.)

CHAPTER 3

PROPORTIONAL COUNTERS

A. Introduction

In this chapter we shall discuss the operation of counters in the proportional region. According to the definition previously given, this is the region which has for its lower limit the lowest voltage at which gas amplification takes place, and for its upper limit the Geiger threshold. The upper part of this region includes the region of limited proportionality.

As we have indicated above, the size of the pulse V in volts appearing on the central wire system is given by eq. (1–1), namely

$$V = Ane/C \tag{3-1}$$

where A is the gas amplification, n is the number of electrons formed in the initial ionizing event. If the pulse size V is to be expressed in volts, then e is the charge on the electron in microcoulombs and C is the distributed capacity of the central wire system in microfarads. Eq. (3–1) assumes that the positive ions have been collected and the space charge is absent.* As each initial electron enters the region of high field near the central wire, it will gain enough energy to produce additional ions by collision, and the new electrons thus produced may in turn produce others. Thus an avalanche or cascade of electrons is produced by each initial electron. The gas amplification A is defined as the number of additional electrons pro-

---

* The transient changes in wire potential while the positive ions are moving out to the cylinder play an important rôle in quenching the counter discharge and will be discussed in Chapter 4.

duced by each initial electron and by its progeny as it travels from the place where it is originally formed to the central wire. Thus A is a measure of the size of the "avalanche" which each initial electron starts, and the avalanches are assumed to be independent of each other. The quantity A is equal to unity in the region below the threshold for proportional counter action, and it becomes very large above the Geiger threshold. In this chapter we shall discuss the determination of the gas amplification A, and the experiments which establish the dependence of A on various factors.

The primary purpose of a proportional counter is to provide a device which will give an output pulse produced by some initial ionizing event of sufficient size to operate a recording mechanism. It is further necessary that some other ionizing event, smaller than this first one by a known amount, shall not produce a pulse large enough to record. This exclusion is essential if pulses are to be studied in the presence of a considerable background of smaller pulses, such as those due to alphas in the presence of those produced by betas, or those due to protons or other nuclear particles accelerated by a cyclotron in the presence of the enormous gamma ray background produced by the same device.

It is evident that any pulse may be amplified to a desired size either in the counter itself (by controlling A) or in the attached vacuum tube circuit. Two independent variables are provided in this manner. We shall discuss the practical limits to counter amplification in this chapter and electronic amplifiers in Chapter 7. In general, only a certain amount of amplification is possible in proportional counters. If we seek to make A greater than a certain value (often about 10^4) the counter becomes a Geiger counter and loses its power of discrimination between pulse sizes. However, the amplification readily obtainable is enough to permit initially quite small ionizing events to be, for example, displayed and studied on an oscilloscope screen.

B. THEORY OF PROPORTIONAL COUNTER ACTION [R3]

1. Development of the Theory. Consider an electron which has been formed at some place within the volume of the counter by an initial ionizing event. This electron will drift toward the central wire under the influence of the field due to the applied voltage. As the electron drifts in, it will make collisions with the atoms and molecules of the gas with which the counter is filled. Since the counter has cylindrical geometry, the field varies inversely as the first power of the radius. Since the field increases toward the central wire, the electron will acquire more energy per unit path near the central wire. We may also assume that the collisions are, at least in part, not elastic, and that the electron loses most, if not all, of its energy at each collision. When the electron gains enough energy in one free path between collisions to produce ionization, the next time it hits an atom it will ionize that atom. We have thus the beginning of the process of cumulative ionization, which is the basis of counter action. If this collision resulting in ionization takes place at some distance from the central wire, we will then have the initial electron plus the new electron. Both start on their next free paths toward the central wire. Since the field increases nearer the wire, any electron which has acquired enough energy to produce ionization by collision at one point, will acquire enough energy to ionize in each subsequent mean free path.

This situation determines at once the threshold voltage for proportional counter action. This voltage is that at which the electron acquires just sufficient energy to ionize in the last free path before it is collected on the central wire. If the voltage applied to the counter is increased, the critical distance at which ionization commences, will move out into the volume of the counter. As the electron begins to ionize at points progressively further out, the total number of electrons produced will increase rapidly, and we have the beginning of the familiar

Townsend avalanche. If we denote by alpha the number of ion-pairs formed by an electron in each centimeter of drift toward the central wire, we get

$$dN = \alpha N \, dx$$

where dN is the number of new electrons formed by N electrons in this process, in a distance between x and $x + dx$. The quantity α is called the first Townsend coefficient and is a function of the field strength, the nature of the gas and the pressure of the gas. If α is independent of x we may integrate this equation and obtain

$$N = N_0 e^{\alpha x} \qquad (3\text{--}2)$$

where the constant of integration N_0 is the initial number of electrons. The values of α appropriate to a wide variety of gas discharge problems, for various gases, field strengths and pressures have been measured by many observers, and the dependence of this quantity on various factors is discussed in detail in treatises on gas discharges.[L1], [C2], [D1] It will suffice to say that Townsend has found an empirical expression

$$\alpha = Ape^{(-Bp/E)} \qquad (3\text{--}3)$$

where A and B are constants determined by the particular experiment, E is the field and p the pressure. The values of A and B for many different gases have been determined.

We shall now apply this theory to the problem of a counter. In this case we have the field varying inversely as the first power of the radius, and for any given condition we can then compute the number of electrons arriving at the central wire. But first we shall discuss positive ions, which also have a part in the Townsend theory.

Each time an ionizing collision takes place a positive ion is formed as well as an electron. These positive ions drift outward toward the cylinder, and we shall discuss in a later section the rôle which they play when they reach the cylinder.

Since the field through which they travel is decreasing as they advance, they do not contribute appreciably to the cumulative ionization process. Because they travel slowly compared to the electrons, they are left behind as the electrons travel in toward the central wire. The entire electron avalanche is completed before the positive ions have moved any appreciable distance. As we shall see below, the presence of these positives produces a space charge which alters the field in this vicinity, and it is this lowering of the field which is in the main responsible for the counter discharge ceasing. However, in the action of a proportional counter, these effects are not important, and we will assume that we may neglect the positive ions and their effects in the present discussion.

We must now make some further simplifying assumptions regarding the nature of the discharge. We will assume first that recombination does not take place to any appreciable extent. If the electrons or positive ions were to disappear through recombination, the picture would be substantially altered. However, at the low pressures and high field strengths found in counters, recombination is extremely improbable, and our assumption that none occurs is substantially correct. In the chapter on Geiger counters we shall justify this assumption by citing numerical values of the recombination coefficient.

Electron attachment to form negative ions occurs only in strongly electro-negative gases such as oxygen, chlorine or fluorine. The effects found with these gases are discussed in detail in a subsequent chapter. Naturally the production of negative ions would substantially alter the avalanche, and indeed the whole character of the discharge. Negative ions move very slowly compared to the electrons. The importance of negative ions in special cases is also further discussed in the chapter on Geiger counters and the numerical value of the electron attachment coefficient is given. We exclude counters containing electronegative gases from this discussion. We shall assume that the electron avalanche is the only agency by which negative charge reaches the central wire, and that no appreciable number of negative ions is formed.

We shall also neglect fluctuations. This assumption is equivalent to saying that the ionization produced along the path of any electron is equal to the average ionization produced by that electron. Due to statistical fluctuations, any individual electron may of course produce more or less than this amount of ionization. The process of taking this into account in a rigorous discussion would be quite cumbersome mathematically. The fact that we obtain good agreement between experiments and a theory neglecting fluctuations shows that we are not seriously in error when we assume that fluctuations may be disregarded and averages used.

We will assume that the photons, if any, formed in the avalanche do not play any important rôle. We shall find later that this assumption breaks down under certain conditions, and there is evidence that the photons are important in certain cases. Where they are present, the ionization will increase more rapidly owing to their presence and the pulses obtained will be larger. We shall see, however, that photon emission may be neglected in many cases, particularly in those in which complex molecules are present. Secondary electron emission due to recombination and positive ion bombardment of the cathode is also neglected. The agreement between theory and experiment justifies these simplifying assumptions.

We shall next consider the formation of an electron avalanche. In the case of a counter, we have two concentric cylindrical electrodes, the cathode and the central wire. Let the wire radius be r_1, the inner radius of the cathode be r_2, and let a voltage V be applied to the counter. Then the field E at any radius r within the volume of the counter ($r_1 < r < r_2$) will be given by

$$E = V/r \log(r_2/r_1) \qquad (3\text{-}4)$$

As the voltage across the counter is slowly raised, a value is attained at which the multiplicative process we have called the avalanche starts. The lowest voltage at which this occurs we call the threshold voltage for proportional counter action, V_p. The physical significance of this voltage lies in the fact that it is the minimum at which an electron traveling toward the central wire acquires energy enough to ionize in its last free path before it reaches the wire. We define the radius r_o as that radius at which the avalanche starts. At the threshold r_o equals the wire radius, or $r_o = r_1$. Now r_o in the region of proportional counting never becomes much greater than r_1 (see discussion of mean free paths below), and we may therefore assume an approximately linear dependence on the potential. Hence we may relate the radius r_o, at which the avalanche starts when the voltage applied is V, to the threshold voltage V_p by the relation

$$r_o = r_1 V / V_p \qquad (3\text{-}5)$$

Thus r_o is defined in terms of the directly measurable voltages and wire radius.

The amplification factor A, defined following eq. (3–1), is determined by the number of ionizing collisions which the electron makes as it travels to the wire, or in other words by eq. (3–2). If we start with a single electron,

$$A = e^{\int \alpha \, dx} \qquad (3\text{-}6)$$

The number of ionizing collisions depends on the mean free path, which is in turn a function of the energy.

We shall next consider how the mean free path for ionization depends on the energy. This dependence has been studied by a number of investigators.[C2] They find that, in the low voltage region, the ionization cross section increases linearly with the energy. The term cross section is used to mean that area, in square cm, which when multiplied by the number of atoms per cc gives the reciprocal of the mean free path; and the "mean free path for ionization" means the average distance an electron must travel, in this gas, before it makes an ionizing collision. In the higher energy ranges, the dependence is by no means linear, and complicated curves have been found experimentally in many cases. However, we are not concerned here with this extension. In the average counter the mean free path is of the order of 10^{-3} cm. A multiplication or amplification of a factor of 1000 can occur if the electron starts to ionize about ten mean free paths from the wire. Hence these avalanches only occupy the last tenth of a millimeter of space next to the wire. The electron travels through almost the entire dimensions of the counter before it acquires a velocity corresponding to the ionization potential of about 15 electron volts. As the electron approaches still more closely to the wire, it receives more acceleration but it loses energy with each collision. Consideration of eq. (3–4) shows that it does not acquire energy in the last tenth of a millimeter differing by orders of magnitude from that which it received in the previous tenth. We may assume that electron energies involved do not ordinarily exceed 30 to 50 volts. In this energy region, experiments show that the ionization cross section varies linearly with the energy. We may therefore write for the cross section σ,

$$\sigma = a\epsilon - B \qquad (3\text{–}7)$$

where ϵ is the energy and a the constant of proportionality, or rate of increase of cross section with energy, and B is a constant which does not concern this discussion. This quantity a has been measured by various workers and a few illustrative values are given in Table 3–1.

Since the mean free paths possess various orientations, we must consider an average energy ϵ_{av}.

If we have N atoms or molecules per unit volume, we may relate ϵ_{av} to α, the reciprocal of the mean free path for ionization, through the equation

$$\alpha = N\sigma = aN\epsilon_{av} - BN \qquad (3\text{–}8a)$$

and we now have the problem of determining the average energy ϵ_{av}.

Gas	$a(10^{17}$ Cm^2/Volt)	Reference
A	1.81	*
Ne	0.14	*
He	0.11	*
H_2	0.46	†
O_2	0.66	†
N_2	0.70	†
NO	0.74	†
CO	0.83	†
C_2H_2	1.91	†
CH_4	1.24	‡

* P. T. Smith, *Phys. Rev.* **36**, 1293 (1930).
† J. T. Tate and P. T. Smith, *Phys. Rev.* **30**, 270 (1932).
‡ A. L. Hughes and E. Klein, *Phys. Rev.* **23**, 450 (1924).

This quantity can only be determined by making approximations. A rigorous treatment appears to involve considerable mathematical complexity. If we write $N(r)$ for the number of electrons at a distance r from the center of the wire, and $n(\epsilon, r)$ as the number having energies between ϵ and $\epsilon + d\epsilon$, then the change in N as r decreases by dr would be given by

$$-dN = N(r)dr \int_0^{\epsilon_{max}} \frac{n(\epsilon, r)}{l(\epsilon)} \, d\epsilon \qquad (3-8b)$$

where $l(\epsilon)$ is the mean free path which is also a function of the energy, and ϵ_{max} is the maximum energy which the electrons have at r, in excess of the average ionization potential of the gas or mixture in the counter. Up to the present time, an exact solution of this integral equation and a determination of the distribution functions has not been accomplished. Certain approximations, however, appear to yield results which are useful experimentally.

First we recall that $n(\epsilon, r)$ has the dimensions of $(\text{energy})^{-1}$ and hence can be written quite generally as

$$n(\epsilon, r) = (1/\epsilon_{\text{av}})\phi(\epsilon/\epsilon_{\text{av}}) \qquad (3\text{--}8c)$$

where ϕ is a dimensionless function and the dependence on r is contained in $\epsilon_{\text{av}}(r)$. We now consider cases where the number of electrons is greatest. Since, of the electrons at r, more than half were formed in the last mean free path, and since the more remote the point of origin, or the greater the energy, the fewer the number of corresponding electrons, the energy distribution will be monotonically decreasing with the most important energy region at $\epsilon = o$. We may thus set $\epsilon = o$ and $-d\epsilon/dr = CV/r$, where $\frac{1}{2}C$ is the capacity per unit length of the counter. Hence from eqs. (3–8a), (3–8b) and (3–8c) a value for the average energy is obtained,

$$\epsilon_{\text{av}}(r) = (\phi(o)CV/aNr)^{\frac{1}{2}} \qquad (3\text{--}9)$$

where $\phi(o)$ is the number of slowest electrons, a quantity which we normalize and take as unity in the discussion which follows. Hence, combining with eq. (3–8a) we have

$$\alpha = (aNCV/r)^{\frac{1}{2}} \qquad (3\text{--}10)$$

Making use of eq. (3–5) and using the definition of A from eq. (3–2) we obtain

$$A = \exp 2(aNCr_1V)^{\frac{1}{2}}[(V/V_p)^{\frac{1}{2}} - 1] \qquad (3\text{--}11)$$

which defines the gas amplification A in terms of experimentally measurable quantities, the voltages, wire radius, etc. A fuller discussion is given in the original paper [R3] and many of the concepts used are described in detail in texts on gas discharges.[L1, D1]

2. Comparison of Theory with Experiment. It will be seen that eq. (3–11) predicts that the gas amplification A should depend on the wire radius (r_1), the capacitance (C) of the counter system, the voltage (V), the pressure of the gas (N), and the kind of gas (a). A series of experiments [R3] was performed to verify the dependence on each of these quantities. The amplification factor was measured, by observing the pulse size in accordance with eq. (3–1), as a function of the voltage, for a counter in which the pressure was varied. Straight lines on semilogarithmic plots were obtained, the slopes and intercepts being those predicted by eq. (3–11). A typical curve, showing dependence of A on V for various gases, is shown in Fig. 3–1. Next methane-argon mixtures were tested, the total pressure being kept constant but the percentage of each gas being changed. This effectively tested the dependence on a, since a for methane and argon are different (cf. Table 3–1). Again, agreement with the prediction of eq. (3–11) was obtained. Finally various polyatomic gas mixtures were tried and again agreement was obtained. The dependence on wire diameter was also checked, and was found to be correctly predicted by eq. (3–11). The amplification increases as the wire diameter is decreased. The practical limit for wire diameters is approximately 3 mils for counters which are to be normally handled in the laboratory. While counters using 1 mil wire have a higher ampli-

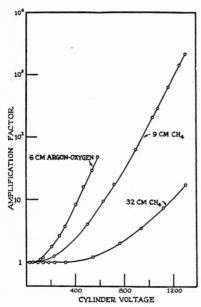

FIG. 3–1. Amplification factor (logarithmic scale) against cylinder voltage for 6-cm argon-oxygen (0.94 A + 0.06 O_2) and two pressures of CH_4. (Rose & Ramsey, *Phys. Rev.* **61**, 199 (1942))

fication factor, this wire is so fragile that the counter may easily be broken in normal use. With the exception of some interesting departures from agreement which we shall discuss below, the good agreement between theory and experiment suggests that the picture we have built up of the avalanche mechanism will satisfactorily describe the proportional counter discharge.

Departures from agreement with the predictions of eq. (3–11) were found in certain cases. These departures are especially interesting in that they throw further light on the nature of the discharge mechanism.

First consider the effects at high voltages. As the voltage is progressively increased, good agreement is maintained until the value of A reaches approximately 10^4. At higher voltages, the pulse size increases with voltage faster than is predicted by eq. (3–11). This is found to occur as the counter enters the region of limited proportionality, traverses this region and goes into the Geiger region. The significance of an increase faster than that predicted by the equation is that something besides the Townsend avalanche is involved. In other words, our limiting simplifying assumptions are not being met. Let us suppose, for example, that ultraviolet photons are formed in the avalanche and reach the cylinder. Here they may liberate photoelectrons which will in turn travel to the wire and start new avalanches. The pulse size will therefore be larger than eq. (3–11), which assumes no photons, predicts. Again, if new electrons are liberated by positive ions reaching the cylinder, the same result occurs. Thus the departure at high voltages is in a direction which indicates that some mechanism, in addition to the simple Townsend avalanche, is operative.

It seems probable that, at amplifications above 10^4, space charge limitations also begin to make themselves felt. The theory of the limitation of the discharge by space charge was developed by the Montgomerys,[M3] and will be discussed fully in the section on Geiger counters. Indeed the main feature of the region of limited proportionality is that large pulses do not increase with voltage as fast as do small pulses. This feature may be ascribed to the effects of space charge, for a large pulse will result in the production of more positive ions and hence more space charge than will a small one. As the field near the wire is reduced by this space charge, the avalanche size will also tend to be decreased, and hence this effect will operate more efficiently on the larger pulses.

Another important departure occurs when gas mixtures are used and the mixture is varied in the direction of an increasing percentage of monatomic gas. Here again another mechanism is evidently at work in addition to the Townsend avalanche, tending to produce more electrons, and hence larger pulses than the avalanche alone, and eq. (3–11) would predict. The experiments reveal an important limitation on eq. (3–11), namely that with monatomic and diatomic gases this equation begins to break down at amplifications of around 100, whereas polyatomic gases may give values of A up to 10,000 before eq. (3–11) ceases adequately to describe the phenomenon. We may tie in this observation by saying that the phenomenon is due to positive ion bombardment of the cylinder. Bombardment by monatomic and diatomic positive ions causes electron emission while polyatomic positive ions, as we shall show, do not. Hence the pure monatomic and diatomic gases, and the mixtures of monatomic with polyatomic, such as equal parts of argon and methane, will exhibit the faster rise of A with V than eq. (3–11) calls for. This positive ion bombardment of the cathode resulting in release of electrons is presumably the main factor in the rapid rise of A with V for low values of A, but this effect is suppressed by the heavier molecules. Thus by adding methane to an argon-filled counter, it is necessary to arrive at a mixture 75% methane and 25% argon before suppression is complete while addition of but 10% of a still larger molecule such as ether to an argon-filled counter produces good agreement with eq. (3–11).

The practical consequence of this circumstance is that any gas or mixture whatever can be made to operate in a proportional counter. However, monatomic and diatomic gas-filled counters are characterized by a much more rapid variation of A with V than are those with polyatomic fillings. The sharp dependence of A on V requires much more critical stabilization and control of the counter operating voltage, and consequently it is usually more convenient to use polyatomic gases in proportional counters. The disadvantage of the polyatomic filling over the monatomic gas lies in (a) the fact that the polyatomic molecules are broken up and consequently the counter changes its characteristics with use, and (b) that the starting and operating potentials of the polyatomic gas counters are generally higher than those filled with monatomic gases. As Spatz has shown [81] a lifetime of about 10^{10} counts may be expected before a polyatomic gas-filled Geiger counter becomes useless due to breakdown of the constituents, and a somewhat longer life may be expected for a proportional counter due to the smaller avalanche size and hence the smaller number of molecules decomposed at each discharge. The starting potentials of counters filled with pure polyatomic gases can be reduced somewhat by adding a monatomic gas; thus, for example, a counter filled with pure methane will actually have its operating potential lowered by adding 10% of argon (the methane content remaining fixed) while the efficiency is also improved by this procedure and its other operating characteristics do not suffer.

In addition to the effects due to positive ions, we must also consider effects due to photons formed in the discharge. Derivation of eq. (3–11) presupposes absence of photons and departures of experimental behavior from agreement with this equation may also indicate that this assumption is, in certain cases, not valid. Photons would produce additional ionization, and consequently the increase of the avalanche size A with V would be more rapid than eq. (3–11) predicts. In the avalanche, photons are presumably formed since collisions result in excitation and atoms in excited states will mostly lose their energy by radiation, the lifetime of these states being of the order of 10^{-8} sec while the mean free time between collisions is somewhat in excess of this figure. Recombination radiation may also occur. As we have pointed out above, recombination is not likely in the avalanche itself, because of the low pressures and high fields. Nevertheless, recombination at the cathode occurs when the positive ions reach it and become neutralized. Again we must consider what happens to the photons.

It should also be pointed out that photons arising from excited atoms of any of the monatomic or diatomic gases normally used in counters, have energies which are mostly greater than the photoelectric threshold of the cathode. Thus, for example, in hydrogen, the Lyman series starts at about 10 volts, and radiation from a helium atom returning to the ground state from, say, the $2P$ level, corresponds in energy to about 20 volts. The photoelectric thresholds of copper and brass are in the neighborhood of 3 volts and consequently the photons from the excited atoms, if they reach the cathode, may be expected to cause emission of photoelectrons. Similarly, the photons which are emitted at the cathode as recombination radiation, also are almost all considerably above the photoelectric threshold in energy. The fact that eq. (3–11), which assumes no photons, fits as well as it does, means that we must explain the absence of both excitation and recombination photons.

The case of recombination photons is discussed at length in the section on self-quenching counters. There it is pointed out that polyatomic ions predissociate instead of radiate upon neutralization. As a result, there are no photons representing recombination radiation in the case of polyatomic molecules. With monatomic and diatomic molecules, such photons will be present and the expected deviations from eq. (3–11), in the direction of faster variation of A with V, occur.

The photons formed by excitation, in the case of monatomic and diatomic gases, are presumably also present, and help to cause the deviations from eq. (3–11) which we have mentioned. There are experimental proofs that photons are present in the discharge. One of these is the experiment on the "localization of the discharge" performed by Wilkening and Kanne [W2] and others. The experiment on localization will be discussed more fully in the next section. There is also an experiment with perforated cathodes, performed by Rose and Korff.[R3] In the latter experiment, A was measured as a function of V for counters with perforated and solid cathodes. It was found that a difference could be detected at large pulse sizes when the counter was filled with a monatomic or diatomic gas. The difference was in the direction of smaller pulses for the perforated cathode, suggesting that the fact that some photons escaped through the perforations made a difference in the pulse size. No difference was observed when the counter was filled with a gas with polyatomic molecules, thus lending further support to the validity of the basic assumption of eq. (3–11) of no photons. The fact that photons are of importance only at large pulse sizes is presumably due to the low photoelectric efficiency. Only a few photons will be generated in a small avalanche, and only a small fraction (10^{-4} or so for most commonly used cathodes) of these will add electrons to the avalanche. Consequently the amplification A must approach the order of 10^4 before excitation photons begin to contribute appreciably to the avalanche size.

The behavior of proportional counters at low values of A has been studied by Rose and Ramsey.[R4] They have investigated the portion of the amplification factor vs. voltage curve near the threshold for proportional counter action, both above and below the threshold. As might be expected from consideration of the statistical nature of the avalanche process, the threshold is not an abrupt phenomenon, but the observed curves gradually trend toward the horizontal. The threshold voltage predicted by eq. (3–11) is the voltage corresponding to the point where the straight line portion of the curve, if extrapolated downward (see Fig. 3–1), would intersect the abscissa for unit A. Fig. 3–2 shows the curves obtained at higher values of A. The experimental curve departs from the computed curve because the theory neglects fluctuations and assumes average energies for the electrons in the avalanche.

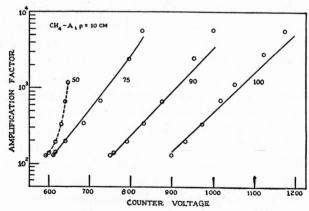

FIG. 3–2. The amplification factor (logarithmic scale) plotted against counter voltage for various relative concentrations in CH_4-A mixtures at 10-cm pressure. The points are experimental and the full curves are theoretical with one point adjusted (see eq. (3–11)). The numbers affixed to the curves give the relative concentration of CH_4 in percent. The dimensions of the counter were: wire diameter 0.075 mm; Cu. cylinder, diameter 1 cm and length 3 cm. (From M. E. Rose and S. A. Korff, *Phys. Rev.* **59**, 850–859 (1941))

Such fluctuations are percentagewise largest for values of A just greater than unity, and become unimportant at values of A greater than 10 or 20.

C. COUNTERS FOR SPECIAL PURPOSES

1. Neutron Counters. *a. Counters for Slow Neutrons.* To detect slow neutrons, proportional counters filled with boron trifluoride (BF_3), which is a gas at normal room temperature, may be used.[K3] A neutron entering this gas may interact with the boron nucleus according to the reaction:

$$_0n^1 + {}_5B^{10} \rightarrow {}_5B^{11*} \rightarrow {}_3Li^7 + {}_2He^4 + Q \qquad (3–12)$$

where the subscripts indicate the atomic number, the super-scripts the atomic weight, the asterisk indicates an excited state, and Q indicates the energy released in the reaction. This reaction has a large cross section (a high probability of occurrence). The resulting alpha particle and also the recoiling lithium nucleus produce dense ionization along a short range or path. The proportional counter can therefore distinguish between pulses produced by this reaction and the smaller pulses produced by beta rays.

Since this reaction is most important in the investigation of neutrons, it has been studied in detail. Bethe [B10] has reviewed the various determinations of the reaction energy, and concludes that the energy Q of this reaction is 2.316 $\pm$ 0.006 Mev. In this case the reaction can actually go in two possible ways:

$$n^1 + B^{10} \rightarrow Li^{7*} + \alpha^4 + Q_1$$
$$\rightarrow Li^7 + \alpha^4 + Q_2$$

where the value of the energy cited is for Q_1. The lithium nucleus emerges in an excited state with an energy of about 0.4 Mev as excitation. It is independently known that the Li nucleus has a level at about this value, so that this explanation is consistent with the known properties of the Li^7 nuclei. Elliott and Bell [E3] give the level in the Li nucleus as 479 $\pm$ 2 Kev and its half-life as approximately 2×10^{-13} sec. Taking Bethe's Q_1 and Elliott's nuclear excitation value, we obtain 2.795 for Q_2. Stebler, Huber and Bichsel [S12] estimate that 92% of the reactions go into Li^{7*} and 8% into Li^7.

By applying the conservation of momentum, it is evident that $7/11$ of this energy is carried by the alpha particle, and $4/11$ by the Li nucleus. Thus, for the more probable reaction, the alpha carries 1.474 Mev and, therefore, has a range of 0.72 cm in standard air. This value for the range agrees closely with experiment. The recoiling Li nucleus, having 0.842 Mev of energy, will have a range of only 3 or 4 mm of air. However, the two particles will be oppositely directed in the counter, and even if the disintegration takes place so close to one wall and the alpha particle is so directed that it hits the wall and loses its energy mostly in the wall instead of in the gas, the Li nucleus will emerge into the gas and hence a detectible pulse will be produced.

Bistline [B11] has measured the average energy required to produce an ion-pair in BF_3, and finds this to be 1.33 times the figure for argon. If we take this latter figure as 25 volts, the value for BF_3 will be 33.1 volts. Hence the Q of the reaction will result in the liberation of about 6.95×10^4 ion-pairs, resulting in the production of a pulse 1.11×10^{-2} volt in amplitude on collector of capacity one micromicrofarad if the gas amplification A is unity. Hence we may operate a proportional counter at moderate values of A and obtain pulses of about a volt in amplitude.

We have thus far discussed the use of the gas BF_3. There are other gases having boron as a constituent. One group of such gases is the family of the hydrides. Unfortunately, problems concerning the stability of these molecules mitigate against their successful use in counters. Thus, diborane, B_2H_6, undergoes thermal decomposition [M8] and decomposition in the discharge, resulting in a variation of the number of molecules per cc, and hence of the operating potential of the counter. The author has tried a number of gases, including B_5H_{11}, and has found considerable variations in the operating characteristics of each gas with use. Further, if the average number of boron atoms per molecule changes with use and dissociation, then the detection efficiency will also change. The gas $B(COH_3)_3$ does not suffer from this latter disadvantage, but is not at the present time as easy to obtain as BF_3 and, since it has no more boron atoms per molecule, presents no increase in efficiency over BF_3.

A reaction similar to eq. (3–12) exists also with lithium, namely, $Li^6 + n = H^3 + He^4 + Q$ giving a 2-Mev alpha.

However, since there is no convenient gas having a lithium atom in its molecule, Li has been used only in the solid form in lining counters. Solid linings are discussed later in this chapter, and eq. (3–18) applies to Li as well as B linings.

Reactions in which alpha particles are emitted are not numerous. The boron and lithium reactions are the only ones with large cross sections. It is, however, possible to use the reactions even if the cross section is not large, although the efficiency is decreased proportionally. This is not too serious a disadvantage if the flux of neutrons is very large, such as, for example, in the neighborhood of piles. Thus Koontz and Hall [K14] have used both the n,p and n,α reactions in nitrogen. For slow neutrons, the n,p reaction gives 0.6-Mev protons; and protons of $0.6 + E$ if $E > 0.4$ Mev. They used a counter filled to $\frac{1}{2}$-atm nitrogen plus $1\frac{1}{2}$-atm argon, at low values of A, with success.

Commercial boron trifluoride is composed of a mixture of the isotopes B^{10} and B^{11}, roughly 19% of the former and 81% of the latter. Unfortunately reaction eq. (3–12) will only apply for the B^{10} isotope and the B^{11} component performs no useful function. The measured [B2] cross section for process eq. (3–12), when the isotope ratio is taken into account, comes out to be $\sigma = 550 \times 10^{-24}$ sq cm, for "thermal" neutrons in equilibrium in water, a figure which we will adopt for all subsequent discussion. Table 3–2 gives the isotopes as found in nature.

The process described by eq. (3–12) operates for slow neutrons. The figure cited refers to "thermal" neutrons, i.e., neutrons in thermal equilibrium in paraffin or water at room temperature. For faster neutrons, the cross section is known to vary inversely as the velocity. We may therefore write

$$\sigma(v) = \sigma/v \qquad (3\text{–}13)$$

where σ is the cross section for the process under discussion.

The efficiency of a neutron counter we shall define as the

TABLE 3–2.   MOLE PERCENT OF ISOTOPES IN NATURAL SUBSTANCES *

Element	Mass No.	Abundance (%)	Element	Mass No.	Abundance (%)
Li	6	7.3	Cd	106	1.22
	7	92.7		108	.98
				110	12.35
B	10	18.83		111	12.76
	11	81.17		112	24.00
				113	12.30
F	19	100.0		114	28.75
				116	7.63

* From F. O. Rice and E. Teller, *The Structure of Matter*, Wiley, 1949.

probability that a neutron, if passing through the counter, will be captured and hence detected. The probability of capture and of process eq. (3–12) occurring is evidently the cross section eq. (3–13) per atom times the average path length for the neutrons passing through the sensitive volume of the counter, times the number of B^{10} nuclei per cc in the sensitive volume. The counting rate, or number of captures per sec, depends on the flux of neutrons and the probability of capture. Consider a counter exposed to a flux of neutrons of various velocities. The number of counts per second n will be given by

$$n = ULp \int i(v)\sigma(v)\, dv \qquad (3\text{–}14)$$

U is the sensitive volume of the counter, L the Loschmidt number and p the pressure in atmospheres, $i(v)\, dv$ the flux of neutrons crossing a sq cm area per second with velocity between v and $v + dv$, and $\sigma(v)$ the cross section for capture. But

$$i(v) = \rho v \qquad (3\text{–}15)$$

where ρ is the density or number of neutrons per cc of all velocities and v is the velocity. Substituting eqs. (3–15) and (3–13) in eq. (3–14), the velocity drops out, we may integrate at once and we obtain

$$n = ULp\rho\sigma_B v_B \qquad (3\text{–}16)$$

Here σ_B is the capture cross section for some known velocity v_B. Numerically we may take these as the thermal cross section cited above and thermal velocity. It is to be noted that the counter measures the density of neutrons ρ, regardless of velocity per cc, and not the flux or number i of neutrons crossing a sq cm area per second. The flux cannot be determined unless the velocity is known. This property of measuring the density is a common characteristic of all detectors obeying the $1/v$ law, eq. (3–13), and is well known in nuclear physics experiments.

If we consider neutrons which all have (nearly) the same velocity, e.g., which are all thermal, then we can compute the efficiency of such a counter. The efficiency E, defined as the fraction of a flux of neutrons which produces counts, is evidently given by the ratio of the counting rate (e.g., eq. (3–16) per unit volume) to the flux, and hence by the relation

$$E = Lp\sigma_B d \qquad (3-17)$$

where d is the average path through the counter of the neutrons to be measured, and where σ_B is the capture cross section for neutrons of the particular velocity being measured. The calculation of the average path through a cylinder presents certain analytical difficulty in the general case, although certain special cases have been computed by Swann.[82] To a sufficient degree of approximation we may take d as a diameter. For example, considering counting slow neutrons with a 7-cm diameter counter with one atmosphere BF_3, $p = 1$, $d = 7$, $L = 2.7 \times 10^{19}$, $\sigma = 550 \times 10^{-24}$, E will be about 10.4%. A smaller counter with $p = 0.1$ atm, $d = 2$ cm, would have an efficiency of 0.29% for thermal neutrons. A counter operating by eq. (3–17), detecting a flux of monoenergetic neutrons is not made more efficient by making it longer, although the total counts recorded will increase, as it will intercept a larger fraction of the flux.

It is also evident that the efficiency depends on the neutron velocities, the foregoing examples assuming the value of σ appropriate for a flux of thermal neutrons. For higher average energies, σ must be decreased according to the $1/v$ law, i.e., must be multiplied by v_t/v_m, where v_m is the velocity of the neutrons measured and v_t the thermal velocity. Thus the efficiency will depend on the arrangement of scattering and "slowing down" material around the counter.

In computing the number of neutrons to be expected at a given distance from a source, it must be recalled that because of scattering the inverse square law does not apply, and that the processes of the diffusion theory must be used. Since almost any source produces neutrons with relatively high energies and since almost any substance slows them down, it is evident that the energy distribution will be a function of the distance from the source and the geometrical arrangement of the counter, source and surrounding material, as well as of the nature of the source and the type of matter near by. The procedures for computing the result for any given arrangement are well known in the diffusion theory and are outside of the scope of this treatment.

Neutron counters have been studied by Fowler and Tunnicliffe, who measured pulse size distributions in BF_3 counters, both at pressures of 60 cm BF_3 and 5 cm BF_3 plus 50 cm argon. They showed that good pulse resolution can be obtained.[F2] They used fast circuits with a time constant of 1.6 microseconds.

It is possible to measure the number of neutrons in a given energy range with BF_3 counters by making measurements with and without certain types of absorbing screens. Thus, for example, a cadmium shield of ½ to 1 mm thickness will be practically opaque to thermal neutrons and practically transparent to neutrons of more than one volt energy. Similarly, borax or boron carbide shields of various thicknesses may be used. In these, the absorption will occur inversely as the neutron velocity, and consequently the effect of any given thickness may be computed. In these calculations, account must be taken of the contribution to the slowing down process due to the water of crystallization in the borax.

The cross section for boron has been measured by a number of observers, and the data have been collected and discussed by Adair [A1] and Goldsmith et al.[G8] The curve of the cross section as a function of neutron energy is shown in Fig. 3-3. The curve is for ordinary boron, with the natural isotope ratio. In

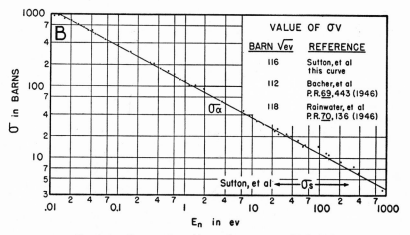

FIG. 3-3.   Cross section of boron for neutrons. (Ref. A1.)

using eq. (3–16) or any other containing the cross section, the values for the cross section must be multiplied by the new isotope ratio if boron with any isotope ratio other than the natural one is used. It will be seen that, for neutrons of "thermal" energies, i.e., at 0.025 ev (corresponding to $T = 300°$ K and using kT; for $\frac{3}{2}$ kt the energy is 0.038 ev), the cross section is 700×10^{-24} sq cm. It is customary, in the slang which originated during the days of the Uranium Project, to call 10^{-24} sq cm a "barn," and we shall use this designation occasionally. It will be seen that the boron cross section for thermal neutrons is larger than the one we cited above, 550 barns for neutrons in equilibrium with water. We may conclude that neutrons in equilibrium with water have, on the average, greater than thermal energies, and this is correct. Because of the capture cross section of the hydrogen in the water for neutrons, the slowest neutrons are captured and no accumulation of truly thermal neutrons exists. In other substances, such as carbon, the neutrons will be slowed down to lower average values since the capture cross section is smaller. The fractional number of neutrons, having original energy E_1 which are slowed down to energy E_2 without being captured, can be shown to be

$$\exp\left(-\frac{1}{2}M\int_{E_2}^{E_1}\frac{\sigma_c}{\sigma_s}\,dE/E\right)$$

where σ_c is the capture cross section, σ_s the scattering cross section. It is assumed, in this instance, that the scattering of neutrons is spherically symmetrical. Here M is the mass number of the scattering nuclei.

In using boron shields to evaluate the number of neutrons, the number of neutrons which will pass through such a boron shield, n, as a fraction of the incident number n_0, will evidently be given by:

$$n = n_0 \exp\left(-Ndt\sigma/w\right)$$

where N is Avogadro's number, d is the density of the boron in grams per cc, t is its thickness in cm, and w its atomic weight. Obviously, Ndt/w is the number of boron nuclei in each square centimeter of shield area. If such a shield is composed of boron carbide, B_4C, compressed to a density of about 1 gram per cc, then there will be about 1.2×10^{22} boron atoms per cc. The energy E at which such a shield transmits $1/e$-th of the incident neutrons is given by:

$$E = (Ndt/w)^2\sigma_B{}^2E_B$$

where σ_B is the capture cross section at energy E_B. For a shield of 1-cm thickness, E is about 44 ev. If we take the cross section of ordinary boron as 700 barns at 0.025 ev, the probability that a neutron of this energy can get through this shield is 2×10^{-4}. The mean free path before capture of this neutron in this shield is 0.12 cm. Since we have a detector sensitive inversely as the neutron velocity, inside a shield which absorbs neutrons also inversely as their velocity, the shield will evidently reduce the counting rate in the detector by the same fraction at all neutron energies.

Let us next consider the case of the cadmium shield. The cross section of cadmium has also been measured by various persons, and the results are presented in Fig. 3–4. The figure

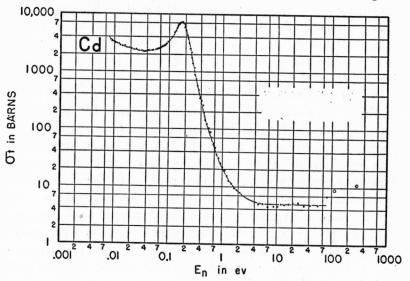

FIG. 3–4.   Cross section of cadmiun for neutrons. (Ref. A1.)

again is for ordinary cadmium, since no isotopically enriched cadmium is at present available. (See Table 3–2 for isotopic percentages.) Cadmium of isotopic weight 113 captures neutrons by the n,γ reaction. The gamma ray varies in energy from 2.5 Mev up to 8 Mev, with a spectrum decreasing sharply with energy [M9] in this interval. Such gamma rays will not ordinarily produce pulses noticeable in a proportional counter set to detect neutrons. The cross section from the figure is seen to be around 2500 barns at 0.025 ev and to fall sharply to 10 barns at 2 ev. There are about 4.5 × 10^{22} cadmium atoms per cc in ordinary metallic cadmium. Hence a shield about 1 mm thick will have a 50% transmission at 0.37 ev and will be quite opaque for thermal neutrons while quite transparent for neutrons of a volt or more in energy. By using boron and cadmium shields, the energy distribution of neutrons may be investigated partially.

There are in addition a number of substances which have very large cross sections at particular energies, showing "resonance absorption." A full discussion of these is out of place in this book, but interested readers will find a large number of cross section curves in the compilation of Goldsmith, Ibser and Feld,[G8] and Adair.[A1]

It follows from eq. (3–17) that greater efficiency is secured at high pressures of BF_3. The practical limit of BF_3 pressures is determined (a) by the fact that high pressures require high operating potentials and (b) by the fact that the pulses due to beta rays increase in size with increasing pressure. Since beta rays have ranges which are long compared to the dimensions of the chamber, at high pressures, more of the range is included. The disintegration particles are entirely stopped in the gas at moderate pressures and therefore increasing pressure produces no increase in neutron pulse size. Thus the ratio of neutron-to-beta background varies with the pressure, and the practical limit is reached when the beta pulses become nearly as large as the neutron pulses.

Improvements in the efficiency of boron trifluoride counters can be secured by using boron in which the isotope ratio has been altered so as to increase the amount of B^{10}. In recent years the Isotopes branch of the U. S. Atomic Energy Commission at Oak Ridge, Tennessee, has made available boron in which the B^{10} isotope was enriched to a total content of 96% B^{10} and 4% B^{11}. They also have boron in which the B^{10} has been depleted, to 10% B^{10} and 90% B^{11}. It is evident from eq. (3–16) that the enriched boron will make a counter, other things being equal, more efficient by a factor of almost exactly 5 over ordinary commercial BF_3. The enriched boron is supplied in the form of a solid, CaF_2BF_3, which when gently heated evolves BF_3 as a gas. The resulting gas must be carefully purified. Bistline,[B11] as well as the AEC bulletins (which may be obtained by writing to the Isotopes Division, AEC, Oak Ridge, Tenn.), describes the purification procedures.

The existence of the depleted BF_3 permits another type of measurement. All counters using BF_3 will exhibit a background produced by large ionizing events, including contamination alpha particles and large cosmic-ray showers or nuclear disruptions. If the counting rate of a counter filled with enriched BF_3 is A counts per minute, and one of the same size filled to the same pressure with depleted BF_3 is B counts per minute when exposed to the same number of neutrons, then we can write $A = (0.96N + b)$ and $B = (0.10N + b)$, where N is the counting rate of a similar counter with 100% B^{10} and b is the background counting rate. The background is assumed to be the same for both counters. Solution of the two equations gives

$$N = 1.16(A - B) \quad \text{and} \quad b = B - 0.10N$$

yielding values of the desired quantities N and b. By an obvious change in the constant multiplying N in the equations for B, this equation may be modified for use with ordinary boron; in fact, any isotope ratio may be inserted.

As an alternative to filling the counter with some gas in which disintegrations are produced as discussed above, counters are sometimes filled with an inert gas and lined with a solid substance from which the disintegration particles emerge. Such a particle must get out into the volume of the counter in order to be detected. The maximum efficiency of a counter of this type lined with boron for slow neutrons will be given by the relation

$$E_{\max} = (N\rho/\mu)R_B\sigma_B \qquad (3\text{--}18)$$

where N is Avogadro's number, ρ is the density of the material of the wall, μ is its atomic weight, R_B is the range of the alpha particles in boron, and σ_B the capture cross section of the wall material (usually boron) for neutrons at the velocity measured. For a boron-lined counter and for thermal neutrons, $E_{\max}$ is about 5%. The boron lining need be only 0.1 mm thick, and added thickness will merely reduce the efficiency. Such counters may employ multiple layers inside, to increase efficiency. Design and construction details are discussed in Chapter 5. The same considerations would apply to a counter lined with uranium and operating by fission, except that alpha particles originating in the uranium would have to be taken into account by setting the minimum detectable pulse size at a high value. Any gas, of course, may be used in such a counter.

Finally it should be pointed out that other gases in which neutrons may produce disintegrations have a possible usefulness in such counters. A uranium compound gas may be used since the fission fragments have a high specific ionization and would produce large pulses. The main objection to fission counters is that, because the fission cross section is small, gas-filled counters are quite inefficient.

b. Counters for fast neutrons. Proportional counters can also be used to detect fast neutrons.[K4] In this case, it is customary to make use of "recoils." A fast neutron may collide with a nucleus of one of the atoms in the gas of the counter or in the surrounding material and cause that nucleus to recoil through the counter. Such recoiling nuclei usually have a high specific ionization and produce counts. The total number of recoil counts n_r per sec produced in the gas of the counter will be given by

$$n_r = ULp \int_{v_{\min}}^{v_{\max}} I(v)\sigma_r(v)\,dv \qquad (3\text{--}19)$$

where $I(v)\,dv$ is the flux of neutrons per sq cm per sec in the velocity interval dv and the recoil cross section σ_r is taken as varying with energy. The experimental evaluation of the limits of integration is discussed below. It will be observed that this is an integral equation and that a simple solution will occur when the cross section may be taken as a constant over the energy range discussed. For example, for hydrogen, the neutron-proton scattering cross section is known to vary between 1.5 and 0.5×10^{-24} in the energy range between 400 kev and 4 Mev respectively. A rough order-of-magnitude estimate of the neutron flux may be obtained, therefore, by taking the cross section as a constant equal to 1×10^{-24} sq cm in this energy interval. A curve of the total cross section of hydrogen is shown in Fig. 3–5. The total cross section is the sum of the scattering and capture cross sections, the capture being the more important at low energies and the scattering of high energies.

The efficiency of a recoil counter is defined as the fraction of

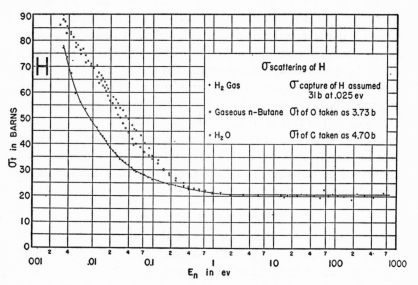

FIG. 3–5. Total cross section of hydrogen for neutrons. (R. K. Adair [A1])

fast neutrons passing through the counter which produces re-coils, it being assumed that virtually every recoil produces a count. The efficiency may be computed for any particular velocity by applying eq. (3–17) and writing the recoil cross section σ_r instead of σ_B. Since the recoil cross section is small, the efficiency of this counter is low. For example, a counter 2 cm in diameter and filled to 28-cm pressure with hydrogen will have an efficiency of about 10^{-5}. The values of the recoil cross section have been measured by various observers for dif-ferent substances and generally are of the order of 10^{-24} sq cm.

For complex molecules, eq. (3–19) must be modified to take account of the cross section of each atom of which the mole-cule is composed. For example, in the case of BF_3 it would include a term $(\sigma_B + 3\sigma_F)$.

Let us next consider the meaning of the limits of integration in eq. (3–19). Physically the meaning of these limits is that the recoiling nucleus must produce sufficient ionization in the counter to initiate a detectable count, and this process will occur only if the recoil energy lies between certain limits. Clearly, if the recoil velocity is below v_{min}, it will not be capa-ble of producing enough ion-pairs to be detected or separated from the gamma-ray background. On the other hand, a very fast recoil will ionize very little, and so a v_{max} must also be con-sidered. Now if we apply classical mechanics and the prin-ciples of conservation to a system in which a particle of mass m collides with one of mass M, assuming that the target is at rest or merely moving with a thermal velocity which is small compared to the velocity of the projectile, then the conserva-tion of energy states that

$$\tfrac{1}{2}mv^2 = \tfrac{1}{2}mv_1^2 + \tfrac{1}{2}MV^2$$

where v and v_1 are the velocities of the projectile before and after the collision, and V is the velocity of the recoiling struck nucleus. The conservation of momentum gives

$$mv = mv_1 + MV$$

and it is assumed that the collision is central. If the collision is not central, then the momentum equation will have two components, and

$$mv = mv_1 \cos \theta + MV \cos \phi$$

$$0 = mv_1 \sin \theta - MV \sin \phi$$

where θ and ϕ are the angles which the recoiling nucleus and the neutron after collision make with the incident direction respectively.

Simultaneous solution of the two equations in the case of the central collision gives as a ratio of the energy of the recoiling nucleus E_r to that of the incident particle E_i

$$E_r/E_i = \tfrac{1}{2}MV^2/\tfrac{1}{2}mv^2 = 4mM/(M + m)^2$$

which, if $M \gg m$ reduces to $4/M$. If the collision be not central, the fraction of energy transferred will have an average energy of $2/M$. For protons, M and m are equal, and in this case the maximum energy transferable is the full energy of the neutron, and the average is one half. Consequently a counter so adjusted as not to detect any pulse that liberates less than 50 kev as ionization in the counter will detect, if filled with hydrogen, neutrons with average energies in excess of 100 kev; but if filled with argon, it will not detect, on the average, neutrons with energies below 1 Mev.

Recoiling atoms will also be ejected from the walls of the cylinder. The number of counts due to wall recoils, n_w, will be given by

$$n_w = \frac{N\rho F}{2\mu} \int_{v_{min}}^{v_{max}} \sigma_r(v)R(v)i(v) \, dv \qquad (3\text{--}20)$$

where N is Avogadro's number, ρ the density of the material of the wall, μ its atomic weight, σ_r the recoil cross section of the nuclei of this substance for the neutrons to be measured, $i(v)$ the flux of neutrons per sq cm per sec, per unit velocity interval, F the cross-sectional area of the counter exposed to the flux, and R the range in cm of the recoiling nuclei in the material of the wall. The factor $\frac{1}{2}$ arises from an integration to give the average number of recoils actually emerging, assuming a random distribution in angle of the recoils. If, from this expression for the total recoils entering the gas from the walls, be subtracted those which have insufficient energy after emergence to produce a count, it will be seen that wall recoils are only important compared to recoils in the gas if (a) the material of the walls is light, (b) the neutrons are of high energy, and (c) the gas pressure in the counter is small, and hence the recoils produced in the gas are few.

The upper limit of integration becomes of importance only in the case of hydrogen. If the recoiling proton has a very high energy, it may pass through the counter without losing enough energy in ionization to produce a recorded count. The upper and lower energy limits are established by the dimensions of the counter, the nature of the gas in the counter, and the energy spectrum of the incident neutrons, as well as by the voltage at which the counter is operated. For a heavy gas such as argon, the neutron energy necessary to produce a recoil too energetic to be counted is so large as to be beyond the range normally encountered and the limit may be considered as infinity. A very high energy neutron of energy above 100 Mev, incident upon an argon nucleus, will cause a disruption of the target nucleus rather than a very high energy recoil. In this case the charged fragments will be highly ionizing and will produce detectable counts. It is evident that increasing the voltage on the counter, other things being equal, is the equivalent of decreasing the lower limit of integration. In those cases where it is not already infinite, the upper limit is also raised.

A proportional counter, whether counting disintegrations or recoils, will also count any other event in which a large amount of ionization is produced. Among such events will be giant showers, nuclear disintegrations produced by the cosmic radiation, and alpha particles present as natural contamination in the walls of the counter. The number of counts due to these several causes may be regarded as a background if surrounding conditions are not changed and can be determined by obvious procedures and subtracted from the counting rate. An important problem in the use of BF_3 counters lies in separating the disintegrations from the recoils. This may be done by varying the integration limits and by the use of cadmium and boron shields as discussed earlier. Further, the number of recoils may be independently measured by using a counter filled with some gas other than BF_3, which does not suffer disintegrations.

It has been pointed out by Hanson and McKibben [H9] that a neutron detector with approximately uniform sensitivity in the range between 10 kev and 3 Mev can be made by surrounding a conventional BF_3 counter with a cylinder of paraffin of suitable thickness. They employed a paraffin cylinder 10 inches in diameter and 12 inches long for this purpose. The neutrons in this energy range are slowed down in the paraffin, and the size is such that approximate compensation occurs for the varying cross section as function of energy.

A device often employed to increase the efficiency of a recoil counter is the insertion of an internal element from which recoils can emerge into the counter. Such an element is called a "radiator," as it can be thought of as radiating recoil protons into the counter. For example, Coon and Nobles [C7] inserted a thin foil of glycerin tristearate on a platinum or gold sheet. Fig. 3–6 shows such an arrangement, and further constructional details of this and other radiating arrangements will be found in Chapter 5.

One advantage of this arrangement is that it is also directional. The distribution of recoils will depend on the direction of the incident beam, and both the upper and lower energy-limits can be evaluated. Barschall and Bethe [B12] have given a full discussion of the recoil problem and have pointed out that a thin radiator is like a gas in that it merely adds more recoiling centers, whereas a thick radiator involves the complex problem, which we already have discussed, of the ability of the recoil to emerge if it originated far inside the radiator. Its ability to emerge will evidently depend on its direction, its energy, and its range in the radiating substance, as set forth in eq. (3–20).

A number of gases and arrangements have been employed by observers in recent years. For example, Pepper [P1] found octane vapor to be useful. The pressure he used was 10 mm,

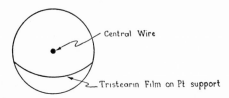

FIG. 3–6.   Internal radiator.   (Coon and Nobles [C7])

which seems low, but since the molecular weight is 114, there will be a large number of protons per molecule capable of recoiling. In order to permit the easy introduction of samples, counters are sometimes operated at atmospheric pressure and the sample introduced through a gas-lock. The gas may be allowed to flow from a tank through the counter throughout the experiment. Arrangements are shown in Chapter 5 for this method. Counters of this type using methane have been developed by Bernstein and Ballantine.[B13] Simpson [S13] has used counters of this type and also ones using air as the gas. In the air proportional counters, Simpson found the thresholds linear from 19 kv at 57-cm to 22 kv at 75-cm pressure. In the study of radiocarbon C^{14}, it may be introduced into the counter directly as radio-methane or radio-CO_2, i.e., $C^{14}H_4$ or $C^{14}O_2$. Since CO_2 is a triatomic molecule, operation of the counter may be improved by the introduction of additional gas. Thus, Miller [M10] found that $C^{14}O_2$ plus ordinary CO_2 at 2-cm pressure works well.

Operating in the ionization chamber region, Wilson and associates [W6] used a high pressure (up to 35 atm) of H_2 and methane for studying recoil protons. They found that filling the chamber with D_2 permitted studying of photodisintegration of the deuteron, since the emerging proton has about an Mev of energy. They also reported that N_2 was satisfactory at the high pressures used, but that O_2, CO_2, H_2S, Cl_2, and H_2O were unsatisfactory on account of electron attachment. Their observations are in agreement with the discussions we already have given of this effect. The same device used in the ionization chamber studies could also be employed as a proportional counter, and they used up to 20 atm of deuterium gas (D_2) in a high-pressure proportional counter with good results.

The efficiency of a counter throughout its volume has been studied by Rossi and Nereson.[R10] They found that in counters filled to a pressure of 22 cm of H_2 and CH_4 an edge-to-center ratio of between 0.80 and 0.83 was observed at values of A of about 500, but that at values of A between 50 and 250, the ratio was unity, i.e., the counter was equally sensitive throughout its volume. The ratio of unity was also found for BF_3, and no electron capture effects were noted for the latter gas at these pressures.

2. Counters for Heavy Ionizing Particles. Proportional counters are well adapted to detecting alpha particles and protons, and indeed alpha particles were the first entities to be counted in the early uses of counters. An alpha particle has a high specific ionization and produces, on the average, some 30,000 ion-pairs per cm in air at STP. Indeed it produces nearly twice this number near the end of its range. The average electron or cosmic ray particle may produce 30 to 100 ion-pairs per cm, and even a slow electron near the end of its range will not produce one tenth as many ions per cm as an alpha particle. Therefore a proportional counter, which produces a pulse whose magnitude is proportional to the number of ions initially formed, will distinguish between alpha particles and electrons with no difficulty at all.

The range of a 1-Mev proton in air is about 2.3 cm. Hence it produces about 12,000 ion-pairs per cm or just over a third as much ionization as does an alpha particle. A proton of this energy is consequently also easy to detect and to distinguish from beta particles.

In detecting alpha particles or protons, any gas whatever may be used in the counter. Some gases are more desirable than others, but any gas can be made to work. Thus, for example, air or oxygen should be avoided because of the possible complications resulting from the formation of negative ions. Particles have a high specific ionization in argon, and this gas also has a low threshold voltage. However, in common with other monatomic gases, argon exhibits a rapid variation of pulse size (amplification) with voltage at high amplification, and hence is somewhat less easy to work with than are the polyatomic gases, which, while they have higher thresholds generally, require less critical stabilization of operating potentials.

One problem in connection with alpha particle and proton counters is to get into the counter the particle to be detected. This is often accomplished by projecting the particle in through a thin foil. The details of possible construction of counters of this type are discussed in the chapter on construction. In other studies, the counter may be directly sealed onto the experimental system in which the particles are accelerated. In this case, the type of gas in the counter is usually determined by the gases used in the rest of the system. Again, weak sources may be put directly into the counter, and some gas flowed through at atmospheric pressure. Illustrations are given in Chapter 5.

The pulse size obtained on the wire of a proportional counter is given by eq. (3–1). The number of ions formed in the initial ionizing event is in turn determined by the specific ionization of the particle being studied in the gas with which the counter is filled. Hence the pulse size V will be given by

$$V = Asple/C \qquad (3-21)$$

where s is the specific ionization, in ions per cm per atm produced by the particle in the gas in question, p is the pressure in atm, and l is the length of the path of the particle through the sensitive portion of the counter. The specific ionization s averaged over the entire path can be obtained from the range of a particle. Thus, for example, the range of 2 Mev alpha particles is about 1.05 cm in air at 15° C and 760-mm pressure.[B2] Since each ion-pair produced in air requires the expenditure of some 30 ev, the specific ionization s will be about 6×10^4 ions per cm. The values of s for cosmic ray particles (fast mesotrons at sea level) are found in Chapter 4, Table 1. The large pulses formed by particles having high specific ionization may, for example, be displayed on an oscilloscope screen, and recording circuits (see Chapter 7) may be made to discriminate against the smaller pulses such as a beta or gamma ray background and record only the large ones.

3. Lifetimes of Proportional Counters. Counters which employ complex molecules, such as BF_3, will have their useful life limited by the number of molecules which are disrupted in the discharge. The minimum number of molecules involved will be equal to the number of ion-pairs formed in the initial ionizing event. For BF_3, since about 7×10^4 ion-pairs are formed when counting neutrons, if we have for A a value slightly over 1000, we shall have 10^8 molecules of BF_3 involved. Not all of the BF_3 molecules ionized will be disrupted, and some may recombine eventually, but since the ionization potential of this gas, about 10 volts, is greater than the molecular bond, many will be dissociated, and predissociation is known to occur. If we consider a counter whose volume is 100 cc, containing 0.1 atm BF_3, we shall have 2.7×10^{20} molecules altogether in the counter. If we should cause 10^8 molecules to become dissociated per count, then many of the molecules will be altered after 10^{12} counts. Long before this figure is attained, considerable changes in operating characteristics will have taken place. Clearly, operating the counter at lower values of A will increase the lifetime. But even 10^{12} counts means 10^4 counts per sec continuously for three years. On the other hand, a counter using only simple gases will not have its lifetime affected by this mechanism. Thus an argon-filled counter will have a much longer lifetime. This lifetime will not, of course, be infinite, as some authors have suggested, for other mechanisms, such as pitting of the central wire by positive ion bombardment or adsorption of gas onto the walls of the counter, will come into play and will limit the useful operation; but these may be several orders of magnitude less effective than molecular dissociation. But again, a lined counter using argon as a gas will have its useful life limited by the decomposition of the material in the lining. If the number of boron atoms per sq cm of lining-area is known, the number of counts may easily be computed before this is, say, 10% depleted.

Resolving times of proportional counters. At low values of A, the principal factor in determining the resolving time of counters is the travel time of the electrons formed in the initial ionizing event. We already have discussed this and have shown that, under the conditions usually found in practice, complete electron collection will take place in less than a microsecond. As the values of A are increased, and larger avalanches are formed, the effects of space charge will progressively be felt. As the counter is operated on higher and higher voltages, the resolving time will be determined more and more by the space charge and by the slow mobility of the positives, until, at the upper end of the region of limited proportionality, the resolving time has extended into the several-hundred microsecond interval that is characteristic of Geiger counters. We shall discuss these effects more fully in the next chapter.

4. Further Discussion of Factors Affecting A. In view of the importance of the quantity A, it is not surprising that a large number of workers have studied this quantity in recent years, and considerable data on A in various gases now exist. In argon, this problem was studied by Colli, Faccini and Gatti,[C6] who obtained curves for A as a function of the voltage for values between 10 and 1000, the voltages here lying between 2600 and 3600. They obtained straight lines in this region. Their curves are shown in Fig. 3–7. Rose and Korff measured A in a BF_3-argon mixture which had been developed for use in neutron counters, and in a methane-hydrogen mixture,

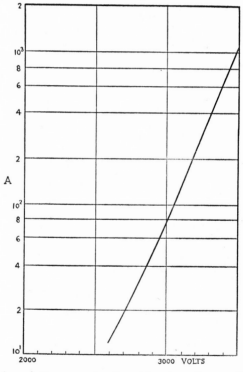

Fig. 3–7. Values of A in argon using β-particle pulses. Counter diameter: 90 mm; argon pressure: 76 cm Hg. Time constant of circuits: 1.5 μsec. (Colli, Faccini & Gatti [C6]).

which had been found useful for recoil counters, as well as in an argon-ether mixture, such as has often been used in regular self-quenching Geiger counters. These mixtures all gave straight lines in the intervals studied. The curves for these three cases are presented in Fig. 3–8. More recently, Rossi

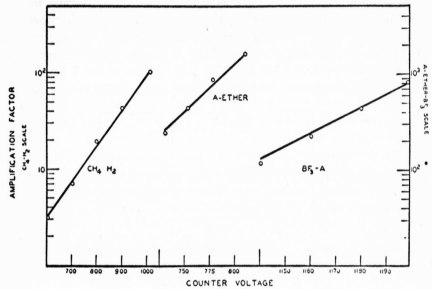

Fig. 3–8. Values of A in BF₃-argon, argon-ether and methane-hydrogen mixtures. (Rose and Korff [R3])

and Staub [R9] have given curves for A measured in tank hydrogen, methane, tank argon, spectroscopically pure nitrogen, boron-trifluoride, and mixtures of 90% H_2 + 10% CH_4; 98% A + 2% CO_2; 90% A + 10% CO_2, and 84% A + 16% propane. In their determinations, the semi-log plots of A against voltage are again often straight lines, in the intervals of A between 10 and 1000. Departures from straight lines are always in the direction of a curve which is concave upward, i.e., which tends to become a horizontal straight line at A equal to unity, and which increases more rapidly than the straight line at high values of A. This effect of departing from the straight line occurs, for example, in low-pressure hydrogen and indicates that, in these circumstances, processes other than those assumed in deriving eq. (3–11) are present. For example, photons were assumed not to play a rôle; in point of fact, however, they do, under certain conditions such as at low pressures in hydrogen and nitrogen. In the more complex gases, for example in boron-trifluoride, the lines remain straight up to values of A of about 1000, indicating that the photons are more strongly absorbed and that they add fewer photo-electrons to the avalanche than in the simpler gases.

Proportional counters using high values of A have been successfully developed by Hanna, Kirkwood and Pontecorvo.[H8] They employed xenon-methane, xenon-argon-methane and argon-methane mixtures.

5. Alternative Derivation of Eq. (3–9). Equation (3–9) may be derived by the following alternative argument. The gain in energy ϵ experienced by an electron moving forward one mean free path l in a field E is:

$$\epsilon = Eel$$

where e is the electronic charge. Now, since the reciprocal of the mean free path is $N\sigma$, and recalling that the field in a counter $E = CV/r$, we have

$$\epsilon = CVe/Nr\sigma$$

But, since by eq. (3–7) σ is proportional to the energy gain, and this in turn to the potential drop traversed ($\sigma = a\epsilon$ and $\epsilon = eV$), we have

$$\epsilon = C/Nra$$

Multiplying each side of the equation by $\epsilon = eV$, we have

$$\epsilon = (CVe/Nra)^{1/2}$$

which is essentially the same result as eq. (3–9), the term Ve being the same as the previous V if it is expressed in volts instead of electron-volts.

6. Fast Practical Method of Testing Counters. The oscilloscope test for the onset of Geiger operation is simple and straightforward. The counter cylinder is connected to an adjustable source of high voltage, and the wire of the counter is fed to the input of an oscilloscope with adjustable sweep speeds and medium gain. A resistor of approximately a megohm is connected from the input terminal to ground. The ground terminal of the oscilloscope is grounded. This is important, for a "floating" system will pick up stray potentials and give unsatisfactory performance. The opposite terminal of the high voltage supply is also grounded. (See Chapter 7 for connections.) The sweep of the oscilloscope is set to a slow value, between 50 and 100 cycles. A source of radiation, usually a small amount of radioactive material, is brought near the counter. The gain on the oscilloscope is adjusted to its maximum. The voltage is then slowly raised, and pulses appear on the screen as vertical lines. As the voltage is further raised, more and more pulses appear. The pulses will not all be of the same size. When the pulses have increased until they approach the limit which can be displayed on the oscilloscope screen, the gain can be turned down. It will at once be evident that there are two controls available, the voltage and the oscilloscope gain. The more the voltage is raised, the more the gain is lowered to keep the pulses of convenient size.

The optimum location of the source can next be determined. The source should be located near enough so that there will be many counts but not so close as to cause the counts to interfere with each other to a serious extent. Moving the source will quickly establish the optimum position.

It will be noted that, as the voltage is increased, a value will be reached at which the pulses will all become approximately of the same size. This voltage is the Geiger threshold. At lower voltages the counter is operating in the proportional region, and at higher voltages it is acting as a Geiger counter.

The flatness of the plateau can be gauged by observing how nearly the pulse sizes are the same. In making this test, the voltage at which the counter starts to go into a continuous discharge can be noted. Care should be taken that the counter is not operated above this voltage, for it is easy to ruin a counter by passing excessive currents through it. A simple test for the continuous discharge consists in removing the source of radiation. If the counting rate does not at once fall to a low value (there will always be a small background because of cosmic rays and stray contamination), then the voltage should be immediately reduced.

Synchroscopes and delay lines are commonly available, and they can also be used in checking counters. If a synchroscope is set for "one-shot" operation, so that the pulse to be studied triggers the sweep, the detailed shape of the pulse can be studied. If the counter is operated at high counting rates, a pattern similar to the "Stever" pattern discussed in Chapter 4 will be seen, and the dead time and resolving time of the counter may be directly evaluated. For the detailed operation the reader is referred to the following chapter.

7. Recent Developments with Neutron Detectors. It is evident that the efficiency of a neutron detector could be increased if the number of boron atoms per molecule were increased. Such molecules exist, and among those available in gaseous form at room temperature are the hydrides of boron, such as B_2H_6. Several tests were made by Korff, but, since they were unsuccessful, they were not published. They are mentioned here because several people have suggested this possibility and have written the author asking why this had not been investigated. The trouble arises from the instability of the hydride. In the discharge, the larger molecules are broken up into smaller ones, so that the pressure, and therefore both the operating efficiency and the operating voltage, vary quite rapidly with the number of times the counter has discharged.

Several successful small BF_3 chambers have been built recently by investigators among whom are Larsson and Taylor [L9] and Caillat, Lallement and Vallados.[C12] The latter also have calculated the optimum signal-to-noise ratio and have presented complete circuits.

Further experiments on the critical potentials of the BF_3 molecule are in progress and will be published, probably by Kaufman, Roots and/or Allen. The absorption spectrum in the extreme ultraviolet has also been investigated by some of these observers, and a considerable amount of absorption, in the form of continuous (structureless) bands at 2200 Angstroms and below, has been found. This bears directly both upon the tendency of the molecule to predissociate and upon the inability of the photons formed in the avalanche to reach the cylinder.

Other experiments upon the dissociation products of BF_3 in the discharge are under way by other members of the New York University Counter Research Project. Preliminary results indicate that the molecule BF_2 is formed at or close to the same voltage as the ionization potential of BF_3. This situation leads to the production of free fluorine in the counter. Should there be any molecules of hydrogen accessible to the gas, whether in gas, vapor, or solid form, the compound HF will be formed, which in turn will produce undesirable action upon the glass envelope. Hydrogenous vapor may get into the counter as a result of the counter having been evacuated by an oil diffusion pump, or from stopcock grease, or from oil manometers.

The factors affecting the flatness of the plateaus of BF_3 counters, the plateau being that for alpha-detection resulting from neutron capture, are also being studied. Again, preliminary results indicate that the purity of the BF_3 gas is of considerable importance, and that contamination by even small amounts of certain gases makes the plateau appreciably less flat. Contamination by the rare gases, however, has no such undesirable effect.

For further discussion of BF_3 decomposition effects see: R. Soberman, S. A. Korff, S. S. Friedland and J. S. Katzenstein, *Rev. Sci. Inst.*, **24**, 1058 (1953).

PROBLEMS

1. A proportional counter filled with argon exhibits background pulses of 0.46-volt amplitude. Assuming these to be due to the 5.9-Mev alpha particles from radium A, compute A. Take the distributed capacity as 16 micromicrofarads.

(Ans. $A = 200$.)

2. Compute the counting rate expected for a neutron counter, filled with 25.3 cm of isotopically enriched (96%) boron trifluoride, 30 cm long and 4 cm in diameter, counting cosmic-ray neutrons in the upper atmosphere. Assume the density of neutrons at that level is 4×10^{-6} per cc.

(Ans. 648 counts per minute.)

3. What is the maximum efficiency of a lithium-lined ionization chamber counting thermal neutrons, assuming ordinary lithium?

(Ans. 10%.)

4. Compute the efficiency of a cellophane foil, one mil thick, for the production of recoil protons by fast neutrons. Assume a cross section of one barn for the recoil process, a density of unity, and a hydrogen-carbon ratio of two. Neglect carbon recoils.

(Ans. 3.43×10^{-5}.)

5. A neutron counter is used to monitor a pile. Assuming a thermal neutron flux of 4×10^8 per sq cm per sec passing through the counter, compute the percentage decrease in efficiency in a month due to depletion of B^{10} by the counting action.

(Ans. 3×10^{-6}.)

6. Find the transmission of a 1-mm cadmium shield for neutrons of 0.37-ev energy.

(Ans. 50%.)

7. If a counter filled with 15.2 cm argon is operated at an A of 1000, about how far from the wire does the avalanche start to form?

(Ans. 5×10^{-4} cm.)

CHAPTER 4

GEIGER COUNTERS

A. Non-selfquenching Counters

1. Theory. *a. Empirical Description of the Discharge Mechanism.* In this section we shall discuss the operation of the counter containing any monatomic or diatomic gas or mixtures thereof. As will be explained, such gases and mixtures pro-

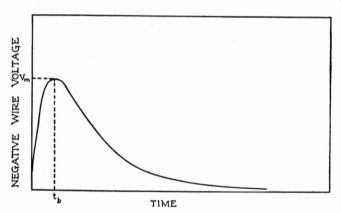

Fig. 4–1. A typical voltage pulse from a selfquenching counter. As viewed on an oscilloscope with a linear sweep, the voltage across R during a pulse is shown here. (After H. G. Stever, *Phys. Rev.* **61**, 39 (1942))

duce non-selfquenching counters. We shall discuss operation at voltages above the threshold for Geiger counting action. In this voltage region all pulses produced by the counter are of the same size, and in general, they are a volt or more in amplitude.

The pulse produced by a counter, if viewed on an oscilloscope screen, has a shape roughly represented in Fig. 4–1. It will be noted that the pulse is characterized by a rapid growth to full value, and then by a slower recovery to normal. The first part is called the "break" as the counter breaks down into a discharge, and the break takes place in a time of the order of a microsecond. The break is due to the sudden onset of ionization inside the counter and to the collection of charge on the central wire, thereby altering its potential. The return of the wire potential to normal is a function of the time constant of the fundamental circuit, Fig. 1-1. It is evident that if the wire is suddenly given a potential V_o by collecting ions, then its potential V at a time t seconds later will be given by

$$V = V_o e^{-t/RC} \tag{4-1}$$

where R and C are the resistance and capacity of the circuit. The total charge Q collected on the wire per pulse is given by

$$Q = \int I dt \tag{4-2}$$

where I is the current flowing and t the time. For small pulses, the measured values of Q are of the order of magnitude of 10^{-10} to 10^{-12} coulomb, corresponding to a current of 10^{-6} ampere flowing for 10^{-5} sec or so. The measurement of Q we will discuss later in detail. This charge arriving on a capacity of 10^{-11} farads produces a pulse of about one volt in amplitude, and, following eq. (1-1), indicates the collection of about 6.2×10^7 electrons. This represents a small pulse at the lower end of the Geiger region, larger pulses being up to 100 times this size.

The early experimenters employed a high resistance for the purpose of "quenching" the discharge. Such counters were therefore called resistance-quenched counters. An empirical description of the operation of the resistance may be obtained by considering the corona mechanism. A continuous discharge is sometimes called a "corona" and we shall consider this, following the treatment developed by Werner [w1] and

others. The fundamental circuit of a counter with resistance
quenching is that shown in Fig. 1–1. If a voltmeter and am-
meter be connected in the battery circuit, it is found that a
steady discharge cannot be maintained inside the counter, unless the voltage exceeds a certain minimum value. A continuous discharge also requires that the current in the gas shall
exceed a certain minimum value. The corona characteristic of
this counter is shown in Fig. 4–2. The minimum voltage and
current, labeled V_{min} and i_{min}
are shown in Fig. 4–2.

Any current flowing in the
counter must also flow through
the resistance R, which has been
called the quenching resistance.
When the counter is operating
at a voltage V_o, larger than
V_{min}, then the overvoltage on
the counter is equal to $V_o -$
V_{min}. When the count takes
place, the current flows, and

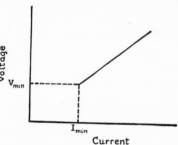

FIG. 4–2.   Corona characteristic of a
counter.

a voltage drop Ri_{min} is, in effect, removed from the operating potential. If $V_{min} > V_o - Ri_{min}$, the operating potential
drops below V_{min}, and since this voltage is no longer sufficient
to sustain the corona, the discharge in the counter ceases and
the counter is said to be quenched. If the voltage V_o is raised,
a potential will be reached at which the overvoltage exceeds
the product Ri_{min} by an appreciable amount, and the counter
will then tend to go into a continuous discharge. The plateau
or operating range of such a counter should therefore be Ri_{min}
volts in extent. On this view the discharge is terminated because of the resistance. We must, however, accept this interpretation with reservations.

The pulse size produced by a counter is defined as the change
in potential of the wire. On the basis of the above mechanism,
this is evidently equal to the overvoltage. The picture which

we may obtain in this way is not strictly accurate and the departures will be discussed below. Indeed, as the Montgomerys [M3] and Danforth [D2] have pointed out, the pulse may be considerably larger than the overvoltage. The counter in this case is said to "overshoot" and the potential of the wire drops below the Geiger threshold. The phenomenon of overshooting will be discussed below.

Unfortunately resistance quenching places severe limitations on the use of such a counter. The minimum currents have been measured for various counters and are of the order of one-tenth of a microampere to 2 or 3 microamperes. Suppose we consider a counter with a minimum current of 0.1 microampere. If operated with resistance R of 10^8 ohms, the product Ri_{min} would be about 10 volts. This would constitute a range in which it would be possible for the resistance-quenching mechanism to work. A "plateau" of 10 volts is quite small, and makes the operation of such a counter difficult and unstable. It is therefore necessary to employ larger resistances. A resistance of the order of 10^9 ohms or more was customarily used in the earlier work. Increasing the resistance still further would increase the usable width of the plateau. Similarly, anything that could be done to increase the minimum current in the counter would also increase the usable plateau. As Werner [W3] and others have emphasized, a high minimum current is desirable.

However, increasing the size of the quenching resistance introduces a serious limitation, since the recovery time of the counter in the fundamental circuit in Fig. 1–1 is determined by the exponential time constant RC, eq. (4–1). The capacity of the counter wire and attached electronic circuits can hardly be reduced below a few centimeters, and if we take the capacity as 10^{-11} farad and a resistance as 10^9 ohms as indicated above, then the time constant RC is of the order of 0.01 sec. This time constant limits the rapidity with which the counter will count. In any random distribution of the counting events, there is a considerable probability that two counts will arrive within a short time of one another. The counter just mentioned would be losing an appreciable fraction of its counts if it had a recovery time constant of 0.01 sec and were counting at the rate of ten random counts per sec. Indeed, no satisfactory compromise is possible between the recovery time constant and the length of plateau necessary for stability, which both increase as R. It is for this reason that the use of resistance quenching has been virtually abandoned, and vacuum-tube circuits which accomplish the same result much faster are used instead. Several such vacuum tube circuits are described in detail in Chapter 7. These circuits drop the operating potential of the counter below V_{min} for a period of 10^{-4} sec or so, allowing the discharge to cease and then return the potential to normal.

b. Discussion of the atomic mechanism. When the quenching mechanism was further examined by Montgomery and Montgomery,[M3] the following picture was arrived at. Let us suppose that an ionizing event occurs and an electron is formed somewhere within the volume of the counter. This electron is drawn by the field toward the central wire and in the neighborhood of the central wire produces additional electrons by the Townsend avalanche process. The avalanche is over in a very short time, owing to the high mobility of electrons. The electrons are actually collected on the wire in a fraction of a microsecond. As Ramsey's [R5] experiments have shown, during this time the positive ions left behind by this avalanche mechanism have virtually not moved at all. The wire is therefore surrounded by a positive ion sheath and this positive ion sheath now begins to travel outwards. The sheath crosses the counter, eventually arrives at the cylinder and is there neutralized.

Immediately after the electron avalanche has taken place and the positive ion sheath has been formed, the field conditions in the neighborhood of the wire are fundamentally and radically altered. Between the sheath and the wire the field is much reduced. It may be reduced to such a value that no further Townsend avalanches can occur. The discharge then ceases. It is thus the positive ion sheath which actually quenches the discharge. As the Montgomerys [M3] have pointed out, the discharge is quenched in spite of the quenching resistance which actually permits charge to leak back onto the wire, and if made too low, would tend to counteract the effect of the positive space charge by allowing the wire potential to recover rapidly. A better name would be the "recovery resistance," as this expresses its true function.

The discharge, having thus been quenched by the positive ion sheath, will now remain quenched as long as no further electrons are formed by any subsequent process. The positive ion sheath travels outward to the cylinder. When it reaches the cylinder, secondary electrons may be created by positive ion bombardment. The details of this process are quite complex and we shall adopt a simplified view. We shall assume that a positive ion, approaching the surface of the metal, draws an electron out through the potential barrier at the surface. This electron then neutralizes the positive ion. The positive ion as it returns to its ground-state will emit its characteristic recombination radiation in one or more spectral lines. For ions such as argon, the recombination spectrum lies in the ultraviolet in a spectral region, the quantum energies of which are larger than the work function of the material of the cylinder. Many of the recombination quanta thus emitted will reach the cylinder and one must therefore consider the emission of photoelectrons. The photoelectric efficiency and the work function of the various surfaces are known and one can therefore estimate the number of secondary electrons which are likely to be emitted when recombination radiation of a given wavelength strikes the metal. The photoelectric threshold of copper lies at about 3000 Ångstroms (roughly 4 volts), and the photoelectric efficiency of many of the surfaces used in counters is of the order of magnitude of 10^{-4}, although this figure can be altered an order of magnitude in either direction by suitable choice of surfaces. Thus, if 10^4 photons strike the cylinder, it is probable that one secondary electron will be formed and the avalanche process will therefore repeat.

The meaning of V_{min} now becomes clear. V_{min} is that voltage at which at least one secondary electron is produced by every sheath of positive ions as it goes out to the cylinder and is there neutralized. If every sheath moving out produces at least one secondary electron, this secondary electron starts a new avalanche which produces a new sheath, and the discharge will continue indefinitely. This continuous discharge is not, as we have pointed out before, really continuous in time, but consists of a series of pulses or spurts at close and somewhat overlapping intervals.

We may now understand the operation of the quenching resistance or the quenching circuit. The function of these is to keep the potential of the wire below V_{min} until all positive ions have been neutralized. Once this has been accomplished, no further mechanism for the ejection of secondary electrons exists and the discharge is therefore terminated. The circuit or resistance may then return the counter to its normal operating potential, and it will then be sensitive to the next event. To reduce the insensitive time, it is desirable that this return to operating conditions should be as quick as possible and may, in general, be of the order of a few times 10^{-4} sec.

In some cases, the initial Townsend avalanche is not large, and the positive ion sheath does not contain enough ions to lower the field in the neighborhood of the wire below the sustaining potential of the discharge. Photons formed in the initial avalanche will travel to the cylinder. When they strike the cylinder, they will cause the ejection of further photoelectrons, and these photoelectrons, coming into the region near the wire, will then cause further avalanches. The result of this phenomenon is the process of "multiple breaks" observed by Ramsey and the Montgomerys.[R5] These experimenters were able to photograph on an oscilloscope the successive changes in the potential of the wire as several groups of electrons due to the photons formed in the various avalanches arrived on the wire. The wire thus attained its full potential drop, not as the result of one electron avalanche, but as the result of several in quick succession. A curve of this phenomenon is shown in Fig. 4–3. When the field near the wire attains a value so low that no further avalanches can be supported, the discharge ceases. The subsequent recovery of the counter to a new operating potential is controlled not by the internal mechanism but by the speed of the external quenching circuit of resistance.

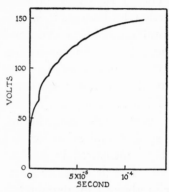

FIG. 4–3. Discharge curve of a counter with a large capacity connected to the counter wire. (C. G. and D. D. Montgomery, *Phys. Rev.* 57, 1035 (1940))

c. Calculation of the efficiency of counters. We will define the efficiency of a counter as the probability that the counter will count when an event of the type to be measured takes place within it. Thus, for example, the efficiency of a beta ray counter counting electrons is equal to the probability that the counter will discharge when one electron is formed inside it or enters it from the outside. Since it is only necessary to have one electron formed inside the counter to start an avalanche, the efficiency of a counter may be readily computed.[D3, C3] We shall consider the probability that any given ionizing event will produce one electron within the active volume of the counter.

Suppose it is desired to detect a particle such as a cosmic ray or a high-speed electron which is passing through the counter. Let x represent the average number of electrons produced by the particle to be detected as it passes through the counter. Then the probability that such a particle can pass through the counter and produce no electrons is e^{-x}. The efficiency G of this counter, which is the probability that one electron shall be produced, is therefore equal to $1 - e^{-x}$.

The evaluation of x is straightforward if the specific ionization of the particle to be detected is known. The specific ionization is defined as the number of ion-pairs per cm of path per atm which is left behind in the gas when the particle in question passes through it. Since high energy rays may produce secondaries capable of producing further ionization, it is customary to distinguish between the total specific ionization and the primary specific ionization. The total specific ionization determines the rate of energy-loss by the primary particle. The primary specific ionization is that used in counter efficiency calculations, since it is the number of ion-pairs formed by the primary, and not the energy of each, that determines whether a counter will register a count. The specific ionization for fast electrons and for cosmic rays has been measured in various gases and is given in Table 4–1 below. Let us consider a few numerical cases. Suppose a counter of about 1 in. diameter is used for the detection of a cosmic ray. Let us further suppose that this counter is filled to a typical pressure of about 0.1 atm of argon. The total number of electrons which would be left behind in the counter by the passage of a cosmic ray mesotron through it would therefore be equal to slp, where s is the specific ionization, l the length of the path through the counter and p the pressure of the gas in atmosphere. Thus, we may write for the efficiency the relation:

$$G = 1 - e^{-slp} \qquad (4\text{-}3)$$

In case cited, if the average path through this counter for the particles in question were about 2 cm, and the specific ionization for argon were taken as 30 ions per cm per atm from Table 4–1, it is evident that on the average 6 ions would be created in the volume of the counter by the passage of the average mesotron through it. The chance that no ion would be created would be e^{-6} and the efficiency of the counter would therefore be 99.8%. Similarly, if the same counter were filled with hydrogen at the same pressure, since the value s is so much less for hydrogen, there would on the average be 1.2 ions left behind in the counter by the passage of each ray. The efficiency in this case would then be about 70%. From this discussion it will be readily appreciated that it is important to employ a gas using high specific ionization, or with high pressure in order to obtain a counter with appreciable efficiency. A counter will be inefficient if the pressure is too low. Several counters which have been reported in the literature employing gases with pressures of about 2 cm are evidently undesirable on the basis of efficiency.

TABLE 4–1. SPECIFIC IONIZATION, s, IN IONS PER CM PER ATM, PRODUCED BY HIGH SPEED COSMIC-RAY PARTICLES, IN GASES WITH n_e ELECTRONS PER ATOM OR MOLECULE

Gas	n_e	s	Reference
Hydrogen (H_2)	2	6.0 ± 0.2	C3, D3
Helium	2	5.9	C3
Helium	2	6.5	H6
Air	14.4	21	D3
Argon	18	29.4	C3
Methane (CH_4)	10	16	S6
Neon	10	12	S8
$C_2H_5(OH)$	26	33 or 42 *	H6
BF_3	32	44	S. K. †
Xenon	54	44 **	S. K. †

* Calculated: 33 if empirical relation between s and n_e is assumed, viz., $s = 1.1 n_e + 3$. The value 42 is obtained if s for $3H_2$, $\frac{1}{2}O_2$ and C_2 are added. The straight line empirical formula breaks down for $n_e = 1$ and 0. It is at best a rough guide to the trend of s.

** The value for Xe seems low but possibly the departure from the calculated value 65 is traceable to the tightness of the binding of the innermost electrons and screening.

† Unpublished.

The efficiency of a counter is of extreme importance. It is important not only when such a counter is used to count single particles, as is done in medical experiments, but is also of vital concern in coincidence studies. In coincidence work, the inefficiencies are multiplicative and in many such experiments an efficiency of less than 98% cannot be tolerated if good results are desired. Indeed, efficiencies of less than this should not be employed for any measuring problem, since too many unknown factors may cause measurements with an inefficient counter to be unreproducible. Since it is easy to make highly efficient counters, there is no reason to tolerate inefficient ones, except for certain special problems which we will discuss later.

We may consider the efficiency of a counter in detecting alpha rays. An alpha particle produces a very high specific ionization. It is possible to compute the number of ions per cm from the well known Bragg curve. The probability that an ion should be formed within the volume of the counter is unity if an alpha particle expends any fraction of its range in the gas of the counter. It is therefore only necessary for an alpha particle to traverse or end its range in any portion of the sensitive volume in order for a count to be recorded. Similar arguments may be advanced in the case of electrons nearing the ends of their ranges. The specific ionization for an electron near the end of its range is obtainable from the ionization curve for electrons. The ionization is heaviest toward the end of the range, and therefore every electron of energy of a few hundred volts or so which enters the sensitive volume of the counter will produce a count. The difficulties which may be encountered in measuring beta radiation from weak radioactive sources with an inefficient counter are at once apparent. Such a weak beta ray may just be able to get through the wall of the counter. If the efficiency of the counter is not high, many of these beta rays may come to the ends of their ranges in some portion of the counter which is not sensitive, or may enter the sensitive volume and still not be detected. The possible errors that an inefficient counter may produce are therefore uncertain and difficult to correct.

Counters may also be used for detecting photons and gamma radiation. In designing a counter for this purpose, it is customary to provide two features which would be undesirable in beta ray or cosmic ray counters. These are (a) a window transparent to radiation and (b) a surface on the cylinder with maximum photoelectric efficiency for the particular radiation. The cathode of the counter may in addition be cut, perforated or otherwise so arranged that a large aperture exists through which the photons to be measured reach the photoelectric surface.

The number of photoelectrons formed in the gas of the counter is usually small compared to the number ejected from the walls. In the case of high-energy gamma radiation, a high-energy photon may produce a Compton electron in the gas of the counter or may eject an electron from the wall by one of several processes. In any event, the gamma ray will be detected only if it produces an electron somewhere within the sensitive volume. Since the photoelectric efficiencies of surfaces are, in general, quite low, a counter will ordinarily have a rather poor efficiency in detecting gamma radiation.

We may also discuss the effect on the efficiency of the introduction of heavy organic vapors into counters. Counters employing argon with an addition of alcohol or other organic vapor have been in common use for some time. Usually, the vapor pressure of the organic substance is of the order of 1 or 2 cm. If the pressure of the argon is between 0.1 and 0.2 atm, the majority of the ionization formed within the counter by the primary ionizing event will be in the form of argon ions rather than organic ions. The efficiency calculations can therefore be made on the basis of the argon content of the counter, and the contribution due to the alcohol will be small. The specific ionization of various types of radiation in the organic vapors has, in general, not been measured, but there appears no reason to suppose that this would be different in order of magnitude from the specific ionization in other gases. The specific ionization is roughly proportional to the number of electrons per molecule and so will be fairly high for alcohol. Hazen [H6] estimates that it is probably about 42 ions per cm for ethyl alcohol. The addition of 10% or so of alcohol vapor to an argon-filled counter will therefore slightly improve the efficiency which is already high. Greisen and his collaborators [G5]

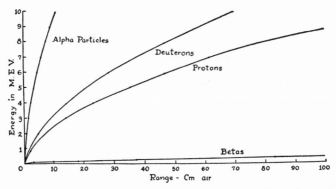

Fig. 4-4. Range-energy relationships for various particles. Range in centimeters of air, energy in million electron volts. (Data from H. A. Bethe, *Revs. Mod. Phys.* 9, 269 (1937))

have measured the efficiencies of alcohol-filled counters and their results confirm the view developed above.

For particles heavier than electrons, the number of ion-pairs produced per cm of path is large. Eq. (4–3) may be used to compute the efficiency of a counter counting alpha particles or protons, but these efficiencies will in almost all cases be unity. The number of ion-pairs produced can be readily computed from the range (see Fig. 4–4) for these particles, recalling that about 35 ev are required to produce each ion-pair.

2. Operation. *a. Introduction.* In this section we propose to discuss the operational characteristics of non-selfquenching Geiger-Mueller counters. We shall consider counters filled with any monatomic or diatomic gas or mixtures thereof. In view of the theory developed above, we shall show what types of operation may be expected, and are actually met in practice. We shall present the characteristic curves and show how these depend on the nature and the pressure of the gas. We shall consider the pulse sizes which are obtained with the various arrangements and the efficiencies of the counters in detecting the radiation of various types. We shall also examine the effects due to negative ions, metastable states, and operation with reversed potentials. The design and construction features and the attached electronic circuits will be discussed in a later chapter.

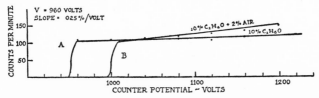

FIG. 4–5. (A) Typical plateau curve of selfquenching counter filled with argon and 10% C_2H_6O vapor. (B) Same counter when 2% air was admitted. Note that starting potential increases and plateau becomes less flat. (Ref. S1)

There are five desirable features which may be realized in counters, to a greater or lesser extent, through proper design. These are (a) low operating potential, (b) long operating voltage range or "plateau," (c) high efficiency, (d) stability with use and time, and (e) pulse size large enough to operate electronic circuits unambiguously. We shall examine the influence of various features on these five desiderata. The purely mechanical features, such as ruggedness, ease of construction and low cost, are discussed in another chapter.

b. Characteristic curves. There are two important characteristic curves exhibited by Geiger counters. The first is the familiar plateau curve, in which the counting rate of a given counter is plotted as a function of voltage, when the gas which it contains and the radiation to which it is exposed are both kept constant. A typical curve of this sort is shown in Fig. 4–5.

These curves are characterized by a rapid rise beyond the starting potential to the Geiger threshold and a more or less flat region beyond this, which is called the plateau. The slope of the plateau and the factors influencing its flatness will be discussed later. At the upper end of the plateau, the counting rate rapidly increases with further rise in voltage, and the counter ceases to be useful for quantitative measurements. This counting rate curve is an integral curve, in which all pulses greater than a certain size are measured. If such a curve shows a flat "plateau," it indicates that, in the region of the plateau, all pulses are of a certain maximum size. A flat plateau may thus be taken to indicate true Geiger counting action, since we have defined this as the process leading to the production of pulses which are all of the same size and independent of the amount of ionization occurring in the initial ionizing event. Moreover, a flat plateau is desirable from an operational viewpoint in that it insures that if the counter be operated somewhere near the middle of the flat portion, the counting rate will be independent of small fluctuations in the operating potential.

The other type of curve which we wish to discuss is that of the starting potential as a function of the pressure of the gas in the counter. Typical curves of this sort are shown in Fig. 4–6. It will be noted that these curves resemble the familiar sparking potential curves and are characterized by a minimum in the neighborhood of a few millimeters and a slow rise toward higher pressures. This rise is practically linear over small changes in pressure. Curves of this sort may be prepared for various kinds of counters and fillings. The rapidly varying portion below one centimeter is of comparatively little significance from the point of view of practical operation, since the efficiency of a counter filled with pressures of 1 cm or less is so small as to make it virtually useless. The usual operating regions for most Geiger counters is in the neighborhood of 7 cm to 20 cm pressure. Operation at still higher pressures is sometimes desirable. To cite cases in which high pressure counters have been found useful, we have those designed by Brown,[B3] in which helium at 1 atm was used, and also the neutron counters,[K5] in which operation at 1 atm and above is desirable from the point of view of efficiency. In the case of helium counters operating at atmospheric pressures, the gas may be flowed into

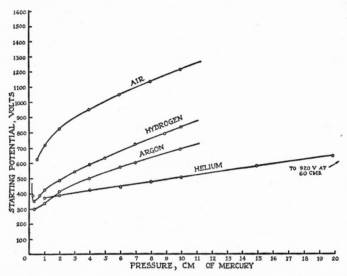

FIG. 4–6. Typical starting potentials with (99%) pure gases. Counter cylinder 1 cm diameter, wire 3 mil. The minimum occurs at about 3 mm. Ordinary operating range 7 to 20 cm. (After C. L. Haines, *Rev. Sci. Inst.* **7**, 411 (1936))

the counter continuously while some portion of it is open to the atmosphere, and the mechanical provisions for introducing a specimen into the volume of the counter are therefore simple. With this arrangement, a radioactive sample to be measured may be introduced into the body of the counter and the radiation emitted in all directions from the substance may be measured.

It is evident from inspection of Fig. 4–6 that the starting potential depends on the nature of the gas. In general, the noble gases produce counters with lower starting potentials than do the common diatomic ones, such as nitrogen or hydrogen. The starting potentials of mixtures will, in general, lie between those of the constituents. Consequently, since a low starting potential is desirable, noble gases have been widely used in counter work.

c. Efficiency. We have shown, in the theoretical discussion, that the efficiency of a counter may be computed from eq. (4–3), and that it depends on the specific ionization of the particle to be counted in the particular gas used in the counter. We have further pointed out that a high efficiency is necessary for good results in most cases. It is comparatively simple to produce a counter with an efficiency of 99.8% or better. The important considerations are the nature of the gas and the pressure. The noble gases, excepting helium, have high specific ionizations, and counters filled to between 7 and 20 cm of such gases will have good efficiencies and low operating potentials.

It is of interest to discuss the case of a counter operating at low efficiency. Counters operating at a low efficiency differ from those operating at a high efficiency in that their operation begins to resemble that of an ionization chamber. As Korff and Danforth have suggested [K6] the exponential for the efficiency—eq. (4–3)—may be expanded and written in terms of its first series member when the exponent is small. Thus the efficiency given by the expression

$$G = 1 - e^{-slp}$$

becomes

$$G = slp. \tag{4–4}$$

Since the efficiency depends on s, the counting rate depends on the size of the ionizing events, and the counter measures a quantity proportional to the total radiation which falls on it, much as does an ionization chamber. A counter of high efficiency counts the number of particles, regardless of the amount of ionization produced by each, whereas one of low efficiency counts particles of high specific ionization preferentially. The counting rate for low efficiencies will be proportional to the volume of the counter while for high efficiencies it is proportional to the cross-sectional area exposed to a flux of radiation. As with an integrating ionization chamber, it is not possible to tell whether a given counting rate with a low efficiency counter is produced by a few particles of high specific ionization or by many with low s. Thus if a counter is exposed to a flux of i ionizing particles per sq cm per sec, and has a cross-sectional area of F sq cm through which the radiation passes, then the counting rate of a high efficiency counter will be iF counts per sec. But for inefficient counters, we must multiply by a value of $G = slp$ less than unity, and since lF is the volume of the counter, which we designate by U, the counting rate will be $ispU$ counts per sec. Thus inefficient counters may have a use in the special case when knowledge of the total radiation is desired, rather than the flux.

Returning to the discussion of counters of high efficiency, the fact that the counting rate depends on the cross-sectional area means that the geometrical relation of the counter and the angular distribution of the radiation must be considered. This is not true for the low-efficiency counters or integrating ionization chambers where the quantity measured depends on the volume of the device and not on its orientation with respect to the particles being measured. Thus for efficient counters, geometrical correction factors are required.

Corrections of this type have been found necessary in the cases in which counters, arranged to cover large sensitive areas, were used for measurement of cosmic radiation.[K6] The cosmic radiation is not incident isotropically on the counter, but falls upon the instruments largely from above. The geometrical corrections are quite sensitive to the angular distribution. Consequently, if the angular distribution varies, as, for example, does that of cosmic radiation as a function of elevation, the intensities at several elevations obtained with electroscopes or ionization chambers cannot be compared with those measured by high-efficiency counters without making the necessary geometrical integrations.

d. Nature and type of gas. (1) *Helium.* Considering first the various monatomic gases, we find that helium has been used by various investigators for filling counters. Counters using helium have been studied extensively by Brown.[B4] Helium has a comparatively low specific ionization, and it is consequently necessary to use a fairly high pressure in order to obtain desirable efficiencies. However, helium counters are also characterized by a low starting potential and therefore comparatively high pressures may be used without encountering excessive operating voltages. One of the features of helium-filled counters is the relative transparency of this gas to radiation in the short-wave regions and the small stopping power which it has for heavy particles.

(2) *Neon and argon.* These two gases are used extensively in counters. Argon, in particular, is inexpensive and has a high specific ionization. Counters with high efficiencies and low starting potentials may readily be made using this gas. Extremely pure argon should be avoided owing to the difficulties which arise due to the metastable states, the effects of which will be discussed below. Ordinary commercial argon, which is often about 98% pure, may be used quite satisfactorily, since the 2% impurity is sufficient to de-excite the metastable states by collision. Krypton and xenon also make excellent gases for counters since both have high specific ionizations and produce low starting potentials. However, expense usually rules them out, and they have, in fact, comparatively little advantage over argon.

(3) *Nitrogen and hydrogen.* Both of these gases are at times used in counters. Each is characterized by a comparatively high starting potential. Hydrogen has an additional disadvantage, namely, a low specific ionization. In order to obtain efficiencies approaching 100% for the detection of beta rays or cosmic rays, considerable pressures of hydrogen are neces-

sary, and the resulting starting potentials may become undesirably high. For example, to obtain an efficiency of 99.8% in a counter with 2 cm average path, the counter would have to be filled to 35 cm of hydrogen and such a counter would require well over 2000 volts for its operating potential.

(4) *Oxygen.* The results obtained with oxygen are somewhat undesirable since in this gas the formation of negative ions is appreciable. The effect of the negative ions will be discussed below.

(5) *Mixtures.* In early experiments, air was used in counters. Air, however, has to a lesser degree the same disadvantage which oxygen has, namely, it permits the formation of a sufficient number of negative ions to produce appreciable spurious counting. In addition, air should be carefully dried in order to remove water vapor which not only may give rise to negative ions, but also may affect the surface of the cathode in time. Mixtures which have been found to be particularly desirable are argon-and-hydrogen or neon-and-hydrogen. In each case, a few percent of hydrogen may be added to the noble gas, and the resulting starting potential is low, almost equal to that due to the noble gas alone, whereas the efficiency is high. The hydrogen molecules remove the energy in the metastable states by collision. Argon-oxygen counters (94% A, 6% O_2) have been studied by the Montgomerys,[M3] and the effects of negative ions were noted.

e. Pulse size. In the theoretical treatment, we showed that the size of the pulse, or in other words, the change in potential of the wire, should be of the order of the overvoltage. That this is indeed frequently the case has been confirmed by numerous investigators. However, in some cases the change in potential of the wire is greater than the overvoltage and the wire drops during the discharge to a value below that necessary for sustaining the discharge. This phenomenon is called "overshooting" and can be produced in any counter by making the capacity attached to the wires small and the overvoltage high.[M3]

If the capacity of the wire system is made high, the counter will ordinarily not overshoot. The phenomenon of overshooting has not been observed by several investigators who sought it, but these observers generally used high capacities on their wire system, and consequently the conditions were not such that the phenomenon would be observed. In Fig. 4–7, a curve of pulse size as a function of overvoltage is shown. In this curve the pulse size would be a straight line for high capacities and departs from a straight line in the direction of pulses larger than the overvoltage at high overvoltages. The experimental data are taken from the observations made by the Montgomerys.[M3]

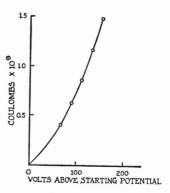

FIG. 4–7. The amount of charge formed in a counter which overshoots, as a function of the potential above the starting potential applied to it. (C. G. and D. D. Montgomery, *Phys. Rev.* **57**, 1034 (1940))

The values of q, the charge collected on the central wire, are closely related to the pulse size. Several observers have measured the charge collected, notably Stever and Ramsey.[S3, R5] One simple procedure for measuring q is to arrange a high-resistance, low-leakage condenser to supply the counter voltage, and then to measure the potential change dV of this condenser after an assigned number of counts n have taken place. The charge q then will equal $nCdV$, where C is the capacity of the condenser. The charge q collected during a pulse was found to be proportional to the overvoltage. It is found to increase somewhat when overshooting takes place. The charge collected is of the order of 10×10^{-6} microcoulombs per volt of overvoltage for small pulse sizes and may run to 100 times this value for larger pulses.

f. Effects due to negative ions. Let us consider the effects due to negative ions. Suppose that a negative ion is formed within the active volume of the counter during the discharge. Accelerated by the field, this ion will drift toward the central wire. The mobility of negative ions is the same in order of magnitude as that of positive ions, and the negative ion will therefore require a few times 10^{-4} second to cross the dimensions of an average counter. Such negative ions may then arrive in the high field region next to the wire after the Townsend avalanche is over and after the positive ion space charge sheath has progressed far enough toward the cylinder, so that the field near the wire has partly recovered to its normal value. The negative ion entering the high field region may lose its electron in the immediate neighborhood of the wire, due to the high field. In this case the electron which is thus freed will start a new avalanche and produce a new count. Alternatively, the negative ion may produce ionization by collision in the neighborhood of the wire and may again thus start a new Townsend avalanche. Since recovery from the first count has partially taken place, the counter would then register a new count. There is therefore the possibility that the counter will discharge at times subsequent to the completion of the initial count, if negative ions are formed within a counter. In other words, spurious counts or an excessive number of close doubles or multiples may be produced by negative ions.

The probability of the formation of a negative ion in the counter subsequent to the discharge may be calculated from the known electron attachment coefficient. The electron attachment coefficient for various gases may be taken from the tables given by Compton and Langmuir.[C2] Numerical values are presented in Table 4-2. The coefficient is defined as the number of collisions which an electron must make with neutral molecules or atoms before it sticks and forms a negative ion. An electron will make approximately 10^5 collisions in crossing a counter, the mean free path depending on the pressure. Therefore, if this coefficient exceeds 10^5, there will be a very small probability that any negative ions will be formed, since the electrons will not have made enough collisions before they are collected. The values reported for the coefficient are high for Argon, H_2, N_2, and ammonia. The value for air is 2×10^5, which is close to the critical value of 10^5, mentioned above, but the figure for O_2 and for H_2O and Cl_2 are all less than this criti-

TABLE 4–2. ELECTRON ATTACHMENT COEFFICIENT *

Gas	n	N
CO	1.6×10^8	$2.2 \ \times 10^{11}$
NH_3	9.9×10^7	$2.9 \ \times 10^{11}$
C_2H_6	2.5×10^6	$4.8 \ \times 10^{11}$
N_2O	6.1×10^5	3.36×10^{11}
Air	2.0×10^5	2.17×10^{11}
O_2, H_2O	$4 \ \times 10^4$	$2.06, 2.83 \times 10^{11}$
Cl_2	$<2 \ \times 10^3$	4.50×10^{11}

* Here n represents the average number of electron impacts which result in one attachment to form a negative ion, and N the number of electron impacts per sec against gas molecules. Data from Compton and Langmuir, *Revs. Mod. Phys.*, **2**, 193 (1930).

cal value. Hence, negative ions will be formed in sufficient numbers to produce significant effects only in the case of oxygen, water, and the halogens. It will be recalled that iodine was used in some counters in the early days. It is evident that this gas and others in that family are undesirable in counters, because of the high electron attachment probability. Water vapor and other similar compounds should also be avoided on this ground.

g. Effects due to metastable states.   Suppose an atom is left in a metastable state as a result of a discharge. The atom will then remain in this state until radiation takes place, or a collision of the second kind occurs and the energy of the metastable state is transferred into kinetic energy. Metastable states occur in the noble gases. In pure argon, for example, metastable atoms may form in the discharge. The lifetime of these metastable states, before radiation takes place, is of the order of 10^{-4} sec or longer. Atoms in metastable states are not affected by the field and drift about within the volume of a counter. Such atoms may collide with the walls of the counter while they are in the metastable state, or (less probably) they may radiate. Either process can give rise to a secondary electron. If such secondary electrons are produced after the positive ion sheath has traversed a substantial fraction of the radius of the counter, a new count will occur. In the new discharge, new metastable atoms are presumably formed, and if these metastable states in turn produce still more secondary electrons, then the discharge in the counter does not terminate. It is for this reason that pure noble gases are not desirable in counters and a foreign gas should be used which de-excites the metastable states by collision. Thus, for example, the addition of a few percent of hydrogen to a counter filled with pure argon insures that a collision between argon and hydrogen molecules will take place within a time short compared to the lifetime of the metastable state, and therefore will result in the elimination of the metastable atoms.

h. Operation of a counter with reversed potential. If the potential on the counter is reversed and the wire is made negative with respect to the cylinder, the counter may still be made to operate as a Geiger counter. The detailed description of the discharge mechanism will, however, be quite different. An electron avalanche will be formed, but the electrons will proceed outward toward the cylinder. Since the electrons move into regions in which the field becomes progressively weaker, the avalanche which they produce will tend to taper off, and the multiplicative process will decrease as the electrons travel outward. The positive ions, on the other hand, may enter the regions of field so high that in one mean free path they acquire enough energy to produce ionization by collision. Additional electrons are thus produced as the ions travel inwards toward the central wire. These electrons will travel out to the cylinder, where they are collected. If they produce additional electrons by bombardment of the cylinder, these electrons are also collected on the cylinder and do not contribute to the continuation of the discharge. The positive ions, however, arrive on the wire and others may produce avalanches at times comparatively long after the electrons have been collected. Thus a count may take place immediately after the ionizing event which caused it, or there may be a considerable time which elapses, depending on whether the initial ion was formed near the wire or far from it. Such random time intervals between the occurrence of the initial ionizing event and the count are called statistical time-lags. Counters with potentials reversed will therefore, in general, show large statistical time-lags. Further, since not all the positives arrive at once, they will also show considerable fluctuations in the size and shape of the pulse. Because of the time-lags, they are of no value in coincidence circuits,[C4] since any effective coincidence-counting arrangement assumes minimum time-lag. The voltage region in which such counters may be expected to give reliable results is comparatively small and the plateaus are not at all flat.

i. Experiments on counters with potential-reversing circuits. Since the fundamental limitation on the recovery time of counters is due to the mobility of the positive ions, it has occurred to many observers independently to attempt to collect these ions rapidly near the place where they are produced. The first successful experiments along this line to be reported in the literature were made by Simpson [84] who employed a square-wave generator (multivibrator) circuit to apply a reverse potential to the counter. If a count takes place in a counter, the positive ion sheath is formed in the immediate vicinity of the center wire. The electron avalanche is complete before the positive ions have moved any appreciable distance. If this arrival of electrons on the wire can trigger a circuit which now rapidly makes the center wire negative and cylinder positive, the positive ions in the counter could travel the much shorter distance to the central wire and there be neutralized. This action would speed up the operation of the counter.

In Simpson's experiment, this was done and a circuit was developed for the purpose. The requirements to be met by such a circuit are quite severe. If the counter normally operates with the wire 1500 volts more positive than the cylinder, it would be necessary to make it several hundred volts more negative than the cylinder, keep it at that potential for a time long enough to collect the positives, and then return it to its original state, all in a time short compared to the travel time of the positives across the counter, i.e., less than 10^{-4} sec. It is therefore necessary to apply a square pulse, 1800 volts or more in amplitude and a few microseconds in duration, to the wire. Most receiving tubes will fail under such operation, and Simpson employed a transmitting tube of type 807. This tube was driven by a trigger circuit, which was in turn actuated by the small pulse due to the electrons arriving on the center wire. Elaborate precautions had to be taken to insure that the final pulse would be really square, eliminating rounded corners and tails to the pulse, and rendering the trigger circuit insensitive during the cycle of operation. A detailed discussion of the circuit is out of place here, and the reader is referred to the original paper.[84] It will suffice to say that the operation was successful, and that it was possible to collect the positive ions in a short time. Simpson reported that the operation could be carried out and the counter restored to a sensitive condition in times of the order of 2×10^{-5} sec, with "no indication that the limit had been reached." Although this circuit is probably not, at the present time, readily adaptable to general laboratory use, it appears probable that future developments in high speed counters will make use of this principle. Circuits of this type will no doubt be simplified and become part of standard laboratory practice. The success of this experiment points the way to important new developments in counter technique and suggests many interesting and significant fields of study. An order of magnitude has already been gained and further progress seems probable.

j. Intrinsic time lags. Most discussions of Geiger counters assume that the count takes place immediately after the ionizing event occurs. It is well to consider this assumption rather carefully, especially if use is to be made of extremely short resolving times. As we have indicated above, once an electron starts to produce an avalanche the action takes place very quickly, and in less than a microsecond the avalanche is over, electrons have been collected and the positive ion space charge sheath has been produced. The electrons, wherever formed, can traverse the dimensions of the counter in less than a microsecond. It was therefore somewhat surprising when various observers reported evidence that a counter did not discharge until some time several microseconds after the primary ionizing event had occurred. The Montgomerys [M1] have given a good explanation of this effect.

The intrinsic time-lag in the counter is attributed to the formation of negative ions. If the electron, formed in a primary ionizing event at some point distant from the wire, is captured to form a negative ion while it travels toward the wire, its speed of travel will be much reduced. Taking the mobility of a small negative ion at about 1.5 cm per sec per volt per cm, a negative ion will travel in a field of 10^3 volts per cm and 0.1 atm pressure, at roughly 1.5×10^4 cm per sec and hence would require many microseconds to traverse a counter. This time would be considerably reduced if the electron were captured near the wire, as it would have traversed most of the distance at the much higher speeds characteristic of an electron, and would complete its journey to the wire faster because it was in the high-field region. The time still would be appreciable compared to that required for the electron to complete its journey in the absence of capture. It is further to be noted that the experiments in which these lags were observed used counters in which oxygen was present as a constituent in an amount of 6%. If short resolving times are to be used, the formation of negative ions must be avoided. This is particularly important in coincidence experiments where a lag of several microseconds may produce an apparent inefficiency in a fast circuit.

k. The use of grids in counters. Experiments have been reported by Korff and Ramsey [K11] and W. F. Libby [L5] in which a grid was introduced into a counter. The cylinder of the counter was 5.6 cm in diameter and a grid of 1 cm diameter was arranged around the central wire. Since the avalanche mechanism occurs only in the immediate vicinity of the wire, the position of the grid does not affect the avalanche. The pulse size is controlled by the potential difference between the grid and the central wire.

When the outer cylinder is made negative with respect to the grid, any electrons produced in the outer space are accelerated toward the grid. Disregarding the few which are collected on the grid, most electrons pass through the grid and produce counts as though the grid were not there. Only a small potential difference between grid and cylinder is necessary. Potential differences of as little as 10 volts were found to serve. Increasing this potential difference to 200 volts made no detectable difference, as the outer region is merely an ion-collecting zone. If the potential was reversed, and the grid made negative by 10 volts with respect to the cylinder, the outer volume ceased to contribute electrons to the discharge and the counter acted as though it were one whose diameter was equal to that of the grid. Varying the magnitude of the grid-cathode potential difference again had no effect.

When the potential difference between grid and cylinder was made zero, the counter went into a continuous discharge. The explanation of this is that any electrons produced in the field free space between grid and cylinder might then drift about and at random times drift through the grid. As soon as each one has passed through the grid it starts a count. A rapid succession of counts at random intervals is the equivalent of a continuous discharge.

The advantages of using the grid are (a) that the total operating voltage of the counter can be reduced and (b) that the resolving time is shortened since the positives cease to influence the discharge as soon as they have reached the grid and thus have only had to travel over one-fifth (in this case) of the radius of the cylinder. The disadvantages are (a) increased complexity in construction and (b) a few electrons are collected on the grid. As to the operating voltage, with a small diameter grid only that voltage needed for a small-diameter counter need be used, plus a grid-plate potential difference of 10 or 22½ or some other convenient low voltage. For a large diameter cylinder, the attainable voltage reductions are quite considerable. This consideration is, for example, of great importance in saving weight in cosmic-ray-balloon experiments.

B. Selfquenching Counters

1. Introduction. In this section we shall discuss counters containing polyatomic gases or vapors. "Polyatomic" we shall use to describe a molecule consisting of four or more atoms. Triatomic molecules will constitute a special case separately discussed below. The counters in question may have monatomic or diatomic gases added. The monatomic component may often be the largest fraction percentage-wise, as for example in counters filled with 90% argon plus 10% alcohol vapor. The polyatomic molecule, however, if present in appreciable amounts, affects the character of the discharge to such an extent that the operation of the counter is entirely different from the non-selfquenching type of counter discussed previously.

It was reported by Trost [T2] in 1937 that the addition of a certain amount of the vapor of some organic compounds caused the counter discharge to "quench" itself, in other words to terminate due to some internal mechanism in the discharge. This property permitted the elimination of the "quenching resistance" or the equivalent electronic circuit. Since the high resistance was the chief cause of the slow recovery time of the non-selfquenching counter, the selfquenching counters exhibited an apparently much shorter recovery time and hence became known as "fast" counters. As we shall show, this is a misnomer, because the actual time required by the "fast" counter to complete one cycle of its discharge mechanism is longer than that for the "slow" or non-selfquenching counter. We shall therefore use the term "selfquenching" when referring to these counters as this more nearly describes their properties.

Since Trost's early experiments, various observers have tried a large number of different compounds in counters. The result of these experiments may be summarized by saying that any polyatomic (gas) molecule will produce the "quenching" action. The molecule need not be organic, BF_3 being an illustration of a non-organic molecule which causes quenching, although most polyatomic molecules are organic. There does not appear to be any great difference in merit between various possible polyatomic molecules, each having certain advantages and disadvantages as compared to others. For example, amyl acetate shows a somewhat longer useful life but a slower resolving-time than does methane. We shall discuss these various properties below.

In selecting a gas for a selfquenching counter we consider the following desiderata: (1) The counter should have high efficiency; (2) it should have a short resolving time; (3) it should have a wide plateau; (4) it should have a flat plateau; (5) it should have a minimum temperature coefficient and (6) it should have a long life. A low operating potential and ease of construction are desirable considerations which we shall also mention. The optimum amount of polyatomic constituent to be added to a monatomic or diatomic gas will be described, as well as the minimum amount needed to produce quenching. In order to understand why a given combination of factors is desirable, we must consider the atomic mechanism of the discharge.

2. Theory. In 1942, Stever [S3] extended the analysis which the Montgomerys [M3] had originally prepared regarding non-self-quenching counters, to selfquenching counters. The Montgomerys pointed out that one of the important differences between the non-selfquenching and selfquenching counters was that when the positive ions formed in the avalanche reached the cylinder, secondary electrons were formed. These electrons caused the discharge to continue indefinitely in the case of the non-selfquenching counter while in the selfquenching type, these secondary electrons were absent. Korff and Present [K7] in 1944 proposed a mechanism to explain the absence of secondary electrons. Stever discussed the formation of the space charge sheath, following the Montgomery theory, and showed how the measured dead times and recovery times depended on the motion of this sheath.

To understand this operation, let us consider the definitions and meaning of the dead time and recovery time of a counter. Suppose a count occurs. There will follow an insensitive time, while the discharge mechanism is operating, during which time, if another ionizing event occurs in the counter, it is not detected. This time is defined as the dead time. At the end of the dead time if an ionizing event should occur, a pulse so small that it can just be detected, would be observed. If the event takes place a trifle later, the pulse will be larger, and finally a time will come when the pulse will be of full height. The recovery time is then defined as the time required by the counter to recover so that a pulse following another by this interval shall be of full size. Stever devised an electronic circuit to demonstrate this phenomenon on an oscilloscope screen and Fig. 4–8 shows a sketch of the pattern seen. The dead time and recovery time are indicated in the figure.

Stever discusses the dead time and recovery time in terms of the movement of the positive ion sheath. This analysis has already been discussed in the section on non-selfquenching counters, since Stever's treatment is substantially the same as the Montgomerys'. The dead time is understood as the time

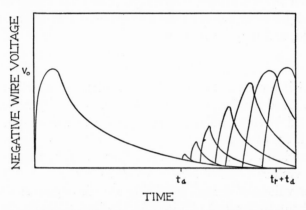

FIG. 4–8. Drawing of oscilloscope pattern of the result of the dead-time experiment. This shows the dead time t_d and the recovery time t_r. The time $(t_d + t_r)$ corresponds to the arrival of the positive ion sheath at the cylinder. The time t_d corresponds to the point in the transit of the positive ions at which the field about the wire has returned to threshold field. (From H. G. Stever, *Phys. Rev.* **61**, 40 (1942))

required for the space charge sheath to move out to a distance such that the field near the wire will have recovered to such a value that counts will again be observed. In other words, as when the space charge sheath is first formed, the field inside the sheath decreases below the value necessary to sustain an avalanche, i.e., below the Geiger threshold. As the sheath moves out, the field between the sheath and the wire increases and returns to normal. Stever shows that the "critical radius" r_c is related to the overvoltage V and the cylinder radius r by the relation

$$r_c = r^{-V/2q} \qquad (4\text{–}5)$$

where q is the positive ion space charge per unit length. The dead time is the time required by the positive ions to move out to r_c.

As the positives continue past R toward the cylinder, the field near the wire recovers to normal. The recovery time is the time required by the ions to reach the cylinder and be neutralized. The dead and recovery times are therefore determined by the mobility of the positive ions. This drift velocity dx/dt of an ion in a field E at pressure P is determined by the field, and may be written

$$dx/dt = kE/p \qquad (4\text{--}6)$$

where k is a constant called the "mobility," and dx is the distance moved by the ion in time dt. The quantity k is usually expressed in cm per sec per volt per cm at atmospheric pressure [cf. eq. (2–2)].

Numerical values of k have been determined by many observers for various types of ions moving in various gases. The numerical values of k and the fields used in counters are such that about 10^{-4} sec is required for the ions to reach the cylinder. The order-of-magnitude agreement between this figure and the known recovery times has been commented on by the Montgomerys and others and has been used to support arguments regarding the natural insensitive time. The case of the selfquenching counter is somewhat complicated since two kinds of ions are often present, those of argon and those of ethyl alcohol, for example. The mobility of argon ions in argon is more accurately known than the mobility of the mixtures in mixed gases. It is therefore not possible simply by referring to values of k in tables, to answer the problem completely. Electron transfer, as we shall show, somewhat simplifies the picture.

The form of the dependence of k on E and on p, the pressure, is complicated, and has been studied in detail by Loeb [L1] and others. Near the wire, where the field is high, k is not constant. Moreover the functional relationship varies considerably from gas to gas. If k is assumed constant, the dead time can be calculated, but experiments do not confirm the values so obtained. The recovery time can be calculated with some degree of success, since most of the travel time of the ions is spent in the low field regions where k may be assumed constant. The expression for the recovery time, t_r, is readily derived from eqs. (4–5 and 4–6) recalling that the voltage $V = \int E dr$, and is found to be

$$t_r = \frac{(r^2 - r_c^2) \log (r/r_w)}{2kV} \qquad (4\text{–}7)$$

where r_w and r are the wire and cylinder radii. The observed values of t_r lie between 1.0 and 2.2×10^{-4} sec for counters operating at between 950 and 1450 volts, $r_w = 0.01$ cm, $r = 1.11$ cm, $r_c = 0.65$ cm and filled to between 5 and 14 cm pressure of a 90% argon + 10% Xylol mixture. The values predicted by eq. (4–7) are generally within 20% of the observed figures. This agreement must be regarded as satisfactory in view of the uncertainties in the problem, the lack of precision in consideration of the exact meaning of the mobility, and the effects of electron transfer which we shall discuss below.

The dead times and recovery times have been measured by Stever [83] for a variety of different gases and mixtures and a few typical ones are listed in Table 4–3. It will be seen that the dead times and recovery times are of the stated order of magnitude, 1 to 2×10^{-4} sec, for the lighter gases, and somewhat higher, up to 8×10^{-4} sec, for the heavier vapors. This is to be expected since the mobilities of the heavy ions are less than that of the light ions.

Eq. (4–7) and the arguments regarding the dead time and recovery time all assume that the discharge spreads along the wire of the counter. A number of experiments have been performed which support this view. Since these experiments also have a bearing on the actual mechanism of the counter discharge, we shall now describe them.

TABLE 4–3. OBSERVED DEAD TIMES AND RECOVERY TIMES

Gases	Total Pressure, Cm	Dead Time, Seconds	Recovery Time, Seconds	Reference
95% argon, 5% xylol	13.4	2.6×10^{-4}	4.3×10^{-4}	S3
95% argon, 5% xylol	11.0	2.4×10^{-4}	4.3×10^{-4}	S3
95% argon, 5% xylol	9.0	2.1×10^{-4}	3.7×10^{-4}	S3
95% argon, 5% xylol	7.0	1.8×10^{-4}	3.6×10^{-4}	S3
94.5% argon, 5.5% ethyl alcohol	10.1	1.4×10^{-4}	2.3×10^{-4}	S7
80% argon, 20% alcohol	10.0	2.1×10^{-4}	2.3×10^{-4}	S7
67% argon, 33% alcohol	9.7	2.2×10^{-4}	2.45×10^{-4}	S7
94.8% argon, 5.2% amyl acetate	10.0	2.0×10^{-4}	4.0×10^{-4}	S7
90.9% argon, 9.1% amyl acetate	10.0	2.0×10^{-4}	4.0×10^{-4}	S7
94.8% argon, 5.2% amyl acetate	15.0	2.8×10^{-4}	4.8×10^{-4}	S7

First we will recall the early and unpublished experiments, made by Ramsey, Brode and others, in which two counters (A and B) were so arranged that the inside region of one counter could "see" the inside of the other. In other words, photons or electrons could pass unobstructed from the region near the wire of one counter to a similar region or could reach the inside of the cathode of the other. The result of these experiments was that when counter A discharged, counter B discharged each time the two were filled with non-selfquenching gases or mixtures. When the counters were filled with self-quenching mixtures, counter B discharged only in a random relation to the discharges of A. By applying a magnetic field which would have so deflected electrons that they could not have reached the other counter, Ramsey further showed that what passed between the counters was photons.

A further extension of this experiment was reported by Stever, who divided the wire of a counter with a small glass bead. He found again that a bead would stop the spread of the discharge in a selfquenching counter and not in a non-selfquenching one. The single counter, with a bead on the center of the central wire, was thus effectively turned into two counters. Either section would discharge independently but would not cause the other to discharge. He then found that a continuous wire might pass through the bead and that the bead would still stop the spread of the discharge. On the other hand, when the cylinder was divided but the wire was continuous the discharge spread into both sections. In other words, the discharge spreads in a narrow sheath along the wire.

The minimum size of the bead necessary to interrupt the discharge was then sought. This size, it was found, depended on the gas pressure and the overvoltage. Thus, for example, a 0.022 in. diameter bead on an 0.008 in. diameter wire stopped the discharge at 10 cm pressure and 1300 volts; but, at 3.5 cm pressure, above 840 volts the discharge was able to pass the bead, while between 840 and the threshold at 790 the bead stopped the spread.

Wilkening and Kanne [W2] made a similar test, with an obstruction (in this case a small quartz disk) on the wire and studied the minimum amount of alcohol vapor which had to be added to an argon-filled counter to prevent the discharge from spreading across the disk. They found that if less than 5% of alcohol vapor were added, the discharge often spread across the obstruction. They further found that the spreading was more likely to occur if the overvoltage was greater. As the processes are statistical in nature, there is no one voltage or pressure at which the spread sets in abruptly. But, if, for example, the voltage is raised, more and more discharges will spread over into the next section.

We are now in a position to inquire into the mechanism of quenching, or in other words to consider the effects produced by the polyatomic molecules. We shall follow the discussions of this problem given by Korff and Present.[K7] It will be shown that the characteristic property of the polyatomic molecule which is important for the operation of a counter is the short lifetime of the excited electronic states against predissociation, i.e., polyatomic molecules, having absorbed a quantum, usually predissociate before they have an opportunity to lose the absorbed energy by radiation. Atoms and diatomic molecules, on the other hand, generally reradiate the energy which they have absorbed.

The excited electronic states of a diatomic molecule have sharp rotational levels well above the dissociation energy of the molecule, and predissociation is only an occasional phenomenon. In polyatomic molecules containing four or more atoms, predissociation is the rule rather than the exception, and the absorption spectrum in the ultraviolet shows diffuse absorption bands with the rotational structure obliterated, as well as regions of continuous absorption. This is essentially due to the opportunities for "crossing over" provided by the many intersections of the potential energy hypersurfaces extending over a wide range of energies. The heavier the molecule, the more diffuse is the spectrum and the more likely is predissociation. Light polyatomic molecules present an intermediate case, and the spectroscopy and photochemistry of each must be considered separately to determine the probable result of a given excitation.

In our definitions, Chapter 1, we have defined "quenching" as any process causing the discharge to terminate. There are three distinct types of "quenching" involved in the operation of a selfquenching counter: (a) quenching of photons in the initial avalanche, (b) electrostatic quenching of the avalanche by the positive ion space charge, and (c) quenching of the secondary emission when the positive ions reach the cathode. The quenching of the discharge involves both the electrostatic quenching and the quenching of secondary emission. We propose to discuss the rôle of the polyatomic gas in quenching cases (a) and (c), since (b) has already been covered.

First let us examine the rôle of the polyatomic gas in the initial avalanche. Common polyatomic constituents of counters are methane and alcohol vapor. Let us consider an argon-methane counter operating in the "proportional" region, in which the size of the pulse is proportional to the number of ions formed in the initial ionizing event. A theory of the formation of the avalanche in this case has been given by Rose and Korff. Assuming that the electrons multiply by collision and that photoelectrons do not contribute to the avalanche, they obtain a formula for the gas amplification which agrees well with experiment as long as a sufficient amount of methane is present in the counter. When the relative or absolute amount of methane is reduced too far, the gas amplification is found to rise more steeply with increasing voltage than predicted by the formula, thus indicating an additional source of electrons. The dependence of this effect on the nature of the cathode surface led Rose and Korff to suggest that photoelectrons from the cathode were contributing to the avalanche. When the counter voltage was raised sufficiently, all the curves deviated from the values predicted by the formula.

They also suggested that collisions which cause electronic excitation of the polyatomic molecule will usually result in decomposition rather than in photon emission. This is in agreement with other evidence to be discussed below, and is supported by experiments of Glockler [G6] in which electrons with 17-ev energy introduced into a methane-filled photo-cell produced no measurable photoelectric current. We wish to emphasize here that in a counter containing a mixture of gases the principal rôle of the polyatomic gas in the avalanche is to absorb the ultraviolet photons emitted by the inert gas (argon). Many photons originate in the avalanche from excited argon atoms. Ranging in energy from 11.5 to 15.7 ev, these photons would liberate electrons from the cathode (photoelectric threshold about 4 ev), were they not absorbed in the gas. Since a gas mixture containing 50% argon to 50% ether shows no evidence of cathode effect, the argon photons must be absorbed by ether molecules before they reach the cathode. This is also in accord with Ramsey's double-counter experiment, cited above, in which it was shown that when counter A discharged, if the photons from this discharge could reach the interior of counter B, then counter B discharged every time if the two were filled with a non-quenching gas (argon), and only at random times if the two were filled with a quenching gas (alcohol).

We inquire next into the details of the absorption act. When a molecule absorbs an ultraviolet photon and passes into an excited electronic state, there are several possible competitive modes of de-excitation: (1) decomposition (dissociation or predissociation), (2) radiation (fluorescence), and (3) deactivation by collision. Process (3) cannot occur in less than 10^{-8} sec, which is the collision time in an ordinary counter. Process (2) involves a radiation lifetime of 10^{-8} sec. Process (1), when possible, occurs within 10^{-11} to 10^{-13} sec, depending on the breadth of the levels. If the rotational structure is obliterated, the lifetime is about 100 times longer than if the vibrational structure is obliterated (continuous absorption). Diatomic molecules, in general, as well as certain light polyatomic molecules, possess stable electronic states with well defined vibrational-rotational structure well above the dissociation limit or limits of the molecule. Excitation of the molecule into this region of energy results in re-emission of the absorbed photon or fluorescence and only rarely in dissociation. Hence, the photons produced in the discharge would not be quenched by diatomic gases. On the other hand, if we examine the spectroscopic and photochemical data for methane, ammonia, and other gases used in fast counters for which data are available,[R6] we can understand why these gases are photon-quenching. The photo-decomposition of methane in the ultraviolet is well known and the absorption spectrum, taken at a pressure of 1 mm of mercury, shows continuous absorption from 1560 Å down to at least 850 Å, the limit of observation. The ultraviolet photons emitted by excited argon atoms range from 1070 Å to 790 Å; hence they are quenched by methane. Ammonia vapor also photodecomposes in the ultraviolet and the spectrum shows continuous absorption below 1200 Å. Hence ammonia also quenches the argon photons.

Evidence of the decomposition of the alcohol vapor in a fast counter has been obtained by Spatz.[81] Decomposition in the initial avalanche is to be attributed partly to electron impact and partly to photo-dissociation. As we shall see later, further decomposition occurs when the alcohol ions reach the cathode. The primary decomposition products are usually free radicals which combine to form a miscellaneous assortment of organic molecules. Some of these decomposition products will be quenching gases. However, with continued use of the counter, all of the larger vapor molecules are broken up and the end products of the decomposition are a non-quenching gas, such as hydrogen or oxygen, and heavy hydrocarbons deposited on the walls. These considerations explain why selfquenching counters "go bad" with continued use. Since about 10^{10} alcohol ions are decomposed at the cathode in each discharge, as will be explained in the next section, and since there are altogether about 10^{20} alcohol molecules in the counter, the counter will go bad after about 10^{10} counts. This is in accord with Spatz's observations. These considerations further explain why a methane counter has a shorter life than an alcohol counter. Methane is already far down the list of decomposition products of alcohol and itself can decompose only once or twice before it is reduced to non-quenching diatomic molecules. We can also understand why a greater proportion of methane than alcohol must be added to argon to produce a selfquenching counter. This is due partly to the greater number of vibration-rotation levels available for inelastic electron impacts in the case of the alcohol molecule and partly to the higher quantum yield of the photo-decomposition of alcohol.

Some of the results of Wilkening and Kanne cited above on localization of the discharge will be examined next. The discharge in the Geiger region normally spreads the entire length of the wire in both non-selfquenching and selfquenching counters. A reduction in the field near the central wire by some artificial means, such as the presence of an insulating bead, will interrupt the spread of the discharge in a fast counter but not in a slow counter. In the latter case, photoelectrons from the cathode spread the discharge beyond the obstacle. Wilkening and Kanne used various devices to interrupt the spread of the discharge and measured the effectiveness of the localizing devices in various gases. Selfquenching counters showed 100% "localization." However, a mixture of 1 cm of methane with 9 cm of argon showed only a 50% localization. This is consistent with the fact that the photon-quenching is incomplete in this case, as we may verify from the gas amplification curves given by Rose and Korff. At 10-cm pressure even a 50% argon-methane mixture shows evidence of appreciable photo-effect. Counters filled with monatomic and diatomic gases showed "zero localization," or complete spread of the discharge, corresponding to the total absence of photon-quenching.

We should expect a close correlation between the extent of localization and the length of the proportional region. It has been reported by Korff [K4] and others that selfquenching counters have a much longer proportional region than slow counters at the same total pressure. This is a consequence of the more rapid rise of the amplification factor of a non-selfquenching counter with increasing voltage, which is in turn due to the photoelectric effect at the cathode. Thus the spreading of the discharge beyond an obstacle and the rapid rise of the amplification factor are due to the same cause: photons in the avalanche. The counters found by Wilkening and Kanne to show

100% localization are all counters containing heavy polyatomic vapors which are present in sufficient amount to absorb the argon photons. The methane-argon counter showing 50% localization has a short proportional region. Counters filled with diatomic gases go over directly into a continuous discharge with very short proportional regions, seldom characterized by values of the gas amplification as great as 100 before instability sets in, and such counters show zero localization.

Consider next the transition from the proportional region to the Geiger region in which the size of the pulse is independent of the number of ions formed in the initial ionizing event. At the threshold voltage of the Geiger region, the amplification factor theoretically rises to infinity; in practice the Geiger threshold corresponds to an amplification factor between 10^8 and 10^{12}. Let us assume that the counter has a negligible resistance in series with it. When the Geiger threshold is reached, a non-selfquenching counter will go into a "continuous" discharge, whereas a selfquenching counter will give a single sharp pulse. Because of the absence of resistance, the counter is at its operating potential during the entire time that the positive ions are moving out to the cathode. The electric field in the vicinity of the wire is below the threshold field until the ions have moved out to Stever's "critical distance." The positive ions then have drift velocities of the order of one-tenth their thermal velocities and the kinetic energy they acquire between collisions is less than 0.1 ev. Thus they can neither excite nor ionize, so that if no further ionizing particles enter the counter nothing happens until the ions reach the cathode and are neutralized. It is at this juncture that the behavior of an argon-filled counter differs from that of a methane-filled counter. Secondary electron emission takes place in the argon counter and, since the counter is at operating potential at this time, the entire cycle is repeated. Thus the discharge in a non-selfquenching counter is self-perpetuating although the avalanches are intermittent. In a methane counter, on the other hand, the discharge terminates when the methane ions are neutralized and no secondary emission can occur because, instead of radiating, the methane decomposes upon neutralization.

Details of the neutralization act and subsequent secondary emission will be considered next. When an argon ion approaches to within 10^{-7} cm of the cathode surface, the field of the ion becomes great enough to extract an electron from the metal. This phenomenon of field emisssion is well known and is substantially the same as that which occurs when a high field is applied between electrodes. In the language of quantum mechanics, the electrons in the metal are separated from the vacant energy-levels in the ion by a potential barrier at the metal surface. Quantum mechanical procedures permit calculation of the probability of an electron from the metal "leaking" through the barrier and neutralizing the ion. The electrons in the metal are at a level of ϕ volts below the top of the barrier, where ϕ is the work function. The vacant levels in the ion are at I volts below the top of the barrier, where I is the ionization potential. The difference in energy which the neutralized atom must radiate is $(I - \phi)$ volts approximately, the exact value depending on the location of excitation levels in the atom. In the case of argon ions and a copper cathode, the neutralized atoms are formed in the excited state at 11.5 ev. The distance of approach at which the probability of neutralization approaches unity has been calculated by Oliphant and Moon,[01] using the Fowler-Nordheim formula. The probability of neutralization is an extremely sensitive function of the distance. For ions of thermal velocities approaching a copper surface the critical distance is about 5×10^{-8} cm. Thus the neutralization must take place before the ions are 5×10^{-8} cm from the wall, after which the neutralized atoms reach the wall in about 2×10^{-12} sec. Many atoms, however, do not reach the wall since the momentum communicated to the ion on neutralization is of the same order of magnitude as its initial thermal momentum.

It has been found experimentally that He+ ions which collide with an outgassed platinum surface at a glancing angle escape largely as neutral atoms in the metastable state. This indicates that an ion may be neutralized without making an inelastic collision with the wall. Many neutralized atoms, however, will approach the surface closely enough to transfer their excitation energy to an electron in the metal, resulting in the emission of a secondary electron if $I > 2\phi$. Another way of putting this is to say that, if the ionization potential is greater than twice the work function, then on the average two electrons will be pulled out of the metal, one of which neutralizes the ion and the other becomes a secondary electron forthwith. The probability of secondary emission by an excited atom approaching the surface has been calculated by Massey.[M4] According to Massey's formula, an atom of thermal velocity must approach to within 2×10^{-8} cm of the surface to make secondary emission probable, i.e., the wave functions of the atomic and metallic electrons must overlap. Since the radiation lifetime of the excited state of argon formed on neutralization is 10^{-7} sec, many of the argon atoms will liberate electrons from the cathode.

Suppose a methane ion captures an electron from the wall. The ionization energy of methane is 14.5 ev, and the neutralized molecule therefore has the same excitation as a molecule which has absorbed light of wave-length 1200 Å. The spectrum of methane, as has been previously mentioned, shows continuous absorption below 1450 Å, indicating a lifetime against decomposition of the order of 10^{-13} sec for the excited molecule. If this figure were exact and if the molecule required 2×10^{-12} sec after neutralization to reach the wall, only about one molecule in 10^9 could reach the wall before decomposing.

Even after the polyatomic molecule comes into contact with the surface, i.e., within range of the van der Waals forces, a transfer of electronic excitation energy from the chemical bond in which it was originally localized, across several other bonds to an electron in the metal, is still less likely than a decomposition. The secondary emission is therefore very small.

We must also note that a radiation lifetime of 10^{-7} sec implies that one molecule per 10^6 will radiate instead of decomposing. Since the photoelectric yield for the cathode surfaces used is of the order of 10^{-4} electron per quantum, the secondary emission from this source amounts to one electron per 10^{10} incident positive ions. We take this figure to represent the total secondary emission. Recombination of secondary electrons with incoming positive ions will further reduce the chance of producing a new avalanche. The average number of ions formed in a selfquenching counter avalanche at the beginning of the Geiger region is about 10^9. Hence the secondary emission is quenched and a single sharp pulse is obtained from a counter filled with methane. Recently Bassi and Beretta [B15] have measured the fraction of secondary electrons liberated and have found this to be of the order of 10^{-10} times the number of incident ions, when ethyl alcohol ions strike the cathode.

In order to determine whether a given gas by itself will make a selfquenching counter, we have to investigate its absorption spectrum at wave lengths corresponding to an excitation energy of $I - \phi$. If the absorption spectrum is diffuse or continuous, corresponding to decomposition in this region, then the gas will make a selfquenching counter. To take an example: The ionization energy of ethyl alcohol is 11.3 ev and the neutralized molecule is formed about 1700 Å above the ground state. The spectrum of the vapor shows continuous absorption below 2000 Å, and this is accompanied by photodecomposition. The quantum yield of the photodecomposition is of the order of unity. Hence, we should expect alcohol vapor to make a selfquenching counter. A diatomic molecule generally possesses discrete states between the dissociation energy and the ionization energy; thus, on neutralization a diatomic molecule will not decompose. Therefore, counters filled with diatomic gases show non-selfquenching counter action. Since, on the other hand, a heavy organic molecule has a large probability of predissociating at all energies, such a gas will invariably make a selfquenching counter. Huber and Alder [H11] find negligible absorption of photons in air-argon counters, but strong absorption when alcohol is added. The halogen family, as Present [P2] has pointed out, may be expected to show quenching properties, since it shows strong absorption in the ultraviolet at around $I - \phi$, which in these substances lies between 1500–2600 Å. Photodecomposition in these substances is well known.

The triatomic gases must be considered separately. The absorption spectra of H_2O, CO_2, N_2O, SO_2, H_2S, and CS_2 show bands with diffuse rotational structure converging on the ionization energy of the molecule as a limit. The broadening of the levels would correspond to a lifetime of the order of 100 times that of a heavy molecule. Hence secondary emission would be much more probable. The mentioned triatomic gases (used in conjunction with low resistances) give no evidence of an appreciable Geiger region. Mixtures of these gases, however, can have selfquenching properties. For example, Miller [M12] has employed CO_2–CS_2 mixtures successfully.

A further consequence of the suppression of secondary emission previously outlined is that the frequency and multiplicity of multiple pulses should increase slowly along the plateau of a selfquenching counter. The numerical estimates of secondary emission given before would lead one to expect about one double pulse in ten or one triple pulse in one hundred at the beginning of the Geiger region. This is roughly in agreement with what one observes on the oscilloscope screen. As the voltage across the counter is raised, the charge collected per count is found to vary linearly with the overvoltage. Measurements [S3] along part of the plateau show that the charge increases by a factor of more than ten. An increase in the number of ions reaching the cathode results in an increased secondary emission and a corresponding increase in the frequency and multiplicity of multiple pulses. From the numerical estimates given above, one would expect that toward the end of the plateau several secondary electrons would, on the average, be emitted when the positive ion sheath reached the cylinder. In these circumstances practically every pulse would be a multiple of large multiplicity; indeed, the oscilloscope shows sprays of multiple pulses toward the end of the Geiger region. If electronic circuits of high resolving power for fast counting are used with a counter operating in this manner, these multiple pulses will give rise to many spurious counts. The slope of the counting-rate plateau is thus to be attributed to the increasing frequency and multiplicity of the multiple pulses leading to an increasing number of spurious counts. The Geiger region terminates when the secondary emission becomes great enough to make the discharge self-sustaining. The Geiger plateau does not terminate abruptly, but as the voltage is raised more and more multiple pulses are observed.

So far the discussion has been restricted to selfquenching counters containing a pure polyatomic gas. If we consider next a selfquenching counter which contains a mixture of a quenching and a nonquenching gas, the question arises of how the secondary emission is suppressed. Since a counter containing 90% argon to 10% alcohol is selfquenching, it is necessary to explain why no argon ions reach the cathode when there is a small amount of alcohol present. The explanation depends on the relative magnitude of the ionization potentials (see Table 4–4) of the two gases: 11.3 volts for $C_2H_5(OH)$ and 15.7 volts for argon. Electron transfer takes place during the passage of the ion sheath across the counter. During this time each argon ion makes about 10^5 collisions with alcohol molecules. Since the ionization energy of the argon atom is greater than the ionization energy of the alcohol molecule, an electron can be transferred from the molecule to the ion. The reverse process, namely, a transfer of an electron from an argon atom

TABLE 4–4. IONIZATION POTENTIALS OF SUBSTANCES USED IN COUNTERS

Substance	Symbol	Mass Number	Ionization Potential	Substance	Symbol	Mass Number	Ionization Potential
1. Monatomic and noble gases				**4. Polyatomic molecules**			
Helium	He	4	24.46	Ethyl alcohol	$C_2H_5(OH)$	46	11.3
Neon	Ne	20	21.74	Ammonia	NH_3	17	11.2 *
Argon	A	40	15.68	Boron trifluor-			
Krypton	Kr	84	13.93	ide	BF_3	68	10.25 *
Xenon	Xe	132	12.08	Ethyl acetate	$CH_2COOC_2H_5$	88	9.5 *
Mercury	Hg	200	10.39	Methane	CH_4	16	14.5
Hydrogen	H	1	13.52	Ethane	C_2H_6	30	11.7
Oxygen	O	16	13.55	Propane	C_3H_8	44	11.21 †
Nitrogen	N	14	14.48	n-Butane	C_4H_{10}	58	10.80 †
				n-Pentane	C_5H_{12}	72	10.55 †
2. Ordinary diatomic gases				n-Hexane	C_6H_{14}	86	10.43 †
				Ethylene	C_2H_4	28	10.60 †
				Propene	CH_2CHCH_3	42	9.84 †
Hydrogen	H_2	2	15.6	1-Butene	$CH_3CH_2CHCH_2$	56	9.76 †
Nitrogen	N_2	28	15.51	Benzene	C_6H_6	78	9.6
Oxygen	O_2	32	12.5	Toluene	C_7H_8	92	8.5
Fluorine	F_2	38	17.8				
Chlorine	Cl_2	70	13.2				
Bromine	Br_2	160	12.8				
Iodine	I_2	254	9.7				
Carbon mon-oxide	CO	28	14.1				
3. Triatomic molecules							
Carbon diox-ide	CO_2	44	14.4				
Water vapor	H_2O	18	12.56				
Carbon disul-fide	CS_2	76	10.4				
Hydrogen sul-fide	H_2S	34	10.42				
Sulfur dioxide	SO_2	64	13.1				
Nitrogen di-oxide	NO_2	46	11.1				

From *International Critical Tables; Handbook of Chemistry and Physics; Smithsonian Physical Tables.*
* R. Kaufman, *Phys. Rev.* **78**, 332 (1950).
† P. Weisz, private communication; R. E. Honing, *J. Chem. Phys.* **16**, 105 (1948).

to an alcohol ion, is energetically impossible because the kinetic energies are only about 0.1 ev. The difference between the two ionization energies may be radiated as one or more photons, or may be manifest as kinetic energy in an inelastic collision. Electron transfer has been investigated by Kallmann and Rosen,[K8] who found that the cross section for this process is of the order of magnitude of the gas kinetic cross section in the case of an ion beam moving through a gas of the same species. For an ion beam moving through a gas of a different ionization potential, the cross section is somewhat less, but no appreciable number of argon ions can reach the cathode after 10^5 collisions. In the commonly used selfquenching counters containing a mixture of gases, the ionization potential of the polyatomic constituent is invariably less than that of the inert gas. If the situation could be reversed, so that the inert gas has the lower ionization potential, then electron transfer would take place in the reverse direction and no polyatomic ions would reach the cathode. In such a counter, photons would be quenched but not the secondary emission. Experimental tests bear this out.

In all cases, initiation of the discharge is assumed to be by the primary ionizing event. That this view is substantially correct even at voltages above the plateau has been shown by Crane [C10] who found that, in an alcohol-argon counter, the voltage alone did not initiate the discharge, even when the potential was substantially above the plateau.

3. Operation. *a. Introduction.* Our discussion of the operational characteristics of selfquenching counters will follow that already given for the non-selfquenching type. The same operating desiderata, namely, low operating potential, long operating range, high efficiency, stability with use and time, and large pulse-size, short recovery time and small temperature coefficient, will be reviewed in turn. The several desirable features are to a certain extent mutually exclusive, in the sense that not all can be attained to a maximum degree with any one arrangement. The interdependence will be discussed and we will point out which have to be sacrificed for the others. It will suffice here to say that there is no ideal "formula" for filling or operating counters, and that the filling substances selected will be determined by the use to be made of the counter and so will differ for different problems.

The chief advantage of the selfquenching counter over the non-selfquenching one is described in the name. In the selfquenching type the discharge terminates or is "quenched" due to the internal mechanism which we have described, and hence no electronic quenching circuit or high resistance is necessary. The disadvantage of the high resistance, as has already been pointed out, is that it lengthens the recovery time of the counter. The equivalent vacuum tube circuit permits a short time constant to be used but adds the inconvenience of an extra stage in the electronic circuits. The advantage gained in the elimination of the quenching resistor or circuit is secured at the price of stability, for the act of quenching also decomposes a fraction of the polyatomic gas or vapor in the counter. We shall show how long a useful life may be expected.

b. Starting and operating potentials. The starting and operating potentials of selfquenching counters are in general somewhat higher than those of the non-selfquenching. When a counter is filled with pure argon, and a cm or two of alcohol or any other vapor is added, the starting potential is raised, usually by several hundred volts. Thus the same counter which might operate at 800 volts filled with argon will require perhaps 1100 when the quenching constituent is added. This is a disadvantage only when batteries are used, for a stabilized voltage supply operating on alternating current (see Chapter 7) and supplying 1500 volts is no more difficult to build than one supplying 1000.

Polyatomic gases in general require higher voltages than do the monatomic ones. For example, a counter filled with pure methane or butane or boron trifluoride will require a higher potential than will the same counter if filled to the same pressure with a mixture consisting of 90% argon and 10% alcohol, ether, or amyl acetate vapor.

The dependence of the starting (or operating) potentials of counters filled with helium or argon plus a hydrocarbon vapor has been systematically investigated by Weisz.[W8] He related starting potentials to the ionization potentials and critical potentials of the hydrocarbons. Since the ionization potential decreases as the number of carbon atoms increases within any one family (such as the methane-ethane-propane series), an inverse dependence on carbon number was found. The more complex the molecule, the more energy levels it will have, and the more opportunities there will be for an electron moving toward the central wire to lose energy upon collision. Hence the electron will have to travel farther before it gains enough energy to produce ionizing collisions. Qualitatively, this is also the chief reason why counters containing complex molecules have higher operating potentials than those containing simple ones.

The fillings for low-voltage counters will be separately considered in a later part of this chapter.

The operating potential increases with the gas pressure and may reach high values. For example, a counter 15 cm in diameter and filled to 50 cm pressure with BF_3 will require about 5000 volts if neutrons are to be detected, and a pulse of 10^{-2} volt amplitude is required. Typical curves are shown in Fig. 4–9 for several cases, in which the starting potentials for a large and a small counter, filled with BF_3, are plotted against pressure. The counters may be used to detect neutrons or gamma rays. The large counter will require higher operating voltages than the small counter and will detect gammas at a higher voltage than is required to detect neutrons because the neutron pulse is larger.

Since argon has a considerably lower starting potential than BF_3, the addition of about 10% of argon to a counter containing pure BF_3 will lower the starting potential somewhat. The total gas pressure will be increased accordingly. The efficiency for detecting neutrons is determined by the amount of BF_3 and hence is not altered by adding argon. Although such lowering of the starting potential was described in the first paper on neutron counters,[K3] and so has been known for eleven years, few investigators have made use of it so far. Further experiments show that similar reduction of operating voltage can be secured by adding helium, neon or krypton.

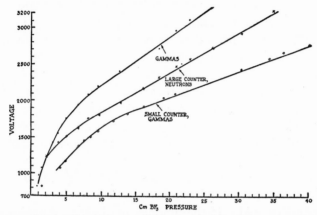

FIG. 4–9.   Curves of starting potentials for neutron BF₃ counters, counting neutrons and gamma rays. Note that the voltage difference between the neutron and beta detection potentials increases with the BF₃ pressure. Large counter 5.5 cm diameter, 22.7 cm long. Small counter 1 cm diameter, 3 cm long, central wire 3 mil. Pulse size, constant, about 0.1 volt. (From S. A. Korff, *Rev. Mod. Phys.* **14**, 1–11 (1942))

c. Flatness and length of the plateau. The flatness of the plateau is determined by the nature of the quenching constituent. If pure argon and pure (absolute) alcohol are used, flat plateaus may be secured. A series of tests was conducted by Spatz [S1] in which he found that (1) the flatness of the plateau was materially reduced by contaminating an alcohol-argon mixture with air and (2) the flatness depended on the amount of alcohol. The flatness of the plateau is defined as the percentage increase in counting rate as the voltage is raised. He found that the plateau could be made absolutely flat to within the experimental error, i.e., a rise in counting rate of less than 1% for a 100-volt increase in operating voltage, if a 95% argon,

5% alcohol mixture were used, and the argon was 99.8% pure and the alcohol absolute. Admitting as much as 2% air caused the plateau slope to increase to a 15% rise per 100 volts. Filling the same counter to a total of 80% argon and 20% alcohol yielded a slope of 5% per 100 volts. He attributed the increase of slope with alcohol content to air dissolved in the alcohol. Similar unpublished tests on other polyatomic vapors yield essentially the same result. As has previously been pointed out, the departure from flatness of the plateau is a measure of the number of spurious counts. The addition of air, resulting in occasional negative ion formation, causes spurious counts.

The dependence of the plateau slope on the nature of the gas was also studied by Brown and Maroni.[B14] They found that the slope did not depend on the nature of the noble gas constituent, but did vary with the quenching gas, being respectively higher for CH_4NH_3, about ten times greater for CCl_2F_2 and a hundred times larger for CCl_4. This was attributed to negative ion formation (see Fig. 4–10A), as we have already mentioned. If the amount of chlorine added exceeds 10%, the effect on the plateau is very marked and increases rapidly with increasing chlorine content.

Organic vapors which (a) do not themselves form negative ions, or (b) do not decompose into fragments which readily attach electrons will provide satisfactory quenching gases. The author has had good success with ethyl acetate, and Morganstern, Cowan and Hughes[M13] report ethylene to yield especially flat plateaus.

The length of the plateau is controlled by the amount of quenching constituent. A diagram conveniently illustrating this relationship is shown in Fig. 4–10B. Rochester and McCusker measured the length of the plateau in an argon-alcohol counter as a function of the amount of alcohol added. The measurements were all made at 40° C, at which temperature the vapor pressure of alcohol is more than 12 cm, so that no alcohol should be present in the liquid phase. It is interest-

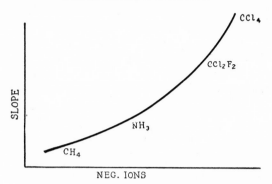

FIG. 4–10A. Effect of negative ions in plateau slope. Plateau becomes less flat as more negative ions are present.[B14]

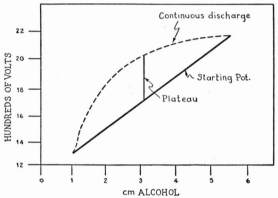

FIG. 4–10B Length of plateau as function of amount of alcohol.[R12]

ing to note that the plateau shortens at the higher concentrations of alcohol vapor.

d. Efficiency. The factors governing the efficiency of counters have already been discussed. Eq. (4–3) may be used in computing the values to be expected. In a counter containing a mixture of gases the number of ion-pairs formed will depend on the specific ionization of each of the constituents and on the pressure of each. A counter 2 cm in diameter (to 10 cm) with argon will have an efficiency of 99.7% and the addition of 1 or

2 cm of alcohol or ether will raise the efficiency to perhaps 99.8%. The specific ionization of many organic vapors has not been measured but it may be assumed to be fairly high because of the large number of electrons per molecule. However, the argon constituent will dominate in the case cited. A counter filled with alcohol vapor alone would have a much lower efficiency, since the vapor pressure of ethyl alcohol is only 4.4 cm at 20° C and hence there would be an insufficient total amount of gas in the counter. Further, such a counter would have a marked temperature coefficient (see below). Filling a counter with quenching gas alone can be done successfully with such gases as BF_3, or methane or butane which can be introduced to a total pressure of from 8 to 15 cm or more without liquefying at normal operating temperatures. The specific ionization of these gases is such that good efficiencies may be obtained with filling pressures comparable to those used in argon-alcohol or argon-ether or argon-amyl acetate counters.

e. *Stability*. As has been pointed out before, selfquenching counters all suffer from the disadvantage that the quenching constituent is decomposed in the act of quenching and hence the characteristics of the counters vary with use. Time, by itself, appears to have no effect, and counters which have been carefully prepared but not used have been found, after a lapse of several years, to be as good as new ones. Chemical stability is obviously essential. It is important that there should be no chemical action, either between gas molecules or with the cylinder or envelope, as such action will clearly alter the number, and perhaps also the kind, of molecules and hence the operating characteristics of the counter. For example, BF_3 slowly attacks hydrocarbons, so that none can be present, even in the walls, of such a counter. Good vacuum technique is recommended to minimize slow evolution of occluded gas. A series of tests of expected "lives" of counters has been made by Spatz.[81] The word "life" is taken to mean the number of counts which the counter can detect before it changes so much as to become useless.

The number of molecules decomposed in each discharge will depend on the overvoltage. Operating counters at high overvoltages will therefore decrease the life, and causing a counter to "flash over" or go into a continuous discharge by applying voltages in excess of the operating potential near the top of the plateau may indeed ruin a counter in quite a short time. In the average case, however, about 10^{10} molecules are decomposed in each discharge. This corresponds to the production, according to eq. (1–1), of about a 100-volt pulse on a wire system, having a 16 micromicrofarad distributed capacity. Since a counter contains roughly 10^{20} molecules of alcohol, we should expect a life of the order of 10^{10} counts, which is in good agreement with Spatz's findings for argon-alcohol mixtures. For methane he finds somewhat lower values, nearer 10^8 counts, which is presumably due to the fact that a methane molecule decomposes directly into a non-quenching gas, hydrogen, whereas more complex molecules may decompose first into other constituents which are still polyatomic and so may be able to "quench" even after they have taken part in several discharges. Further, methane polymerizes in the discharge. Heavy hydrocarbons, solid or liquid at room temperature, are formed, and these coat the electrodes. A long lifetime will hence be gained by (a) using a heavy, complex molecule, taking care to avoid those which polymerize readily, (b) having as much of it as possible in the counter, and (c) operating always at low overvoltages. These features, if incorporated, will usually entail some sacrifice of flatness of plateau, a high operating voltage, and a longer recovery time.

As the quenching constituent is decomposed, the total number of molecules in the counter increases. We should expect therefore that the pressure in a counter would increase with use. This is found to be the case. Spatz reports changes of pressure in both argon-alcohol and methane counters. Concomitant with such changes in pressure, there is to be expected an increase in starting potential, since this depends on pressure. This also is observed. The starting potential may change by 100 volts or more during the life of an argon-alcohol counter. Further, the plateau is also observed to become less flat with use, and a counter with a plateau initially flat to within experimental error will show an appreciable slope after a certain amount of use.

Consequently, as the counter is used, the following changes take place: (a) the operating potential increases, (b) the pressure increases, (c) the plateau becomes less flat. These changes in characteristics can usually be allowed for and will not interfere with accurate measurements, provided they are recognized. The life of 10^{10} counts will serve for most experiments. Eventually, however, a selfquenching counter will have to be pumped and refilled. A non-selfquenching counter is better, in that its operating characteristics are more stable with use and its life is determined not by decomposition of the gas but by pitting of the central wire under repeated discharges. A longer life will generally be secured for non-selfquenching counters.

Since the theoretical treatment by Korff and Present of the quenching mechanism suggested that the organic molecules should progressively dissociate, a number of investigators have made observations which bear upon this interesting process. In particular, Friedland [F3] studied the dissociation process as a function of the number of counts which the counter had recorded. A number of counters were equipped with break-off tips and simultaneously filled to a known pressure with an inert gas (in this case, argon) and a quenching vapor. The counters were then caused to count at high rates for varying periods; they were next attached to a mass spectrograph, the break-off tips were broken, and the contents were analyzed for mass number distribution. The presence of the inert gas provided a convenient constant reference-mass. It was found, as might have been expected from the theory outlined above, that the larger mass numbers decreased and the smaller ones increased as a function of the number of counts. We shall employ the short word "use" to mean the number of times the counter has discharged. The amplitudes of the mass numbers at 101, 89, 46, etc., attributed to the large molecules (e.g., ethyl acetate or alcohol) decreased as a function of use, as also did the intermediate spots at 87, 61, 70 and 45. On the other hand, it was found that spots 44 and 28, corresponding to CO_2 and CO, increased with use. Thus apparently in the discharge the large molecules are progressively broken up, first into medium-sized fragments, and finally are caused to rearrange themselves into stable permanent gases.

Decomposition, however, is only one part of the complete story. In the discharge another kind of molecular rearrangement can also take place. In a counter filled originally with a methane-argon mixture, the methane mass 16 will decrease, but masses 27 and 28 are observed to increase, corresponding to polymerization and formation of such compounds as C_2H_4 and others. Whether a complex molecule will decompose into smaller fragments or polymerize into larger ones preferentially depends on the exceedingly complicated possible processes operating competitively in that particular compound. In general it was found that gases in the methane series polymerized more than they dissociated, and that the reverse happened with such compounds as ethyl acetate and the alcohols.

The effect of polymerization is particularly undesirable. As soon as the compound acquires more than five or six carbon atoms, it becomes a liquid or solid at room temperature and deposits out on the walls and central wire. It requires only a small amount of material on the electrodes to render the counter almost useless. Let us consider this matter quantitatively. Suppose a counter contains a partial pressure of 7.6 mm of ethyl acetate. This will correspond to 0.01 atm, or to 2.7×10^{17} molecules per cc. If the counter is about 2 cm in radius and 16 cm long, so that its volume is 100 cc, there will be about 2.7×10^{19} molecules of this vapor in the counter. Now let us assume that the counter is producing 10-volt pulses. Then according to eq. (3–1) there will be 6×10^8 electronic charges collected on the central wire and therefore the same number of polyatomic ions suffering predissociation at the cylinder walls. After 4×10^{10} counts, we might expect that, on the average, practically all the quenching vapor will have been used up. Actually, the effects of the depletion of the quenching constituent will be observable after a considerably smaller number of counts, say, 4 or 6×10^9. Hence, in this case, the observed life and the expected life on the basis of dissociation are in reasonable agreement. But now let us consider polymerization. If 3×10^{14} molecules polymerize, this number will suffice to cover the entire wire with a monomolecular layer; and indeed 3 or 6×10^{17} will suffice to cover the cylinder also. Hence we may expect that a counter filled with methane will show important effects after 10^8 to 10^9 counts, because the electrodes have been covered to a greater or less extent by a dielectric material. This again is in accordance with observations and accounts for the fact that certain types of counter filling appear to deteriorate faster than others.

Two subsidiary observations also support this view. Several observers including Shepard [S15] reported that methane-filled counters which had gone bad through use were rejuvenated by heating the central wire. This process drove off the polymerized material. Further, Weisz [W10] tried an experiment in which he removed the gas from a methane-filled counter which had gone bad through use, transferred the gas to a new counter, and found that the new counter counted properly; then he admitted new methane into the old counter and found that it did not operate. He found, however, that the counter could be made to operate again by cleaning and baking, thereby driving off the heavy compounds. Again this explains why a gas such as methane appears to deteriorate before enough molecules have dissociated actually to produce such an effect. Methane will eventually decompose into hydrogen, a nonquenching gas, to the extent that it does not polymerize, but the polymerization appears to be a more probable process in this case.

A number of further mass spectrographic studies have been made recently, for example those by Friedland and Katzenstein,[F5] who find CO_2 as one of the decomposition products of ethyl acetate. Geerk and Neuert [G9] studied the decomposition of methane and of methyl alcohol and found the expected stable end-products. It should further be added that the decomposition of ethyl alcohol shows some water vapor formation. This, in turn, through the process of negative ion formation, shows up in the fact that the plateau becomes somewhat less flat after the counter has been used than when the counter was new.

The smallest amount of organic vapor which will produce quenching was investigated by Krumbein.[K17] He employed the criterion that the plateau had to be five or more volts in length in order to permit the statement that appreciable quenching action was taking place. It is clear that a knowledge of the minimum amount of vapor, combined with the theory of electron-transfer and predissociation, will permit calculation of the effective cross section of the transfer process. He obtained curves of the minimum amount of vapor required to quench Q_m as a function of cathode radius in the gases A, Ne, and He, using methane, butane, and ethyl acetate as the quenching constituents. Counter cylinder radii were varied between 0.14 to 1.84 cm, with 5-mil tungsten central wires. From these data he computed the number of collisions between the gas ion and polyatomic molecules, and the minimum number of such collisions required to effect transfer of charge.

Clearly, when the cathode diameter is small, the amount of quenching constituent must be larger, other things being equal, in order for the number of collisions to be the same. The data bore out this relationship. Another approach was to measure the dead time and resolving time and to compute the number of collisions from Stever's analysis. The two approaches yielded substantially similar figures except in the case of helium, where the mobility is in doubt. The results may be stated in the following way: Argon-ethyl acetate counters require about 150 collisions to effect ion-transfer; argon-butane, 250; argon-methane, 540; helium-ethyl acetate, 200; helium-butane, 600; and helium-methane, 1200. The figures for the argon counters are believed to be within 10%, while those with helium about 20%, subject to a possible discrepancy of a factor of two in the mobility. These data show (a) that transfer is more favorable for argon than for helium and (b) that ethyl acetate is a more effective quenching agent. For example, Q_m of 0.002% of ethyl acetate was found sufficient to produce quenching in a counter of 1.8-cm radius filled to 30 cm pressure with argon. On the other hand, butane-helium counters had comparatively short recovery times, of the order of one half that in the butane-argon case.

f. Recovery time. The natural insensitive time of a counter is determined by the migration time of the positive ions. This we have already discussed, and we have cited the measured times for selfquenching counters as of the order of 10^{-4} sec. Thus Simpson finds between 1.0 and 2.9×10^{-4} sec for argon-alcohol counters, while for the heavier amyl acetate molecule in the same counter, 6 to 8×10^{-4} second. Similarly, a non-selfquenching counter, employing argon, might be expected to have a shorter recovery time because the mobility of the argon ions is greater than that of the organic ones. This is also found to be the case, and thus the commonly used designation of "fast" counter for the selfquenching type is exactly the reverse of a true description. Here again the interdependence of the desirable characteristics of counters is to be noted, since the heavy molecules which will give the longest useful counter lives also give the counter a longer resolving time. For fast counting problems, therefore, light molecules should be used, or non-selfquenching counters employed, while for long-period observations at not too high counting rates, fillings using heavier molecules will be advantageous.

By using the method of Stever for dead-time measurements, ionic mobilities may be investigated. In this manner, Weisz and Kern [W9] have found a definite correlation between molecular size and the mobility k, obtaining, for example, for C_2H_6 a value of 3.5 for k, for C_4H_{10} a value of 2.5, and 1.5 for C_7H_{10}. A number of other dead-time and resolving-time measurements have recently appeared, some by other methods, as for example by exciting the counter by pulsed X rays. The various experiments all agree on the order of magnitude of a few hundred microseconds for these quantities. Reduction of the dead time has been attempted by Collinge [C13] by the use of a potential reversing circuit. He found that the dead time could be reduced to 20 microseconds in this way. Curran and Rae [C14] put beads on the wires, which because they terminate the spread of the discharge also have the effect of reducing the dead time. With no beads, a counter with a cylinder 3.2 cm, an 0.2-mm wire, filled with 7 cm argon plus 1.5 cm alcohol at 90 volts overvoltage, showed a dead time of 350 microseconds. A counter 1.2 cm in diameter, at 80 volts overvoltage, with the same wire and filling and with 15 beads on the wire, showed only 50 microseconds for its dead time. The effect of the RC values in the circuit was computed by Thomas,[T1] who found that this had very little effect on the dead time but found that the shape of the pulse at the end of the recovery time depended on the resistance R if R was small. Electron transit times have also been studied by several investigators, among them Quaranta et al.,[Q1] who report that the electron velocity in an alcohol-argon counter is around 5×10^6 cm/sec and is independent of the field at fields exceeding 200 volts per cm.

g. Temperature coefficient. Various observers [K9] have commented that the counting rate of selfquenching counters exhibits a temperature dependence which can at times be troublesome. This effect has been explained as due to the fact that most of the heavy organic compounds are vapors at room temperature, and therefore a decrease in temperature of any substantial amount may cause some of the quenching constituent to condense out. Two results follow: (a) there may be insufficient quenching material left to quench completely the discharge and (b) the liquid may condense near the electrodes in such a way as to cause semi-conducting paths across the insulating material between the wire and cylinder. Leakage across such paths can manifest itself as spurious counts. Hence care should be taken in filling counters not to introduce organic vapor to such an amount that any will condense at the lowest temperature at which the counter is to be used. Other observers [C5] report that non-selfquenching counters show negligible temperature coefficients. This is also to be expected, provided the counters are so constructed that the inner surfaces are chemically stable and do not evolve gas if the counter experiences moderate temperature changes. Thus, for example, the use of hard rubber plugs for the ends of counters, or inadequate cleaning, may give rise to temperature effects. Temperature coefficients are largely produced by variations in the total number (and kind) of atoms or molecules; while if the total number is not varied and the pressure rises because of increase in temperature, little trouble is experienced.

Recently temperature coefficients have been studied by Parkash and Kapur.[P3] Using a glass-envelope, copper-cylinder counter with 8.5 cm argon and 1.5 cm alcohol, they found no effect in the temperature range 23 to 48° C; and a decrease in plateau at 8° C. This is in agreement with the previous observations.[K9] He attributes the effects at low temperatures to the formation of semi-conducting paths, and notes that at high temperatures the slopes are somewhat poorer.

h. Operating resistance. The choice of the operating resistance of a selfquenching counter is important. By referring to Fig. 1–1, it will be seen that a resistance R is necessary to permit coupling the counter to the vacuum tube circuit which follows. It is the voltage pulse developed across this resistance which is detected. In the case of the resistance-quenched counters, it is this resistance which produces the long time constant referred to above. For selfquenching counters, no resistance is needed to quench the discharge, but one is required in order to produce a voltage swing for transmission to the grid of the tube and also to permit the counter wire to recover rapidly to its initial voltage so that it will be sensitive for the next pulse. If the resistance is made too high, the recovery time constant will be too long. If the resistance is too low, the voltage swing of the grid will be small.

Let us assume that the counter wire is connected directly to the grid of a vacuum tube. The distributed capacity of the counter wire, tube grid and leads may then be of the order of 10 micromicrofarads, or higher if the counter is far removed from the grid and long connecting cables are used. If the resistance R is chosen of 1 megohm, the RC time constant will be 10^{-5} sec. This is shorter than the natural insensitive time of the counter, and hence little is gained by making the resistance lower. An additional factor of ten is sometimes used, if extremely short revolving times (10^{-6} sec) are required and the counter is operated on the "break" of the discharge. In this case a resistance of the order of 10^5 ohms is used and sensitive circuits are required as the pulse is small. In general 10^5 ohms can represent a useful lower limit. On the upper side, a resistance of more than 10 megohms will introduce appreciable time delay into the recovery. Hence a resistance of between 0.1 and 2 megohms is the best for most cases.

If the resistance is lowered below 0.1 megohm, the pulse received on the grid of the vacuum tube becomes small. Further, the resistor serves as a protective device. A megohm will limit to a milliampere the current that can flow if (at 1000 volts) the counter should be accidentally operated above the Geiger plateau and go into a continuous discharge, or if the operator should inadvertently come into contact with portions of the device.

i. Effects of mercury vapor. Many investigators have speculated regarding the effect of small amounts of mercury vapor on the operation of a counter. It will be recalled that the vapor pressure of mercury at room temperature is about 10^{-3} mm, and since precautions to exclude it entirely are usually not taken, it may be assumed that it is present to this amount in many counters. In a series of tests, Korff and Present [K7] sought to ascertain what effects might be ascribed to it.

First it should be pointed out that mercury vapor is monatomic and hence a non-selfquenching gas. Second, in amount it is roughly 10^{-5} of other gases. Hence we might expect that it would have roughly the same effect as a like amount of some other non-quenching gas present as an impurity. Such effects are so small as to be undetectable. An occasional mercury atom becomes ionized, and the positive mercury ion will progress to the cylinder and be neutralized along with the other positives. The percentage present is not enough to affect the starting or operating voltages.

A possible effect may be expected because of the magnitude of the ionization potential, 10.4 volts. This is less than that of some organic molecules (see Table 4–4) and hence we might expect that electron transfer would occur in such a sense that positive mercury ions would reach the cylinder. In being neutralized these might be expected to emit recombination radiation and hence provide a source of secondary (photo) electrons. However, since the amount present is so small, say one part in 10^{5}, and since the average ion on its way out to the cylinder only makes between 10^{4} and 10^{5} collisions, the number of mercury ions which are produced either in the avalanche or by transfer is small. Now since the photoelectric efficiency is low, about 10^{-4}, then 10^{4} mercury ions would have to become neutralized at the cathode in order to produce even one secondary electron. Therefore we might expect, as experiment bears out, that no significant effects are to be observed at room temperature.

If, however, the mercury vapor pressure were increased by a factor of 100 or so, enough mercury ions would be neutralized at the cylinder to produce observable effects. This was accomplished in the experiments cited by introducing a small drop of mercury into the counter and then heating the counter to about 82° C, at which temperature the vapor pressure is 0.1 mm. When mercury is present at these pressures, the behavior of a normal selfquenching counter becomes erratic. Occasional enormous pulses are observed and at slightly higher pressures the counter tends to go into a quasi-continuous discharge.

Thus it is a matter of good fortune that the pressure of mercury vapor at room temperature is sufficiently low so that mercury produces negligible effects. For this reason, no especial pains need be taken to exclude it from the counters, and in the discussions we shall disregard its presence.

j. Delayed electron emission. It was found by Paetow [P4] that electrons might, in certain circumstances, be emitted from surfaces at considerable intervals after the excitation process had taken place. This "delayed electron emission" or the "Paetow effect" is of importance in Geiger counters. It is clear that it is one possible source of spurious counts. The effect has been recognized and studied by a number of investigators.[M1] Thus, for example, Lauterjung and Neuert [L7] found that after irradiation of a counter cylinder with ultraviolet, the background of spurious counts slowly decreased with time, the decay constant being a function of the material of which the cylinder was made. The effect was especially noted, and the decay-time longest, in the highly photosensitive cathode materials such as magnesium. Similarly, Chaudhri, Fenton and Fuller [C11] concluded that the photosensitivity apparently induced in counters by operating them at a high counting rate is a surface phenomenon. The Paetow effect is therefore one

additional argument for using stable materials and good vacuum technique in making counters.

k. Field inside a counter. The magnitude of the field inside
a counter can be computed by eq. (3–4), but the actual values
obtained by this computation are often not appreciated. Consider a counter in which the wire radius is 5×10^{-3} cm, corresponding closely to the 4-mil central wire often used, a cylinder
with 1-cm radius and a potential difference of 1000 volts across
it. Then the field will have the values indicated in Table 4–5

TABLE 4–5. VALUES OF THE FIELD IN A TYPICAL COUNTER

Radius, cm	Field, volts per cm
5×10^{-3} (wire surface)	37,400
0.01	18,700
0.05	3,740
0.1	1,870
0.5	374
1.0 (at cylinder)	187

for various values of the radius. The field in this typical
counter is plotted in Fig. 4–11. The reduction of the field near
the wire, produced by a positive ion space charge sheath is also
shown, as is the effect of a grid. The total potential being the
integrated area under the curve, the reduction of operating
voltage effected by the grid is seen at once.

Further, it will be noted that the high field region occupies
a space about half a millimeter in radius around the wire. In
this region the field is high enough so that the electron will
gain 15 volts or more in each free path of advance toward the
wire and will therefore be able to produce additional ionization
by collision. Hence all the Townsend avalanche effects we
have been discussing take place inside this small volume.
Most of the counter is clearly just an ion-collecting space,
where the electron travels in a field below the average value
and gains only a tenth of a volt or so per free path.

l. Low-voltage counters. In recent years it has come to be realized that there are two special applications for counters in which it is particularly important that the operating potential

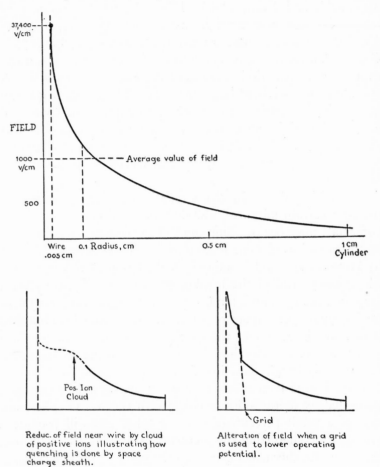

Reduc. of field near wire by cloud of positive ions illustrating how quenching is done by space charge sheath.

Alteration of field when a grid is used to lower operating potential.

FIG. 4–11.

be at a minimum. These are (1) portable survey instruments and (2) instruments to be flown in unmanned balloons. In each case, the saving of weight in the high-voltage battery is important. This situation has led to a study of the factors controlling the operating voltage, some of which we have already discussed. The first approach to this problem was made by Curtiss and Korff, who in 1936 constructed counters for balloon-borne cosmic ray flight instruments operating at around 450 volts. These counters were of the non-selfquenching types, filled with neon plus a small addition of hydrogen. Subsequent experiments with triode counters have also led to reduction of operating potentials of large counters. The simple expedient of reducing the gas pressure in order to operate the counter at or near the minimum of the characteristic curve is obviously undesirable, as the efficiency is reduced so much that the counter becomes useful only for the special purposes already discussed.

A careful study of the characteristics of mixed gases reveals that, for certain mixtures, well-developed minima in operating potentials may occur. Simpson [S16] has investigated these gas mixtures and used some in counters. The excellent summary by Druyvesteyn and Penning [D5] is the basis for this investigation. They studied the breakdown between coaxial cylinder systems usually containing one principal noble gas component plus a small percentage of another. It should be remarked here that almost all of the gases used in these studies have metastable states and that the presence of these greatly influences the discharge characteristics. Extremely pure noble gases cannot be used in counters because of the secondary electrons generated by metastables colliding with the walls. The addition of a small percentage of some other gas will provide a means of de-energizing the metastables by inelastic collisions. However, another effect can also take place. Suppose that the energy of the metastable state of one gas exceeds the ionization potential of the other. Then the de-excitation process can result in the ionization of the gas with the lower ionization potential. It is this process which is partly responsible for the low potentials realizable in certain circumstances.

Table 4–6 gives the potentials at which metastable states occur in substances which have been used in counters. From inspection of this table and comparison with the ionization potentials listed in Table 4–4, certain mixtures immediately suggest themselves. Thus, for example, the metastable state in

TABLE 4–6. METASTABLE LEVELS IN THE ENERGY-LEVEL SYSTEM CHARAC-
TERISTIC OF THE SEVERAL LISTED SUBSTANCES

Substance	Symbol	Metastable States (in electron volts)	
Helium	He	20.55	19.73
Neon	Ne	16.6	
Argon	A	11.6	
Krypton	Kr	10.5	8.8
Xenon	Xe	9.4	8.3
Mercury	Hg	5.43	4.66

helium at 20.55 volts is close to the 21.47-volt ionization potential of neon; while the neon metastable level at 16.6 volts just exceeds the argon ionization potential at 15.69.

Next consider a counter filled with neon, at pressures of 6 to 15 cm Hg, with 0.002% argon. This will be about the minimum amount of argon required to remove metastables. Such a counter will have a broad minimum in the curve of starting potential plotted as a function of neon pressure and will have a starting potential of a little over 100 volts. Increasing the amount of argon to 0.012% makes little difference; but increasing the argon percentage to 0.1% causes the minimum to be narrower, to occur at about 5 cm Hg, and to increase to 140 volts; while at 0.4% argon, the minimum is about 160 volts and occurs at about 4 cm pressure. It is important to avoid mercury contamination in these counters, for the percentages of gas are so small. The amount of mercury present at room temperatures is not enough to affect most counter behavior, as we have shown above, but in these cases does become of importance.

Another feature of interest in these cases is that the central wire diameter is not so critical and indeed is sometimes preferably coarser than with conventional counters. For example, the position of the minimum in a counter filled with neon with 0.012% argon is independent of wire size, and the starting potential does not become an important function of wire size until the pressure in the counter exceeds 15 or 20 cm Hg. At 15 cm, a wire 0.0635 will have a starting potential at around 150 volts, and decreasing the size to 0.0025 only lowers the starting potential by 20 volts. Thus a factor of almost 30 in wire size corresponds to a change of less than 20% in operating potential.

Penning's breakdown curves have another peculiarity which should be noted. In certain cases the breakdown occurs at lower potentials when the sign of the voltage is reversed from that at which counters are usually operated. As we have noted above, counters are almost invariably operated with the wire positive and the cylinder negative. This gives the lowest operating potentials in most cases. But in the case of the counter containing neon with 0.002% argon, the curves cross at around 9 cm pressure, and at 30 cm pressure, the counter will operate at perhaps 130 volts if the wire is negative, whereas it operates at above 250 volts when the wire is positive. The radii in this case were 2.3 cm and 0.087 cm for cylinder and wire respectively. At pressures of less than 9 cm the minimum occurs with the normal arrangement of polarities.

The extremely low voltages thus possible occur in noble gas counters, and these counters are non-selfquenching; they are customarily used with electronic quenching circuits. It is further evident that accurate control of purities is required and that contamination of a few parts in a hundred thousand will completely nullify the very low voltage characteristics of these counters.

m. Halogen-filled counters. Whereas halogens have long been considered undesirable as gases for use in counters because of their tendency to form negative ions, nevertheless as Present [P2] pointed out, these gases have some of the same properties as have most organic vapors. The gases are normally diatomic, but in their absorption band structure they show the tendency to photodissociate. The absence of well-defined energy levels in their ultraviolet bands indicates that within a considerable range of energies absorption of energy results in dissociation of the molecule. This property of these molecules has been understood for twenty-five years at least, but only recently has it been applied to making counters. Liebson and Friedman [L8] found that a mixture of four parts of argon plus one of chlorine plus a lot of neon gave good results. Only about 0.25 mm of the halogen-argon mixture was required to act as a "quenching vapor." The neon pressure was varied between 5 and 60 cm, and satisfactory operation over this range was observed. At the lower neon pressures, the counter operated at a comparatively low voltage, about 300 volts, and as is usual in neon-filled counters, this potential increased but slowly with increasing neon pressure.

Another characteristic of such fillings is that they operate satisfactorily with quite coarse central wires. Increasing the central wire size from the usual 3 or 4 mils up to 30 mils was found not to cause any great increase in operating potential.

Naturally, provision must be made to prevent chemical action of the chlorine on the walls or other parts of the counter. This can be accomplished by using glass envelopes and electrodes of tantalum, carbon, or stainless steel. The usual copper, brass, or silver gives poor results. Adding nitrogen, oxygen, or air will increase the plateau slope as might be expected. The counters exhibited no temperature dependence in the range between $-50°$ and $100°$ C. Dead times of the order of 350 microseconds were found.

Absence of marked effects due to negative ions is presumably due to the fact that so small a fraction of the gas is halogen. For a counter using 10 cm neon, the halogen would be

present in the amount of 0.06%. Taking the negative ion capture probability from Table 4–2, it is clear that the average
electron in traversing the counter will not make enough collisions with halogen molecules to be captured. The electron will
make around 10^4 collisions, of which 0.06% will be with halogens; i.e., only around six per traversal. But it requires on the
average 2000 collisions to produce a negative ion, and hence
few such are formed. At higher halogen pressures this effect
would be troublesome.

The lifetime of such counters is longer than for the organic
vapor-filled types. A halogen molecule, when it dissociates
into two atoms, will recombine after a period of time, provided
the gases in the counter are inert and the walls are chemically
inactive. The ionization potentials of the halogens are below
that of neon so that the electron-transfer mechanism can
operate. Enough halogen must be present to make this process
probable; yet small enough to cause negative ion formation to
remain improbable. Hence the amount of the halogen is quite
critical. Further, not all combinations will work, for a fluorine-
argon counter would have the ionization potentials reversed,
and thus electron transfer from the halogen to the rare gas
would be energetically impossible.

Such counters have also been studied by LaCroisette and
Yarwood,[L10] who examined counters filled with Br_2, A, and Ne.
They pointed out that a neon metastable colliding with a neutral argon atom can produce an argon ion and that the argon
ion will in turn ionize the bromine by electron transfer. They
found the lowest operating voltage when there was just enough
argon present to de-excite the neon metastables.

The plateaus of many halogen mixture counters are not very
flat. The factors affecting flatness were studied by Hull,[H12]
who used a small source of radiation and found a considerable
dependence on where the source was placed. He obtained
slopes of 11% per 100 volts when the source was near the
center of the counter and 42% when it was near one end. The

lack of flatness of the plateau may be a symptom of negative ion formation in these cases.

n. Long-life fillings. We have mentioned earlier that the factor operating most rapidly to limit the life of selfquenching counters is the decomposition of the molecule at the wall, which is part of the selfquenching mechanism. In a search for ways to prolong the life of counters, two approaches have thus far been employed.

The first of these is to find a compound which would not only be decomposed in the act of quenching but which might also be synthesized at some point in the operation of the counter. One such compound is ammonia. Ammonia is synthesized in the Haber process by running an electrical discharge in a mixture of hydrogen and nitrogen. Hence we might expect that if an ammonia molecule decomposes in quenching a discharge, the constituent nitrogen and hydrogen atoms might at some later discharge find themselves in a position to reunite in the Townsend avalanche to re-form ammonia. With this expectation in mind, Korff and Krumbein [K16] filled a group of counters with ammonia and ran them in a life test. It was found that these counters actually did have longer lives than might have been expected on the hypothesis that decomposition was the only process and that no synthesis occurred. Mixed fillings, ammonia plus neon or argon, were also tried, as were various cathode materials such as copper, silver and carbon. No marked dependence on cathode material was observed, nor did the argon or neon content change the results. The chief disadvantage seemed to be that the cathode became extremely photosensitive after prolonged use. The factors controlling this effect are at present under investigation.

Ammonia counters have also been studied by Witten [W12] and by Neuert and Geerk.[N5] These observers report that the reactions occurring within the counter are probably not the simple Haber process, but more complex ones, possibly involving the formation of clusters of molecules. Mass spectroscopic analysis of the counters after use shows that the amount of molecule N_2 increases, as does also NH_2 and N. It is possible that some hydrogen is adsorbed or that it forms hydrides on the surface, thus leading to a lowering of the work function. In summary, we may say that there is evidently some regeneration of the ammonia molecule which takes place, and that the disadvantage of these counters lies in their increasing photosensitivity with use.

The second avenue of approach lies through complex mixtures of stable gases. Here one might hope that enough complex processes of energy-transfer might take place to simulate the predissociation effects; or that some constituent may predissociate. For example, Shore [S17] found that a mixture of 15 mm xenon, 1 mm oxygen, 15 mm nitrogen and argon to bring the total to 73 cm operated in a satisfactory manner. Quenching with a resistor as low as 1 megohm was observed, and a plateau extending from 1600 to 1900 volts was noted. It is possible that, with this mixture, some complex equilibrium involving one or more of the oxides of nitrogen is involved. In any event, since the constituent gases are stable, life limitation by decomposition into smaller fragments does not occur.

o. External cathode counters. Although it has been known for thirty years that ions can slowly migrate through glass, the application of this fact to the construction of counters is quite recent. Maze [M14] constructed counters by painting a conducting cathode on the outside of the glass envelope of a counter having no internal cylindrical cathode. In this case the positive ions arrive at the glass surface and migrate through the glass in order to reach the conducting layer where they are neutralized. Some kinds of glass are much better than others for this purpose. The soft glasses, including soda-glass, work quite well, whereas pyrex is almost impervious to this ionic migration.

Counters of this type have the advantage of ease of construction. As with other external cathode counters, they are usually operated with the cathode grounded and with the wire at a high potential with respect to ground. The appropriate circuits will be found in a later chapter. The disadvantages of these counters are (a) that they cannot be made of pyrex, which is universal in some laboratories, and (b) that they have a slow resolving time, because of the length of time required for the migration through the glass. At high counting rates the glass polarizes and the counter becomes inoperative. The resolving times have been measured by Beretta and Rostagni,[B16] who find times of the order of 0.1 second. This limits the use of these counters to applications in which the counting rates are slow. However, it should also be stated that the production of secondary electrons at the glass surface by the positive ions is much lower than the production at metal surfaces, (a) because the work function of glass is high, and (b) because no conduction electrons are available for multiple emission processes. Hence these counters have very nice quenching characteristics and exceptionally flat plateaus.

p. Liquid-filled counters. Instead of filling the counter with a gas, as has been assumed in most of the discussions above, it is possible to fill counters with liquids. For example, Davidson and Larsh [D4] have employed a counter filled with liquid argon. This gas has a freezing point at $-185.7°$ C, so that it is not difficult to maintain a counter filled with liquid argon with the aid of a liquid air bath. They reported large conductivity pulses in the counter when alpha particles from polonium entered the sensitive volume, at fields between 1000 and 10,000 volts per cm. The electrons formed by the primary ionizing event will drift through the liquid, and except for somewhat slower drift velocities will behave much the same as they do in a gas. Indeed it is even possible to induce the formation of Townsend avalanches, although the mean free path of the electron is small. The same authors also tried liquid nitrogen and heptane and found no pulses. Presumably conditions are not favorable for the migration of electrons in the latter liquids.

The obvious disadvantage of the liquid-filled counter is the necessity of operating at such a low temperature. On the other hand, the advantage is that the specific ionization is very high. Thus such entities as photons, which ionize only occasionally in a gas, will have a much greater probability of producing detectable ionization. These counters are therefore of especial value in problems where high efficiency for entities of low specific ionization is desired.

q. Spread of the discharge along the wire. If we examine the details of a discharge when a counter is operating in the Geiger region, we find the following situation. The initial electron travels in toward the high field region near the wire where it starts to make ionizing collisions and initiates a Townsend avalanche. Geometrically, such an avalanche is presumably pyramidal in form, with the electron at the apex and the wire at the base. Certainly such an avalanche usually occupies a very small space. In sparks, where this phenomenon has been extensively studied, it usually occupies a small fraction of a square millimeter in cross-sectional area. Also, the avalanche itself is fast. The electrons, having to go a distance of perhaps 0.01 or 0.02 cm at average velocities of around 10^8 cm/sec, will reach the wire in times between 10^{-9} and 10^{-10} second after the start of the avalanche process.

However, it has been known for about twenty years that a thin glowing sheath can be seen around the entire central wire when a counter discharges. This phenomenon can better be seen in non-selfquenching counters filled with a gas such as neon, which has strong emission lines in the visible. By looking into such a counter axially and examining this discharge spectroscopically, Locher (unpublished) found the recombination spectrum of the filling gas to be emitted. From this observation it is evident that the discharge spreads along the length of the wire. Hence we may inquire into the mechanism by which this spread is accomplished, and about the time required for it to do so.

A further bit of evidence along this line recently came to light when Hodson, Loria, and Ryder [H13] arranged a counter inside a cloud chamber. Since the cloud chamber contained an argon-alcohol mixture, it had a selfquenching atmosphere, and it was not necessary to have any envelope around the counter electrodes. Moreover, since the cathode merely serves to distribute the field, an arrangement of six or eight rods spaced around the corners of a hexagon or octagon, with their lengths parallel to the central wire, would serve as a counter with external shell, so that radiation could reach the interior of the counter without passing through anything except, of course, the gas. When the chamber was expanded, a cloud was formed wherever there was ionization, and this included the avalanche. Consequently, the avalanche was rendered visible. By this technique, it was observed that, when the counter was operated in the proportional region, a narrow spot of ionization was formed. If the chamber was expanded a short interval after the initial avalanche, the expanding annulus representing the positive ion cloud could be seen on its way out to the cathode. This experiment verified what had been believed from other evidence, namely, that the swarm of positive ions was of small extent and stayed quite closely together during its outward motion. The most important feature of this experiment from the point of view of the theory was the smallness laterally of the ion cloud in the proportional counter.

We shall next consider in detail the longitudinal spread of the positive ion sheath. The longitudinal spread represents the difference between the proportional and the Geiger mechanism. In the proportional region, the avalanche is localized; in the region of limited proportionality, the sheath starts to spread along the wire; and the Geiger threshold is reached when the sheath has spread to cover the entire wire. Hence, all pulses are of the same height, for the sheath controls the pulse size, and the initial ionizing event does not. The sheath spread consists of a series of (possibly overlapping) Townsend avalanches, adjacent to each other, and it is clear that some entity originating in one avalanche initiates the next one. We shall develop below the evidence that the entity causing the spread is a photon, but first we must describe the measurements of sheath spread velocity.

As in many other instances in the progress of science, whenever a particular set of observations is required to establish a particular point, several independent and simultaneous observations are made, often by widely separated groups. In this case, the work by Wantuch at New York University and that by Huber and his colleagues at Basel in Switzerland were in progress simultaneously. Wantuch's experimental arrangement [W11] consisted of a long counter, with probes at each end consisting of a loop of coarse wire wrapped around the central wire and separated from it by a millimeter or so. The counter itself was about 25 cm long. Each probe was independent of the rest of the counter electrically, and one was connected to a circuit initiating the sweep of a fast oscilloscope. The second probe was then connected to the vertical deflecting plates of the oscilloscope. Thus, when the first probe received an impulse, the sweep started across the screen. When the second pulse received an impulse, the sweep was deflected vertically. The distance between the start of the sweep and the point where the beam departed from horizontal travel was a measure of the time between the arrival of the pulse at the two probes. If, for example, an event occurred in the middle of the counter and the sheath reached both probes simultaneously, the time lag thus found would be zero. The maximum lag would occur when the initial event occurred in the immediate vicinity of the probe initiating the sweep, and the sheath had to travel the entire length of the counter before it came to the deflecting probe. Thus the distribution of pulses starting in the half of the counter between its center and the initiating electrode gave a measure of the travel time of the sheath. These velocities were found to be of the order of a few times 10^7 cm/sec.

Huber's [H14] more extensive work with a more complex electronic shuttering arrangement confirmed this situation and helped to systematize the data, since many measurements at differing voltages and fillings were made. Other observers including Saltzman and Montgomery [S19] and Hill and Dunworth,[H15] using slight modifications of the foregoing systems, have also measured sheath travel times as functions of various counter parameters. The bulk of these observations can be summarized by saying that the observed spread velocity lay between 1 and 2×10^7 cm per sec, for a wide variety of voltages and fillings. Only with unusual combinations of parameters does the velocity pass outside these limits in either direction by any large amount, and deviations by as much as a factor of ten have almost never been observed. The most noticeable systematic effect was a gradual increase of velocity as the overvoltage was increased. Also, most counters used in these studies were between 0.6 and 2 cm in radius and had central wires of 2-, 3-, or 4-mil diameters. Large deviations in geometry have thus far not been investigated. We must next inquire into what mechanism can be postulated which will account for sheath spread velocities of this order of magnitude.

In the Townsend avalanche, there are many collisions between electrons and atoms resulting in excitation and ionization. Most of the collisions resulting in excitation will result in radiative de-excitation by the atoms, for the mean free time between collisions at the pressures obtaining in most counters will be of the order of 10^{-8} sec. The lifetimes of the excited states against radiative de-excitation for many of the states (for example, the higher levels in neon or argon) are of the order of 10^{-8} to 10^{-9} sec. Hence, many atoms will have time to dispose of their excess energy by radiation before they suffer a collision, which, should they still have this energy, would be an inelastic collision. The photon radiated in this manner will then travel through the gas until it is absorbed by another atom or molecule. Clearly, radiation resulting from excitation will not usually have enough energy to ionize another atom of the same kind as that from which the radiation originated. But, if another gas is present, the ionization potential of which is below the excitation potential of the first, then ionization can result from the absorption of the quantum. As soon as ionization has occurred, a new Townsend avalanche will be formed, and quanta of many different energies will again be emitted, thereby further spreading the discharge.

If we take the mean life of the excited state as 10^{-8} sec, then a spread velocity of 10^7 cm per sec will correspond to ten absorption and emission acts per centimeter travel, or, in other words, the mean free path of the average photon will be about a millimeter. This figure is in excellent agreement with the size of the beads known to stop the spread of the discharge down the length of the wire in selfquenching counters. A bead of 2 mm or so will be an effective barrier, whereas one substantially less than a millimeter will be jumped over. Naturally, at higher overvoltages, when the avalanche starts farther out and is bigger, the bead diameter must be increased. Again, in non-selfquenching counters, the absorption is much less for there is only the line series absorption and not the numerous bands in the ultraviolet which most complex molecules exhibit. In this case some of the photons may even reach the cathode and liberate secondary electrons from there, starting new avalanches in totally different parts of the counter. Thus in a counter containing only a single noble gas, we shall have a photon diffusing out to the cylinder, experiencing one or more absorption and re-emission acts on its way. In a counter with two such gases, owing to the difference in ionization potential, we can have one gas photoionizing the other; and in counters containing the usual mixture of a vapor plus a vehicular noble gas, we shall have the radiation from the excited states of the noble gas photoionizing the vapor molecules. It is now also clear why the velocity of the sheath spread is not very dependent on any of the usual counter variables. For example, at 1000 volts, a 100-volt change in the overvoltage or a 10% change in the operating potential is a considerable change. Yet it will make only a small change in the sheath diameter and virtually no change in the mean free path of the photons. It will increase the number of photons, but only slowly increase the spread velocity, which depends largely on the mean free path before absorption. One might expect the velocity to depend more on the amount of vapor present, for this can be varied over wide limits and have the counter still quench.

The view that photons are responsible for the spread of the Townsend avalanche is further supported by the experiments of Van Gemert, den Hartog and Muller,[V1] by Colli, Fancini and Gatti,[C15] and by Craggs and Jaffe.[C16] The latter performed experiments with long counters, beaded wires and divided cathodes, as well as tested the effect of oxidized copper cylinders in which the work function was high. That the avalanche spread can be stopped and the resulting deadtime of the counter thereby shortened has also been recognized by several observers. Both Smith[S20] and Collinge[C9] have employed potential reversing circuits to accomplish this successfully.

C. Spark Counters

1. Spherical Electrodes. It was discovered in the 1920's that, if a potential difference close to the sparking potential were applied to a pair of electrodes in air, then the spark actually occurred at the very instant that an ionizing event took place between the electrodes. It is clear from our previous discussion that any gas is an electrical non-conductor unless there are ions in the gas. On the other hand, if there are ions present, the conductivity of the gas is determined by the number of ions present. Ionization is, therefore, necessary in these circumstances to initiate the spark. The applied voltage should not exceed the sparking potential by large amounts; otherwise, the phenomenon is complicated by other effects, for example field emission. The formative time lag of such a spark, defined as the time interval between the instant the potential across the gap exceeds the sparking potential and the instant at which the spark occurs, can, in proper circumstances, be quite short. In experiments on this time lag it is customary to irradiate one of the electrodes with ultraviolet light to insure that a supply of photoelectrons will always be present. If this is not done, so that ionization between the electrodes is only that produced by the occasional random cosmic rays or radioactive ionizing events in this region, the lags may be quite long. On the other hand, when such an arrangement is used as a counter, the potential is kept at a lower value, the spheres are not irradiated, and the initial ionization is provided by the particle to be detected.

One of the difficulties encountered in this work arises from the fact that, after several sparks have occurred, chemical action on the electrode at the point where the spark originated may change the surface enough to affect the results. Consequently, chemically inactive metals are used as electrodes. Such counters were studied by Frey,[F1] who found that platinum spheres provided particularly stable gaps. He tried atmospheres of H_2, N_2, O_2, and CO_2 as well as air. He concluded that counters containing dry, dustfree air had a particularly long plateau.

Since with spherical electrodes the field is so shaped that the spark takes place almost invariably at the place where the spheres are closest, sphere-gap spark counters have a limitation in the effective volume in which counting action can take place. This limitation can be overcome by using parallel plates, and we shall next discuss this type of counter.

[*Note:* Point counters have not been used much in recent years, but a review article on the theory and operation of these was published by J. Morgan and J. L. Bohn, *J. Franklin Inst.* **237**, 371 (1944).

Studies of the time required to form a spark are to be found in such papers as "Formative time-lags in spark breakdown in air at uniform field and low overvoltage," by L. H. Fisher and B. Bederson, *Phys. Rev.* **81**, 109 (1951).]

2. Parallel Plate Electrodes. When accurately parallel plates are used as electrodes in a spark counter, the spark will occur at or exceedingly close to the point where the ionizing event takes place, as long as it is anywhere in the area between the plates. In order to secure a uniform surface and uniform conditions between the plates, it is usual to pump and bake the electrodes thoroughly. Accurate parallelism of the plates is necessary, as otherwise the spark will tend to take place, where the spacing is least.

The problem of terminating the spark is more difficult than that of terminating the discharge in Geiger counters. It has been found that by employing both a "selfquenching" mixture and a quenching circuit, this action can be achieved in a comparatively short time. However, it is seldom possible to complete the process of terminating the discharge in times shorter than about 10^{-3} sec. Also, sparking conditions are favored by operation at a comparatively high pressure.

Thus, for example, Hereford [H7] operated parallel plate counters with 2-mm separation and 9-sq cm area, in an atmosphere of 85% argon and 15% ethyl alcohol, to a total pressure of 70 cm Hg. He reports that the spurious counting rate is reduced by operating the counter at a high temperature, around 70° C. Similarly, Keuffel [K13] employed disks, with 2.5- and 3-mm spacing, 35 and 3.1 sq cm in area, with mixtures of ½ atm argon plus 6 mm xylene, and potentials of about 2500 volts. He found a plateau slope of 3.6% per 100 volts. He also found a quenching time of 0.05 sec necessary. He reports a "reaction time" or time lag of 5×10^{-9} sec. He found practically no plateau at all when the counter was operated with air between the plates. Again, Madansky [M7] tried varying spacings and found that with an argon plus 10% butane mixture plus a Neher-Harper quenching circuit he obtained good operation at 0.5-mm spacing and 100-cm pressure. He used 2400 volts to give 200 volts overvoltage under these conditions. With 1-mm spacing and 200-cm pressure, the counter operated at 5500 volts. He estimated the efficiency as 98% in the latter case. He reports that a quenching time of 10^{-3} sec is suitable, and that the time lag is below 6×10^{-9} sec. He found the dead time longer for Al, Au, Pt and brass electrodes, and shorter for Pb and Sn. Hudson [H16] built large cylindrical spark counters. He used a xylene-argon mixture at $\frac{1}{2}$ atm, a gap of 137 mils, and found an operating voltage of 2250 volts.

Parallel plate ionization chambers can also be used. Such devices have been studied by Sherr and Peterson,[S10] who report very rapid operation. They find the rise time of the pulse to depend on where the electrons originate. Hence it is possible to distinguish, by examining the pulse shape on a fast oscilloscope, between such an event as a cosmic ray burst, in which uniform ionization is produced throughout the counter, and a heavy particle, in which the ionization is all produced at one place or along one comparatively short track. Clearly, it is possible by electronic circuitry to distinguish between these two types of events, so that the device may be made permanently recording without the need for an operator to study the oscilloscope screen. Thus in spite of the fact that the same amount of ionization and hence the identical pulse height will have been produced by the two different events, it is possible to separate them by the differing rise-time. This is an important advance in that it enables two otherwise similar portions of the background of a chamber to be separated and greatly facilitates the study of large ionizing events connected with the cosmic radiation.

The two important features of parallel plate counters are (a) the short time lag, which will permit accurate timing of events, and (b) the exact localization of the spark. The latter feature permits such counters if used in coincidence to give accurately reconstructible path determinations. Further, by interposing a magnetic field, track curvatures can be measured.

The disadvantages are (a) the long quench time and (b) the small sensitive volume. The result of the small volume or path length is that a comparatively high pressure must be maintained in order to secure efficient operation, for the probability that a spark will occur is, of course, determined by the probability that ionization will occur, and the efficiencies are controlled by the considerations discussed in connection with eq. (4-3). For example, a 1-mm gap in argon at 1 atm is comparable to a 1-cm counter at 7.6 cm argon, and the gap cannot be increased or the pressure decreased by more than a factor of two without very appreciably lowering the efficiency.

D. Recent Experiments with Grids in Counters

The present author has conducted some unpublished experiments on the use of grids in counters. The results can be briefly recapitulated. If the counter is operated in the Geiger region, and if only one electron is formed in the initial ionizing event, then the probability that a count shall be initiated is equal to the probability that the electron will pass through the grid or that the electron will be originally formed in the space between the grid and the wire. The probability of passage through the grid is determined by (a) the number and size of the wires of which the grid is composed and (b) the potential distribution in the counter. Thus the grid may be thought of as presenting an "obscuring area" to an electron the effectiveness of which is not only dependent on the geometrical factors but also upon the fields. The effective obscuration can be made greater or less than the geometrical value by proper choice of potentials. This fact is well known to designers of radio tubes. Further, the ratio of the probability of an electron being initially formed outside or inside the grid is roughly the ratio of the volumes of the two regions, and for cylindrical geometry is in the ratio of the squares of the radii. If several electrons are formed in the initial ionizing event, it is evident that only one electron has to succeed in passing the grid to initiate a Geiger count.

When a counter with a grid is used as a proportional counter, a different situation obtains. In this instance the grid introduces fluctuations, for the number of electrons which pass through it will depend upon the orientation of the track of the ionizing entity and the distribution of the initial ions with respect to the holes in the grid. The author tried several models filled with BF_3 for neutron counting. He found that the plateaus were less flat and the behavior less satisfactory than in counters of the same size without grids.

An attempt was made by Sherwin [S11] to speed up the collection of electrons by using grids and applying a high potential between the cylinder and grid. This procedure usually led to breakdown between these two electrodes, and no noticeable improvement was found.

In connecting such a counter to the potential supply, it is possible to employ a high-resistance potentiometer as a voltage divider to control the potential of the grid with respect to the other elements. This procedure was found by Korff [K15] to yield a useful simplification. It is the opinion of the present author that much additional experimentation with grids can be done, with a reasonable expectation of useful results.

E. Eccentric Positioning of the Central Wire

It has commonly been assumed that the central wire should be axial. An experiment was tried by Korff (unpublished) in which a counter 6 cm in diameter was equipped with a central wire the position of which could be adjusted by turning a ground joint while the counter was in operation. The central wire always remained parallel with the axis, but its radial position was thus variable. It could be moved from the center to any position, limited only by contact with the cylinder. As the wire was moved away from the center, the operating voltage was found to be lowered, since the controlling voltage was that necessary to maintain a field between the wire and the nearest point on the cylinder high enough to produce counting. The rest of the counter operated as an ion-collecting volume. The satisfactory operation ceased when the wire came within about 2 mm of the cylinder, and a large number of spurious counts then appeared. Presumably the field is so distorted in this instance that local emission takes place.

Finally a word should be said about the tightness of the central wire. If the wire is either not tight or not parallel with the axis, then the potential will be correct at only one point and will be progressively more wrong as one departs from this point. Hence the plateau will not be flat, for the pulse height will depend on where the pulse was formed. In the event that the wire is not tight, the operating potential can also vary if the counter is moved about, so that the sag differs in position or amount. Thus the wire must be tight and parallel with the axis, but it need not be axial and may indeed be quite eccentric.

F. Photon, Gamma- and X-ray Counters

Counters may be used to count quanta of electromagnetic radiation or, in other words, photons. The controlling consideration is that the quantum must produce an electron in the sensitive volume in order to initiate the discharge. There are two possible sources of such electrons: (a) the walls and (b) the gas. There are two processes operative in each: in the gas, the processes are direct photoionization and the Compton effect; from the wall, electrons can be ejected either by the usual photoelectric effect or by a high-energy collision process. Each of these four processes is a function of the photon energy. Moreover, the probability of such a process happening per unit traversal of the counter by the photon is generally much less than unity, so that photon counters are likely to be inefficient.

In order to eject a photoelectron from the wall, the photon must have an energy equal to or greater than the photoelectric work function of the surface. The photoelectric efficiency of most surfaces is small. Often 10^4 photons are absorbed per electron emitted, and great care must be taken with surfaces to bring the yield up to 1% or greater. The special treatments which a surface must experience are still largely in the "cookbook" stage and depend on such factors as amount of oxide present, outgassing, and heat treatment. At high photon energies, as for example with X rays or gamma rays, where the photon energy is many orders of magnitude greater than the work function, the possibility of the emission of several electrons exists. Indeed, such electron-sprays may be ejected by a photon either entering or leaving a metal. The controlling factor seems to be the atomic number of the material. Hence it has been usual practice to make the cathodes of gamma-ray counters of heavy materials, such as lead and bismuth. Moreover, in order to increase the surface, the heavy material that is used may be in the form of screens or have an irregularly contoured or wavy surface.

For the production of ionization directly in the gas, the photon must have an energy equal to or greater than the ionization potential of the gas. This is usually greater than that of the work function of the walls, by a factor of three or so. Many metallic substances used in counters have work functions of 3 to 5 volts, corresponding to photoelectric thresholds of 4000 to 2500 Å; the ionization potentials of most gases are about 15 volts, which corresponds to a photon of less than 1000 Å. Now such photons have very little penetrating power and indeed must have originated within the counter itself, for they will not pass through any windows. Hence photoionization of the gas itself by a photon from outside is not an event that need be considered in most counters. At higher photon energies, in the X-ray domain, when the photon has 10^4 or more volts of energy, then its penetrating power again increases and, in this event, can reach the interior of the counter through the walls or windows. Ionization in the gas in this instance can be produced by the Compton effect, and the Compton electron can initiate the discharge. However, the probability that a

Compton electron will be produced by a photon passing through a few cm of gas at a reduced pressure is not very large, and the majority of X-ray counts are not initiated in this manner.

A number of successful photon counters have been built in recent years, and we shall summarize some of the experience thus gained. For example, Mandeville and Scherb [M15] made counters using ultraviolet transmitting windows and photosensitive surfaces and report efficiencies between 0.1 and 0.01 in the 2000–3000 Å wave-length interval. Others for this region have been built by Labeyrie [L11] who used Fe-Ni cathodes. X-ray counters with cylinders of bismuth were tested by Hart and colleagues, [H17] who report efficiencies of 0.7% at 0.7 Mev increasing to 2% at 3 Mev. Lead, brass and aluminum cathodes for gamma rays from 0.5 to 2.5 Mev were studied by Bradt and associates [B17] and also by Maier-Leibnitz [M16] who reports that the lead cylinders showed uniform sensitivity in the range 0.15 to 1.5 Mev, while with brass the sensitivity was proportional to the energy in the interval from 0.1 to 3 Mev. At low energies, below 0.1 Mev, he found a thin-wall tin cylinder most satisfactory. Dependence on wall thickness was studied by Suffczynski [S21] who found that, as the gamma ray energy increases, greatest sensitivity is secured by increasing the wall thickness. He used lead and brass cylinders and gamma rays from Ra and MsTh filtered through 2 cm Pb. Barrere [B18] studied the X-ray sensitivity of counters of the Maze type, using the K radiation from copper and trying various gas fillings. Brown [B19] used a microwave discharge counter to measure gamma rays. The counter was a part of a cavity resonator operated at 3000 megacycles. An organic quenching mixture was used. Very fast resolving times were reported. In summary of the work thus far published, it may be said that practically no observers have studied the systematic dependence of counter behavior on more than one or two parameters and that most of the existing experience indicates how to make good counters for a particular wave-length interval.

G. Time Lags

The time lag of a counter is defined as the time interval between the instant that the initial ionizing event occurs in the counter and the instant that a detectable pulse appears on the central wire and electrically attached system. Much difference of opinion as to time lags has appeared both in the literature and in discussions. It is therefore worth while to review the pertinent factors governing such lags, for lags will be one of the most important controlling factors in determining the maximum counting rate obtainable with a given counter.

As we have pointed out above, during the time interval just defined, the following events take place. First, one or more electrons are formed in the ionizing event. Then the electron or electrons drift in toward the central wire. The time required for this drift we shall refer to as the "electron transit time." Next, the Townsend avalanche is formed. Third, the avalanche spreads along the length of the wire, with a velocity which we call the "sheath spread velocity." Fourth, the positive ions move out to the cylinder. Let us consider these four operations in turn.

First, consider the electron transit time. Suppose first that we consider only one electron, and further that this electron is not captured to form a negative ion. This electron must then travel a distance equal to or less than the radius of the counter. Most of its path lies in the low-field region. Here the fields are between 100 and 1000 volts per cm, and the pressures are of the order of 0.1 atm. Hence taking the known electron mobilities, we conclude that the electron will require between 10^{-8} and 10^{-7} sec to complete this transit.

Second, consider the Townsend avalanche. This takes place within a few free paths of the wire, where the fields are high and the electron gains 10, 20, or more electron-volts of energy per free path. The average velocity of the electron will be of the order of 10^8 to 10^9 cm per sec, and since it has to go a distance of only a mm or less, it will take about 10^{-10} sec to complete. The time required for this process therefore is substantially smaller than the electron transit time, and we shall ignore it in the following discussion.

Next we evaluate the effect of the sheath spread along the wire. This has been discussed before and it has been shown experimentally to be of the order of 10^7 cm per sec. A counter 10 or 20 cm long will therefore require one or two microseconds for the discharge to spread along the wire.

Fourth we must consider the motion of the positives. If all the electrons were held by electrostatic image-forces and prevented from flowing along the wire, we should find that quite long times were required. Indeed just such long times are required for complete recovery. But it is possible for a fast circuit to detect a small fraction of the total number of electrons which will eventually be liberated. The geometry of image-formation in a cylindrical conductor permits some of the electrons to escape almost immediately after the first Townsend avalanche is finished and long before the sheath speed is completed. Hence, the long times imposed by the motion of the positives can also be disregarded.

We see therefore that the factors determining the time lags are the following. The electron transit time is controlled by the field and the gas pressure and cannot be varied by as much as an order of magnitude in either direction. It will, of course, be less if the ionizing event takes place near the wire. If the electron is captured and travels for any appreciable distance as a negative ion, the time lag can be greatly lengthened.

The sheath spread time also depends on the usual parameters, the voltage gas pressure and size of the counter. This time can be minimized by several procedures. In a self-quenching counter, we can place beads along the central wire, thus limiting the distance the sheath travels. Clearly ten equally spaced beads will reduce the sheath spread time to one tenth the former time. We can operate the counter with a potential reversing circuit, in which case the wire potential can be dropped before the sheath has spread, and again cut down the time. We can operate the counter in the proportional region, in which case the sheath does not spread anyway.

In summary, we can reduce the time lag to little more than the electron transit time, and hence we should expect that time lags of 0.1 or 0.2 microsecond or, with favorable circumstances, even less than 0.1 could be attained. We may now consider recent measurements.

Experiments support the foregoing view. For example, Mandeville and Scherb [M11] find 4×10^{-8} sec for the case of an alcohol-argon counter, and Sherwin [S14] obtained 10^{-7} sec by a method of firing a narrow beam of β rays into a counter in a direction parallel with the wire and at various radial distances. Sherwin measured transit times at various voltages up to 250 volts overvoltage. He found a mobility $k = 4.5 \times 10^6$ and a dependence on field and pressure given by $v^2 = k^2E/p$. Further, den Hartog [H10] also obtained similar values in alcohol-argon counters and reported that the lags were proportional to the square of the diameter of the counter and the mobility was independent of the field. Rossi and Nereson [R11] found that an alcohol-argon counter, 20 cm long and 2.5 cm in diameter, with gas at 10 cm pressure, a 7-mil central wire and 120 volts overvoltage, showed lags of the order of 0.1 to 0.2 microseconds.

Further experiments to study lags systematically, as a function of the various parameters such as gas pressure and composition, counter size and voltage are in progress. From these measurements Laufer [L12] and others have drawn conclusions in support of the arguments cited. A comprehensive study is clearly needed and is under way.

That negative ions are an important agency in producing time lags has been understood for some years. We shall briefly review the situation. First, should a negative ion be formed in the volume of the counter, it will traverse the counter at a speed determined by its mobility, as we have already discussed, and may take up to 200 microseconds to complete a traversal. In the event that only one electron is formed in the initial ionizing event, the probability that this will be captured can be computed as we have already indicated. Should two or more electrons be formed and one or more of these escape capture or negative ion formation, the electrons will move quickly to the high field region, there initiate a discharge, and the negative ion or ions will follow more slowly and may, in turn, initiate discharges after the first one. This production of spurious counts also has already been mentioned. However, all the complexities of the situation are not now catalogued.

Should the negative ion be formed only a small distance from the wire, the lag thus produced may only be a microsecond or a few microseconds. Suppose, for example, that the quenching constituent in the gas is one which decomposes into fragments capable of forming negative ions. Suppose we deal with an alcohol molecule; this molecule by itself has a comparatively low coefficient for negative ion formation. But the molecule can dissociate into a fragment H_2O or oxygen, both of which form such ions with greater probability. We shall then have two effects. First, the lags in the counter will change with use, for the amount of oxygen will increase as dissociation takes place. Second, short lags may be encountered. These short lags will depend on the number of electrons formed in the initial event, for if several electrons are formed, only one must survive to initiate the avalanche with a time lag controlled by electron-transit time alone. If negative ions arrive in the high field region either while the avalanche is still building up or before the positive ion sheath has moved an appreciable distance away, the field conditions will not have recovered enough to permit a new avalanche to be formed and the negatives will merely be collected on the central wire. But if one electron alone is formed, which may or may not be captured, then we shall find short time lags in some discharges and no lags in others; or if n electrons are formed and the probability of each being captured is P, then we shall have a chance of $e^{-n}(e^{Pn} - 1)$ of having a lag. Thus the same counter, if it is used to detect radiation which produces many electrons in the initial event, may show no lags, while if one or a few are produced, it may show lags. This situation has been investigated experimentally by Laufer [L12] and by Kitchen,[K18] as well as by Montgomery and colleagues.[M17, W7] All of these observers reported effects due to negative ions; Montgomery not only found effects in instances in which oxygen had been added, but also reported negative ions formed by CO_2, which in turn was presumably formed in the disintegration of ethyl alcohol, none having been intentionally introduced. Marked negative ion effects in methyl bromide quenching mixtures were reported by Carver and White,[C8] and in low-voltage halogen counters by Loosemore and Sharpe.[L13]

For further discussion of Electron Transit Time Lags, see J. Heirtzler, *Rev. Sci. Inst.*, **25**, 243 (1954). For discussion of discharge and sheath propagation mechanism, see S. A. Korff, *Rev. Sci. Inst.*, **24**, 1031 (1953).

PROBLEMS

1. Compute the efficiency of a counter filled with 15.2 cm of helium, assuming the average path length of the particle to be 2 cm in the counter. Assume the counter to be counting cosmic ray particles.

(*Ans.* Efficiency 91%.)

2. An anticoincidence arrangement of three counters, similar to that in problem 1, is used to study the lifetime of mesons. Compute the probability that a wrong value is obtained by a coincidence being missed when, in fact, it occurred. (*Ans.* 0.25.)

3. Will a methane-xenon mixture be expected to be a good filling-mixture for a selfquenching counter?

(*Ans.* No. Ionization potential of methane is greater than xenon.)

4. Will the addition of 0.75 mm chlorine to a counter of 1-cm radius filled with an argon-alcohol mixture at 7.6 cm be expected to show an appreciable change in flatness of plateau?

(*Ans.* Not much change.)

Further References Regarding Operation of Counters:

"The Speed of Operation of Geiger-Muller Counters." H. den Hartog, *Nucleonics* **5**, 33 (1949).

"A Review Paper on Counters." D. R. Corson and R. R. Wilson, *Rev. Sci. Inst.* **19**, 207 (1948).

"A Review of the Mobilities, Dissociation Processes at Surfaces." P. B. Weisz, *J. Phys. Coll. Chem.* **52**, 578 (1948).

CHAPTER 5

PREPARATION AND CONSTRUCTION OF COUNTERS

A. General Considerations in Construction

1. Construction. In constructing a counter to be used in the detection of any type of radiation, electromagnetic or corpuscular, it is desirable to attempt to approximate as closely as possible several desiderata. First, the counter must be designed with regard to the nature and distribution of the radiation being studied. This includes providing means whereby radiation with small penetrating power, such as alpha particles, can reach the sensitive part of the counter. Second, the counter should have as low a natural background as possible, and undesired radiation should be excluded. Third, the counter should not have spurious counts, for these will vitiate interpretations based on a statistical analysis of the data since their probability of occurrence is not random, and will introduce a variable background which it is difficult to allow for accurately. To these features may also be added simplicity of construction, ruggedness, forms convenient for use, and low cost.

The methods that will be described, for the preparation and construction of counters, have been developed as a result of the application of two fundamental principles. The first is that the construction and preparation should be such as to permit the mechanism of the counter discharge to operate, with a minimum of disturbing effects due to unwanted agencies. The second principle is that the procedures should insure that the desired conditions remain as permanently as possible. An illustration of the application of the first of these principles is the following: The cylinder of the counter should be made of substances with high work functions and alkali metals should be especially avoided. This is important because the supply of secondary electrons, which causes the discharge to continue, and thus tends to defeat the processes quenching the discharge, is dependent on the work function. The number of secondary electrons can be greatly reduced by proper choice of cathode surface, and the counter will accordingly have better operating characteristics. An illustration of the second principle, to insure permanence, is in the desirability of cleaning the counter thoroughly before filling and sealing it. If, for example, the counter contains adsorbed films of material which, over a period of time, will change, then the chemical composition of the gas in the counter will alter with time and the properties of the counter will change accordingly.

In the past, many persons have claimed that some of the precautions suggested below were unnecessary. While it may be possible in individual cases to disregard certain ones and still occasionally to produce a good counter, yet the reason for each of the procedures appears sufficiently cogent to warrant its use. Over a period of some years during which some thousands of counters have been constructed, it has been found possible to make counters in lots of 100 at a time and to have all but one or two be acceptable, in the sense of having long, flat plateaus and low backgrounds. Other counters have been kept for years before use; and had they not been chemically stable they would almost certainly not have remained constantly usable. Several are still serviceable which were made nine years ago. The problem is similar to that of the construction of radio tubes. While it may be possible to get an occasional good tube if the thorough cleaning and evacuation techniques are neglected the production of many with reproducible and predictable characteristics is greatly facilitated by attention to these details.

B. CONSTRUCTIONAL FEATURES

Counters can be constructed with an astonishingly wide variety of characteristics and physical dimensions. To illustrate the possible ranges in size, counters 4 mm in radius and 9 mm long may be contrasted with others 75 mm in radius and 1 meter in length. Both these sizes are in successful operation at the present time and there appears to be no reason why these dimensions cannot be considerably exceeded in either direction should it prove desirable to do so. The nature of the problem to be studied largely determines the size and shape of the counters used. For example, if a large sensitive area is required, as often occurs in cosmic ray investigations, it is usual to arrange a layer or tray of long narrow counters and to connect the wires either together or in coincidence (see Chapter 7). A single counter of great size would perform this same function but would also have a considerable sensitive volume not used directly in the experiment and hence would contribute unnecessarily to the background. In addition, a single big counter would require a higher operating potential. On the other hand, for detecting a small number of neutrons, such as the number produced by the cosmic radiation at sea level, a large sensitive volume is desired and a single counter of maximum dimensions is indicated. Still another problem is the detection of weak beta radiation from small samples, a common phenomenon in tracer research in medicine or biophysics. Here a small counter with low background but with a maximum efficiency in terms of sensitive solid angle is necessary. We shall describe such counters in the paragraphs on thin windows.

The geometry of most counters is cylindrical. The optimum length and diameter of the cylinder will be determined by the problem. There are no fundamental limitations on either, except that a cylinder whose radius is larger than its length will have a field distribution which varies along its axis, so that different parts of the counter will be operating at different effective potentials. Further, spherical geometry can be used if desirable. A small round bead on the end of a wire projecting into the center of a sphere will serve as a collecting electrode and the shell as the spherical cathode.

A desirable feature which should be included whenever possible is that both ends of the central wire should be electrically available from the outside of the counter. This is important in that it will enable the wire to be glowed while the counter is evacuated. This operation will effectively remove microscopic bits of dust or lint or metal or sharp points on the wire. If left, these would create local irregularities in the electric field, which in turn may cause local ionization and hence spurious counts. Further, glowing the wire drives off occluded gases and hence contributes to chemical stability.

The wire diameter is one factor determining the operating voltage. It is desirable, in order to secure low voltages, to have this diameter as small as possible. Ordinarily, 3 or 4 mil tungsten wire is used, for larger diameter wire causes the required voltages to increase unnecessarily, while smaller diameter wire is so fragile that the wire is too readily broken in ordinary handling. Tungsten is a good material for the wires because (a) it can readily be sealed to glass and (b) it can be heated successfully while the counter is being pumped.

Sharp points in the high field regions must be avoided as these give rise to local ionization and spurious counts. The ends of the cylinder should be slightly rounded outward, to decrease the field gradually, and the inside of the cylinder should be free from burrs, scratches or irregularities. Similarly the wire should be smooth. The places where the wire is welded onto the supports should be shielded, preferably with glass sleeves, so that high local fields are avoided. Such sleeves are shown in Fig. 5–1A and elsewhere.

Copper is a good material for the counter cylinder. Brass may also be used and is frequently available in suitable shapes.

If anything, it is a little less good than copper, due to the increased photosensitivity of the zinc content. Any trace of the alkali metals must be scrupulously avoided. Aluminum is undesirable for two reasons. It is often porous and hard to outgas. Further, with certain filling gases, electrons may be liberated from its surface by chemical action, and thus it may produce spurious counts. Soft solder on parts of a counter is undesirable as the counter can then not be heated enough to outgas thoroughly. In certain types of construction, this is hard to avoid, but it should be regarded as a definite disadvantage. Soft solder is also attacked by cleaning solutions.

Light should be kept from reaching the interior of the counter. This is especially important if the ultraviolet content of the light is high. This can be accomplished in many ways. The counter may be operated inside a suitable shield. Black paper is opaque to light yet does not affect any but the softest beta rays. The glass surfaces of the counter may be coated with an opaque wax (see below), or the shape of the envelope may exclude virtually all ambient illumination. The purpose of excluding light is to reduce the number of photoelectrons and spurious counts.

Waxed joints of any kind should also be avoided. These can seldom be made permanently tight. They are attacked by cleaning fluids, and prevent the counter's being heated to outgas it. Moreover, they are often attacked by the organic filling materials and hence are chemically unstable. Further, they may evolve gas and render the counting-rate temperature dependent.

C. Envelopes

Counters can be made with either glass or metal envelopes. In the metal envelope type, the tube itself is usually also the cathode of the counter. For safety in handling, it is customary to operate such counters with the cylinder at ground potential. The appropriate circuits are given in Chapter 7. Glass con-

tainers, on the other hand, permit either cylinder or wire to
be operated at ground potential. Glass counters are also somewhat better adapted to the cleaning techniques which we shall
describe in the following section. Most metal envelope designs

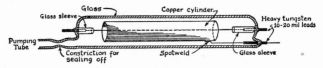

FIG. 5–1A.   Glass envelope counter.

involve soldered joints which would be attacked by the cleaning acids.

Several designs which have been used successfully are shown in
Figs. 5–1A and B, those indicated by A being in glass envelopes
while those marked B employ a metal cathode as the outside
element. The cylinder can be quite thin in the case of the
glass envelope types. Seamless copper tubing of 0.2 mm thickness will serve admirably. When the cylinder also serves as
the wall of the counter, it must of course be rugged enough to

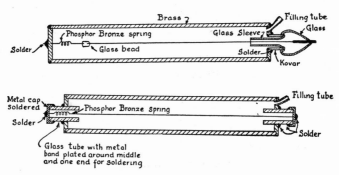

FIG. 5–1B.   Metal envelope counters.

withstand atmospheric pressure and also the shocks of ordinary handling. Consequently thicker stock is required, 0.5 mm
brass often being used. Thus the metal exterior counters require more metal; but they require less glass blowing and are

somewhat easier to mass-produce if a good glass blower is not available. The glass counters can usually be cleaned more thoroughly.

In the early days of counters, it was often the custom to employ a brass tube as a cathode and to wax hard rubber stoppers into the ends. Such construction should be avoided because (a) it is virtually impossible to clean, (b) the parts give off gas and change the counter characteristics with time, and (c) in the case of BF_3 counters, the gas attacks the ends and the counter soon becomes useless.

In making glass envelope counters for neutron measurements, the neutron absorption due to the boron content of glass must be considered. Thus for measurements in which very low neutron intensities are expected, the types of glass such as Pyrex having high boron content should be avoided. If it is necessary to use such glass, the absorption of neutrons in the glass should be computed and allowed for [see eq. (6–8)].

D. Thin Window and Large Solid Angle Counters

The problem of getting the particle to be detected into the counter is especially important with (a) weak sources and (b) the types of radiation which have small penetrating power. Two procedures are in general available, first to place the source of radiation inside the counter, and second to employ a thin window on the counter through which the radiation may be projected into the sensitive volume. To illustrate the thinness required of the window, we recall that most alpha particles have a range of only 4 or 5 cm of air. The window must consequently not be thicker than a few centimeters of air-equivalent, or say some 0.05 mm or less of glass.

Extremely thin glass bubbles can be blown on the ends of glass tubing, and hence an arrangement such as is shown in Fig. 5–2A is readily constructed. If the source of alpha or other radiation of low penetrating power is put next to this window, the particles will have the maximum opportunity of entering the counter. The source cannot be moved many centimeters in air from the window because of the short range in air of the radiation. Placing counter and source in an evacuated container is possible but is inconvenient, and further a

FIG. 5–2A.   Counter with thin end window for alpha particles.

thin window will be able to withstand quite a pressure differential only if the glass is always under tension. The counter should thus have less pressure on the inside than outside.

Re-entrant thin glass windows as in Fig. 5–2B may be used, through which alpha particles can be projected into proportional counters for calibrating purposes. If the thickness of the window is known, the amount of ionization produced by the particle in the counter can be readily estimated. If the

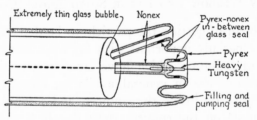

FIG. 5–2B.   Construction of thin window on counter to permit alpha particles for calibration to be projected into the sensitive volume with minimum loss of range. An extremely thin glass bubble is attached to the end of a tube entering the volume of the counter, and a rod with some mesothorium or polonium on one end is lowered through the tube and brought near the window.   (Ref. K4)

source is now withdrawn one cm in air from the window, the amount of ionization produced in the counter is less by the amount produced in the 1 cm of air. In this manner a curve can be obtained of the pulse size as a function of the amount of ionization liberated in the counter. The thickness of the window can be determined by raising the voltage on the counter until it is operating in the Geiger region. The source is now withdrawn until the counter just ceases to count the particles

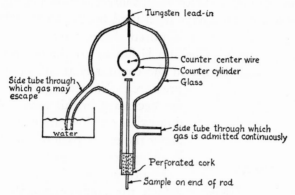

FIG. 5–2C. Counter arranged to contain gas at atmospheric pressure so that samples may be readily brought near sensitive volume with no intervening windows. Helium or argon at atmospheric pressure will produce counters with reasonable starting potentials. (After S. C. Brown, B3)

which the source emits. If we designate by D the distance of the source from the window at which counts are just detected, and by W the window thickness in air-equivalent, then the range R of the particles is evidently equal to $D + W$. Since R is known for the various alpha radiations and D has just been measured, W is determined. This term also includes the

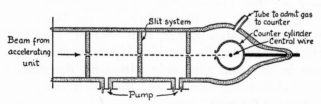

FIG. 5–2D. Counter attached directly to accelerating apparatus.

thickness in air-equivalent of the gas inside the counter which the particle must penetrate to reach the sensitive region. The particle need produce only one ion, once it has reached the sensitive region, in order to record a count if the counter is operating in the Geiger region. The end of the range is thus readily found.

Another arrangement for weak sources is shown in Fig. 5–2C. Counters of this type have been used by Brown [B4] and others. In this case, the source is raised directly into the sensitive volume. A stream of helium is flowed continuously through the counter, and the gas in the counter is at full atmospheric pressure. No sealing-off provisions are necessary in this case. No window exists and ionization is produced along the entire path of the particles in the gas of the counter.

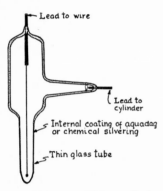

In other cases it is possible to attach the counter directly to the accelerating apparatus, and to project the particles to be studied into the counter directly. A typical arrangement of this sort is shown in Fig. 5–2D, where the beam passes through narrow slits into the counter. The pressure in the counter can be kept high enough for counting action by admitting gas through an adjustable leak, while pumping between the slits will keep the gas out of the accelerating chamber. If the particles in the beam have any appreciable penetrating power, thin windows may be placed over the slits and the slits considerably increased in size. The windows in this case need only withstand the difference in pressure between the counter and the accelerating tube, perhaps a total of 0.1 to 0.2 atm.

FIG. 5–3A. Thin-walled counter suitable for immersion in liquids containing minute radioactive traces.

For the detection of weak beta radiation, a problem which arises both in medicine in radioactive tracer research and in certain problems of nuclear physics, another design is often used. Not only has the beta radiation often low penetrating power, but it is frequently so small in absolute amount as to render its detection above the normal statistical background difficult. It is therefore important that as large a fraction as possible of the beta radiation emitted by the source should reach the sensitive portion of the counter. This in turn means

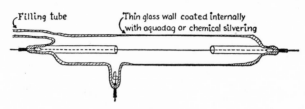

FIG. 5–3B. Thin-walled beta ray counter.

that the radiation in all directions from the source should be available to the counter, or in other words that the counter should have a large sensitive solid angle.

Radiation from a solution may be measured either by lowering a thin-walled counter such as shown in Fig. 5–3A into the solution or by placing a thin-walled counter directly above it.

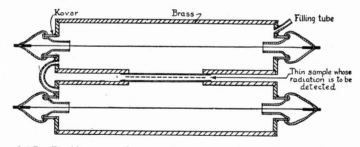

FIG. 5–3C. Double counter for measuring radiation from both sides of thin sample.

A beta-counter suitable for this purpose is shown in Fig. 5–3B. Virtually all the radiation from one side of a thin foil may be measured with counters of this type by curling the foil to the same diameter as the thin portion of the counter and laying it on the thin part.

For coverage of still greater solid angles, such as for detecting radiation from both sides of a foil, Simpson [85] has devised an arrangement of two counters as shown in Fig. 5–3C. Here each counter has a section covered by a thin window which can be made of any suitable substance such as cellophane or nickel silver foil, and the two thin sections are placed together. The wires of the counters may then be connected together and the discharges of both recorded. If the opening in the counters is to be large and the window thin, it may be necessary to provide some support behind the window to prevent the window from collapsing under atmospheric pressure. This can readily be arranged by placing a wire mesh or narrow reinforcing strips behind the window. These reinforcements will somewhat reduce the sensitive aperture but can generally be made narrow enough not to obscure too large a fraction of the area.

2. Evacuation and Filling. *a. Washing and cleaning.* It has been repeatedly emphasized by Locher [L2] and others that it is important to remove dirt, dust and contamination from the inside of counters. Dust and particles will tend to become electrified in the strong fields, will distort the field and give rise to spurious counts. Contamination may give off gas which will alter the operating characteristics of a counter over a period of time. It is important therefore adequately to wash and clean the inside of the counter. In the glass envelope types, this can readily be accomplished by washing the inside of the counter with a dilute mixture of sulphuric and nitric acids, allowing the solution to stay in the counter until it has vigorously attacked the cathode and removed all surface contamination, and then cleaning out all the acid with distilled water. In the metal envelope types, the ends are usually attached with solder and the acid treatment cannot therefore be used. In this case, washing with ammonia and organic solvents will remove most of the impurities and, while not as thorough as the acid, will have to serve. For special counter shapes or designs, special techniques should be devised, but the purpose should always be to remove dust, wax, grease or other extraneous matter.

The chemical stability of the cylinder may be insured by suitable treatment. The cylinder may be either oxidized, by admitting oxygen and heating, or reduced, by heating with hydrogen. Ordinarily, hydrogen should not be used as a filling gas in a counter with an oxidized cylinder, for a chemical reaction will take place which will slowly alter the constituents, and therefore the operating characteristics of the counter.

In making the thin-walled glass counters such as shown in Fig. 5–3B, in which the cathode is chemically silvered or coated with colloidal carbon (Aquadag), the glass must be thoroughly cleaned before the cathode surface is applied, so that the painted surface will adhere firmly. Both chemical silvering and graphite have a tendency to peel off in flakes if the surface is not clean, and these flakes are immediately so oriented in the field that they form sharp points and hence may give rise to spurious counts. Baking to outgas counters of this type is not practicable as it tends to destroy the cathode surface; but the central wire can be glowed in the design shown in Fig. 5–3B.

b. Evacuation. The thoroughly cleaned counters may next be sealed onto a vacuum system and evacuated. It is desirable to obtain a good vacuum. Prolonged pumping with diffusion pumps is recommended. The counters should be heated if feasible, to drive off gases occluded on the surfaces. This procedure is of course to be carried out with caution if the counter has soldered joints or is internally silvered, but glass-envelope types can be given extensive heat treatment. If a group of counters is to be filled, they may all be mounted on a manifold and the entire arrangement placed in an electric furnace. Baking under vacuum follows the customary techniques for obtaining high vacua. It is not necessary to take elaborate precautions to eliminate mercury vapor, for experiments have shown [K7] that the amount present at room temperature is of no consequence.

The wire should be glowed. This can readily be accomplished by connecting the ends of the wire to a Variac, and slowly raising the voltage. Usually a few volts is enough to produce incandescence. The importance of this procedure has been emphasized by Locher, who points out that it not only burns off dust and sharp points on the wire but also alters the crystalline structure to give greater uniformity and reduces die-scratches on the wire. To enable the wire to be glowed it is necessary that both ends be available electrically. While this cannot always be achieved, as for example in the counter shown in Fig. 5–3A, the importance of glowing the wire is such that serious consideration should be given in the design to arranging for the possibility.

After a good vacuum has been secured, the counter may be filled. The gas chosen will depend on considerations which we have already discussed. Usually it is convenient to store the gases to be used in glass bulbs connected to the counter filling system by stopcocks. The glass bulbs can be thoroughly evacuated and the gases purified if desirable. Stopcocks permit easier and more accurate control of the flow of gas than do the valves on the commercial steel cylinders of gas. A diagram of a suitable system is shown in Fig. 5–4. Mercury manometers should be provided to enable pressures to be measured. Whenever an organic vapor is used, care should be taken that no air is admitted at the same time. The stopcocks should be watched, for many organic liquids suitable for quenching counters also dissolve stopcock grease. Similarly, BF_3 attacks stopcock grease slowly, and occasionally stopcocks should be cleaned and regreased. Enough time for diffusion of heavy vapors should be allowed. In preparing vapor-filled counters the vapor should be admitted first, and then the inert constituent. At least an hour should be allowed for diffusion equilibrium to be established after the mixture is made. The counters should in general be tested while still attached to the system, so that errors in filling can be rectified or operating conditions altered by admitting or removing gas. An oscilloscope and an adjustable voltage supply, as well as a small sample of radioactive material, are all that is necessary for such testing. After filling and testing, the counter is sealed off, and the system pumped to remove the organic vapors,

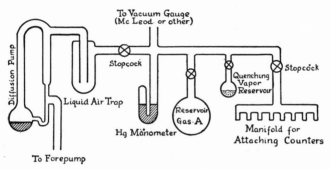

FIG. 5–4.   Vacuum system for filling counters.

since these are inflammable, and constitute an explosion hazard if left.

c. External treatment.   After a counter has been filled and removed from the system, it is well to wax the glass surfaces. The purpose of this is twofold. The photo-sensitivity of the counter is reduced if an opaque film of wax covers those parts through which light can reach the interior. Various black or dark red fat-soluble dyes (e.g., Sudan IV and others) can be added to the wax to increase its opacity. The second important feature is that this procedure gives the glass surfaces a high resistance, and reduces the formation of surface films of moisture and surface leakage. Since high fields and potentials are used, it is important to eliminate leakage. A very minute amount of charge, leaking across an imperceptible moisture film on a glass surface, or even merely redistributing itself on the surface, can cause spurious counts. A high resistance moisture proof wax, such as Ceresin, is therefore indicated.

3. Summary. We may summarize the recommended techniques thus: Avoid procedures which will (a) leave sharp points of any kind in the volume of the counter, or (b) cause chemical or mechanical or electrical changes with time. The first category includes avoidance of dust or microscopic fibres in the counter, or scratches or burrs on the cylinder or welds on inside connecting leads or pits or die-scratches on the wire. Glowing the wire is helpful. The second group of causes of trouble may be minimized by care in preparation, chemical cleanliness, proper choice of materials, good vacuum technique and construction avoiding features such as organic materials which give off or absorb gas over long periods of time. The desirability of any new features in the construction of counters may often be determined by seeing to what extent the proposed features conform to the two principles mentioned.

SUMMARY OF OPERATIONAL EXPERIENCE

We may summarize experience with counters by citing some "rules" which, while by no means complete or infallible instructions, seem to the author to embody the most important factors in the successful construction and operation of counters.

In order to secure maximum operational effectiveness the following items should be observed:

1. A counter should never be operated above its rated voltage. To do so may damage or ruin it.

2. A counter should not be permitted to go into a "continuous discharge." If it does, the high potential should be immediately disconnected and not connected again until the voltage has been reduced.

3. The counter should be disconnected from the high potential supply, or the high voltage should be shut off when not in use.

4. The voltages in the various circuits, as well as the high voltage, should be stabilized and free from major fluctuations.

In construction, the following features should be considered:

1. Avoid dust inside the counter.

2. Avoid any sharp points on the inside, i.e., on the wire or cylinder.

3. Use pure (99%) gases and good vacuum technique, and particularly avoid contamination with air.

4. Avoid getting anything into the counter which will change with time, or which will give off gas or produce chemical reactions.

5. Avoid photosensitive surfaces (except in photocounters).

6. Arrange or treat exterior surfaces to minimize electrical leakage.

Recent Developments in Design and Construction

The most marked development in recent years is the manufacture of counters in quantity by commercial concerns following the procedures used in making vacuum tubes. We shall discuss and comment upon some of these procedures. Further, since it is often necessary to make counters in some special design or shape, we shall describe a few new and successful constructional details.

First we shall remark that, although much progress has been made in the quantity production of counters, the situation is still far from satisfactory. Not all the manufacturers use adequate vacuum techniques or do enough pumping and baking previous to filling. The results show up in counters being nonstandard and in their changing with time. The problem of making good counters is not essentially different from that of making gas-discharge tubes such as the VR tubes and thyratrons that are now made in large lots. Automatic vacuum-tube making machinery is readily adaptable to this problem. A few standard sizes and shapes are self-evident. For radiological monitoring, counters should be roughly 10 to 15 cm long, 2 cm in diameter, and should be based. They should have identical characteristics, so that counters can be interchanged as easily as radio tubes with no change in operating potentials required. As is well known in the vacuum-tube industry, the secret of reproducibility is control in the various processes. The counters should be made with identical dimensions, pumped and baked thoroughly, and filled to accurately determined pressures. It is almost impossible to do work by hand to the requisite tolerances and still produce tubes in lots of ten thousand at a low price. Much thought needs to be devoted to the problems of arranging the assembly and manufacture to be as nearly fully automatic as possible, including automatic tolerance controls.

In the paragraphs that follow we shall occasionally refer to particular counters made by particular manufacturers. It should be understood that any such mention, or lack of mention, does not constitute an endorsement or a criticism, but is merely an illustration of a point under discussion. The author does not pretend to have all catalogs of all manufacturers at hand, and often particular designs are made by several companies with only slight variations. If one counter is used to illustrate a point, it does not imply that this counter is better or worse, in the opinion of the author, than some competitive and perhaps almost identical model. Further, it is impossible to get a patent on a mixture of gases, the vast majority of which have been tried and described in the literature. Hence some manufacturers take refuge in "trade secrets" and pretend they have a wonderful new mixture. During the past ten years, however, the developments which have taken place have been those described in this text, from which it is clear that many new and interesting avenues have been followed but no major discoveries have been made. With the very large number of possible gases and organic vapors available today and with the need for specialized applications and geometries, it seems reasonable to expect that improvements will continue to be forthcoming, and that the subject will continue to expand. We shall next outline some of the improved design and construction details recently developed.

a. Cathode material and construction. It was found by Louw and Naude [L15] that ground and polished cathode surfaces showed large numbers of spurious counts, decaying to the normal background in a few hours. This they attributed to delayed emission. This effect has not been observed, however, in counters that were thoroughly cleaned and baked, and it can therefore probably be avoided.

A technique for evaporation of copper onto the inner wall of a glass envelope counter was described by de Vos and du Toit,[D6] which is especially suitable in applications where it is desired to have a thin glass wall for beta-counting. The cathode in this instance adds a negligible thickness to that of the glass walls. Evaporated or chemically applied silver had previously been similarly used. The counters made in this manner resemble the type illustrated in Fig. 5–3B. Detailed descriptions of the metal-wall types shown in Fig. 5–1B have been published by Regener,[R13] and by Shamos and Hudes.[S22]

b. Note on glass. An important point has been emphasized by Montgomery [M18] about the kind of in-between glass used in the seals shown in Fig. 5–2B, to seal Pyrex to Nonex. It is that the Pyrex blue glass Number 542 should be used, and the common intermediate glass Number 3321 should be avoided, for the latter contains uranium and therefore adds to counter background.

c. External cathode counters. Following the original paper by Maze,[M14] Blanc and Scherer [B20] have also described counters of this type, and Bassi, Beretta and Rostagni [B15,B16] have measured the dead times of these counters, which they report as of the order of 0.1 sec (corresponding to a resistance of the glass of perhaps 10^9 to 10^{10} ohms) and a coefficient of liberation of secondary electrons of the order of 10^{-10} when hit by positive ions. For detailed discussion see Chapter 4.

d. Rejuvenation. Several investigators have considered measures to rejuvenate counters which have "gone bad." The results may be summarized by saying that, if the counters that have gone bad were filled with a vapor which decomposed, the procedure is to admit a new gas. If the major problem is polymerization, then it is necessary to clean the electrodes. For example, Shepard [815] found that heating the wire sufficed to rejuvenate some alcohol-argon counters he had been using. Hagen and Loughridge [H18] put in a new wire, with the same effect. Farmer and Brown [F4] found that cleaning the electrodes was useful when the fillings were of methane, ethane, ethylene and acetylene, all of which polymerize readily in the discharge, and Scherb [823] also found rejuvenation in an argon-butane counter when the electrodes were heated.

e. Needle and dip counters. Counters which are of extremely small diameters are useful for biological applications, for example, when one has to be introduced into the brain. Such counters diagrammatically are of the type shown in Fig. 5–3A, with, in some instances, longer and thinner extensions. Counters of this type have been described by E. Strajman [824] and by Robinson.[R14] Robinson's counters used diameters from 0.25 to 0.038 inch and wires from 2 to ½ mil. He reports good results with diameters as small as 0.067 inch, the very smallest giving poorer results. The chief difference between these counters and the one shown in Fig. 5–3A is that a small bead is placed on the wire near the end, and a coarse wire is used through the large part of the counter and as far down as the bead. A fine wire starts at the bead and goes to the end of the thin part of the counter, where the other end of the wire may be held by an insulating substance to keep it from vibrating or touching the cylinder. The large portion of the counter serves as a gas reservoir and therefore helps prolong the life. Robinson used a sensitive volume 27 mm long and finds optimum ratio of wire to cathode to be 150 or more. He employed copper cathodes and an argon-ether mixture with 5% to 16%

ether at total pressures of 7 to 16 cm. The operating voltages are rather low because of the small diameter and are about 735 volts with a 120-volt plateau. He also experimented with higher pressures, up to 2 atm of argon plus 28 mm ether. Except for a slight increase in efficiency, there seems to be not much advantage in the higher pressures.

f. Internal radiators. Quite a number of designs have appeared in recent years in which internal radiators have been inserted to increase the efficiency of counters. Of the many, two are selected as representative of the two main kinds of radiator. The first kind we shall call the disintegration radiator, of which a typical example is that used by Lowde.[L6] In this counter, Lowde employs multiple layers of solid boron for counting neutrons. As we have shown before, the maximum efficiency of a boron-lined counter is far below 100%. But by the use of multiple layers, in the form of a "sandwich" this efficiency can be considerably raised. Consider alternate layers of solid boron, a small separation occupied by the counter gas, and then collecting electrodes. For neutrons diffusing in a direction to penetrate more than one boron layer, the efficiencies of the several layers become additive, approaching 100% asymptotically as the number of layers increases. If the boron layers are thin and both sides are exposed to the gas, the disintegration particles can emerge from either side and be detected. Fig. 5–5A shows such a counter. It is clear that modifications in the geometrical arrangement can readily be made should this be desirable for any special applications. Lithium may be used as well as boron if the alpha particles are to be detected by the (n, alpha) reaction. Other substances could similarly be used should other reactions be under investigation. Multiple-layer fission counters have been described in the literature. The (n, alpha) reactions have the advantage that (a) the cross section for these substances is large and so the counter can be quite efficient, and (b) the emerging particle has a high energy but short range, permitting much smaller counters to be used than would be the case if a less heavily ionizing particle, such as a proton, emerged.

The other type of radiator is the recoil radiator. In this case the entity to be detected transfers part or all of its kinetic energy to a nucleus in the radiating surface, and the recoiling nucleus produces the ionization which is detected. Since the majority of such counters are built for the detection of fast neutrons, we shall discuss them as though this were the only

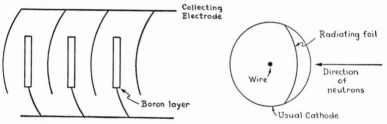

FIG. 5–5A. Boron sandwich.[L7]   FIG. 5–5B. Internal piston radiation for fast neutrons.[C7]

purpose. The reader will readily appreciate the modifications to be used when other entities are to be counted by this process. The energy transfer is most efficient when the masses of the projectile and target are similar. Hence for neutrons we generally use recoiling protons.

Hence it is not surprising to find, described in the literature, a number of arrangements in which hydrogenous radiators are placed inside counters. One such is shown in Fig. 5–5B. Here Coon and Nobles [C7] have placed a hydrogenous radiator inside such a counter. They tried several substances and found glycerin tristearate to be especially satisfactory. The substance is placed on a thin platinum or gold foil, and the shape of the arrangement is such as to minimize distortion of the field. The heavy atoms in the foil do not contribute much to the recoil process because of the momentum transfer inefficiency which has been discussed above. The special advantages of arrangements of this type are (a) that the counter is directional and (b) that it is possible to calculate both the upper and lower limits of the detectable recoil energies. (See Chapter 3 for calculation of recoil cross section, etc.) Various geometrical modifications will at once occur to the reader, and a number have been tried successfully; the one cited illustrates the principle as well as any.

g. Counters with special shapes. As was pointed out in previous chapters, the cathode merely serves the purpose of distributing the field in the counter. It can be of many differing shapes and still operate. Cylindrical geometry is merely a matter of convenience. Counters employing spherical geometry, with the active anode consisting of a tiny central sphere, were devised several decades ago but, being somewhat more difficult to construct, did not encounter widespread use. Flat-wall and/or rectangular counters have also been employed. Examples are the rectangular types used by Curran and Reid [c17] and shown diagrammatically in Fig. 5–6. They

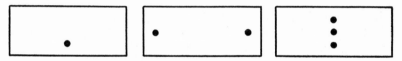

FIG. 5–6. Rectangular counters.

tried both single-wire and multiple-wire types. As we have pointed out before, the rectangular types have certain disadvantages. For the single-wire kind, the field in the corners is quite low, and ions may take an appreciable time in emerging if formed there. In the multiple-wire types, there are regions of low and even zero field between the wires. These effects show up in the non-flat plateaus noted. The same authors also reported using cylinders with off-center wires. The present author's experiments several years before led to the same result. Flat-box counters made by a commercial firm have come to the author's attention. Wire-and-plate counters, in which five wires were spaced between two parallel plates, the wires being uniformly separated and all in the median plane between the plates, were described by Hashimoto.[H19] These counters have applications in problems in which a geometry that fills a given volume is required, since it is sometimes not convenient to use an array of cylinders.

Toroidal counters have been described by at least two observers, Haigh [H20] and Ensell and Chatterjee.[E4] In this case the counter resembles a doughnut and is suitable for certain applications in which this geometrical arrangement is desirable, as, for example, in surrounding a beam or source with a detector. Multiple-wire types have also been used by Chambers [C18] who used the modification of a square array in which alternate wires were cathodes and anodes. Such an arrangement reduces collection time. An arrangement of six anodes in an annular counter was used by Raeth, Sevold and Pederson [R15] to replace a bundle of six counters connected in anti-coincidence. Such an arrangement of six anticoincidence counters around one conventional counter will serve as a shield and will automatically subtract effects due to ionizing particles passing through the entire device. Other special disposition of electrodes include a counter with two electrodes, one at each end, used by Frank [F6] to localize the discharge by timing the arrival of the pulse on each electrode. This is similar to the arrangement used by Wantuch [W11] in measuring the spread velocity of the Townsend avalanche around the wire.

h. Thin-window counters. Several designs of thin-window counters have recently appeared and deserve mention. One important development is already in commercial use in manufactured counters. For alpha counting, thin mica windows have been used for some time. The problem has been how to fasten the mica. Metal clamps around the edges are not very satisfactory for the mica is rather fragile and easily crushed. But if a metal or ceramic envelope is used on which a flange of several mm thickness is made, the thin piece of mica can be cut to size, placed on the flange, and cemented with powdered glass or other high-fusing cement. The powdered glass can be sprinkled over the edge so that it covers both the flange and the mica, the radius of the mica window being somewhat less than the outer radius of the flange. Then the entire arrangement is placed in a furnace and heated until the powdered cement melts and flows over the junction. Similarly, thin duralumin foils can be attached as end windows, according to Good,[G10] by first tinning the duralumin and then using Lenk aluminum solder. Double-wall counters for liquids have been described by Van Hecke [V2] who used concentric Pyrex cylinders, the inner of which was very thin and internally silvered. The liquid to be measured is then poured into the space between the walls. This design has a large solid angle efficiency. Similar concentric cylinder counters for liquids are made commercially.

Bell-shaped counters placed above automatically changing sample-trays have been used by a number of observers and are made commercially. The design devised by Peacock and associates [P6] may be cited as an example and is quite similar in appearance and operation to a type employed by Robinson which will be illustrated later in this chapter.

i. Gas flow counters for tritium and carbon 14. Counters through which gas flows continuously have been used by a number of workers. They are similar in principle to the one shown in Fig. 5–2C, and may or may not contain arrangements for introducing the samples into the sensitive volume. If either tritium or carbon 14 is to be detected, the substance can be made into a gas and introduced directly into the counter. The various gases $C^{14}O_2$, $C^{14}H_4$, and CT_4 (or CH_3T) can be used.

Both C^{14} and tritium are weak electron emitters; both are valuable and widely used in tracer research. The period of C^{14} is given as 5720 ± 47 years by Engelkemeier, Libby *et al.*[E5] and the electron has an energy of about 145 kv. The half-life of tritium is about 12.5 years and its electron has only 12 or 15 kv of energy.

One system developed by Libby [L15] consists of a counter that uses a gauze cylinder for a cathode, the whole being enclosed in a glass envelope of diameter considerably greater than the gauze. The radiocarbon to be measured is then applied to the inside surface of a cylinder which is slipped inside the envelope but outside the gauze. Electrons originating from the carbon will produce ionization in the gas, which is then detected. But if the chamber wall is made positive with respect to the central wire and gauze system, the electrons will be drawn toward the outer wall and will not initiate counts. The background of the arrangement is measured in this manner; the potentials are reversed and the counting rate produced by radiocarbon plus background is found. The entire arrangement [A2] can be surrounded (a) by a lead shield to cut out stray contamination radiation from the room and (b) by an anticoincidence set of guard counters to cut out cosmic rays

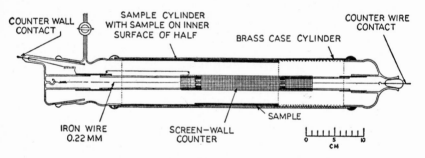

FIG. 5-7.   Screen wall counter assembly. (Ref. Libby [L15].)

which would penetrate the entire set. A diagram of this counter is shown in Fig. 5-7. Other systems for C^{14} in which the radiocarbon is introduced inside the counter have been used by Novis and Inghram;[N6] Wiedenbeck [W13] designed removable activable cathodes as well as thin windows arranged

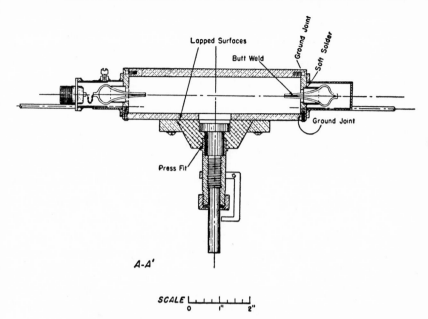

FIG. 5–8. Cross-section view through plane *A–A'* of assembled gas-flow proportional counter. Spindle and sample platform are shown in lowered position.

inside the outer envelope, thereby reducing the pressure-differential which this window must withstand.

In Fig. 5–8, a counter designed by Simpson [S13] is shown, in which again the sample is brought close to the sensitive part and within the envelope.

One counter previously mentioned and designed by Damon [D7] is shown in Fig. 5–9. This device uses a loop of wire for its anode, and, in addition, uses a 50-mil wire below the loop as its cathode. Loop anodes were also used by Simpson.[S13]

Purbrick, Cherry and Carpenter [P7] studied the problem of end-window counters for C^{14} and report the optimum length of the counter to be about 1 cm. Brown and his colleagues [B21] designed a counter for respiratory problems which was open to the air at 1 atm. Eidinoff [E6] designed counters especially for tritium, using hydrogen-argon-ethyl-alcohol mixtures. The hy-

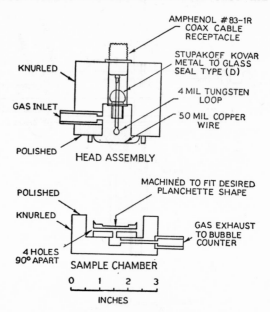

FIG. 5-9. Loop-line counter.

drogen mixed in with the counter gas can contain the tritium to be studied.

Further References on Thin-window Designs:
H. L. Baumgart and O. C. Yens, *J. Clin. Invest.* **4**, 1 (1927)
L. F. Curtiss, *J. Res. Nat. Bur. Stan.* **30**, 157 (1943)
Delasso et al., *Phys. Rev.* **58**, 586 (1940)

j. Gamma-ray counters. In the previous chapters we discussed the principles underlying the operation of gamma-ray counters. As has been pointed out, the usual procedure employed to increase gamma-ray detection efficiency is to make the cathode of a heavy material. We shall now cite some examples in which this has been carried out with success.

For example, a counter with a lead cathode ½ mm in thickness was constructed by Jurney and Maienschien.[J3] The cylinder was 8 cm long and 2.2 cm in diameter with a 5-mil central wire, and it was filled with 9 cm argon plus 1 cm ethyl alcohol.

The gamma-ray efficiency was found to be around 10^{-3} at 1 Mev and to increase slowly with gamma-ray energy in the interval from 0.2 to 3 Mev. Optimum wall thicknesses for Cu and Al for gamma rays in the range from 0.2 to 5 Mev are given by Marty [M19] as follows:

Gamma-Ray Energy (Mev)	Optimum Wall Thickness	
	Aluminum (cm)	Copper (cm)
0.2	0.016	0.0048
0.5	0.064	0.019
1	0.19	0.036
2	0.3	0.09
3.5	0.6	0.18
5	0.88	0.27

Various geometrical arrangements to increase efficiency have been reported. Thus Saltis [S25] reports an increase of efficiency by a factor of 2.5 by placing three concentric brass grids inside the counter and dividing the voltage applied to them by a voltage-dividing network so that the field is the same as it would be with no grids. Heavy gases have been used in soft X-ray counters, Borgren [B22] reporting that counters filled with krypton and xenon using ethyl ether or amyl acetate quenching vapors operate well, as do those filled with tetramethyl lead. The latter compound is known to operate well as a quenching agent, but as it is extremely poisonous it has not been commonly accepted for this purpose.

Increases in gamma ray efficiency may also be achieved by the use of multicell counters. Such devices have been described by Lind [L16] and also by Graf.[G11] The latter employed 24 counters in parallel inside a single envelope. Each counter had a cathode made of a screen on which bismuth was plated. A conventional argon-alcohol quenching mixture was found satisfactory, in this case 20 cm argon plus 3 cm alcohol. Gamma rays of 0.28 to 2.6 Mev were found to be detected with good efficiency.

Finally it may be said that, as in any instance in which the efficiency of a detecting system (a) is controlled by the walls and (b) is appreciably less than unity, internal radiators are indicated. Not many good designs have come to the author's attention, but by following the principles already discussed a number of possible arrangements at once suggest themselves.

Description of Survey Instruments:
A. G. McLellan, *New Zealand J. Sci. Tech.* **27,** 263 (1945)

STUDENT EXPERIMENTS

1. Making and Filling Counters

Apparatus: Blank counters can be obtained from several manufacturers, or they can be made to order by professional glass blowers. Counters of the metal-envelope type can be made by the student following the directions and diagrams in this book. A vacuum system is next required. Bulbs containing the gases to be used are sealed on to the system and evacuated and then filled with the gas. A small bulb to contain the organic quenching constituent is next attached and filled.

Procedure: Attach the counter to the vacuum system and evacuate thoroughly. Shut counter off from pumps and then admit about 1 cm of the organic vapor. The pressure can be read on a mercury manometer. In filling the bottle with the quenching constituent, care should be taken to remove all air from above the liquid. This can be done by first pouring in the liquid and then opening the connecting line to the pumps and pumping out the air; after the manometer indicates that the vacuum is fairly good, close the stopcock and wait for a while, then open and pump again. Repeat several times.

After the quenching agent is admitted, add the vehicular gas, such as argon. Fill to a total pressure of 10 to 15 cm Hg, again determined by the manometer. Next, wait for several hours or overnight to assure complete mixing by diffusion of the gas and vapor. The counter is next tested while attached and, if satisfactory, is sealed off.

Testing is accomplished by connecting the wire of the counter to the vertical deflection plate of a cathode ray oscilloscope. The sweep is set to a slow repetition rate, perhaps 50 to 100 per sec. A one-megohm resistor should be connected from this terminal to ground.

The high voltage is next connected. A source capable of being varied from a few hundred volts up to 2000 should be used. The positive terminal is grounded; the negative connected directly to the cylinder. A source of radioactive material should be placed near the counter (the luminous dial of a wristwatch will do), and the voltage should be slowly raised while the student watches the oscilloscope. The gain on the oscilloscope should be set to a high value. The oscilloscope sweep is set to a low repetition rate, 50 to 500 per sec. As the voltage is raised, a value will be reached at which point counts will appear on the screen of the oscilloscope. These should be vertical lines of small width and should greatly diminish in number as the radioactive source is removed. If all pulses are of substantially the same height, the unit is operating as a Geiger counter. If the pulses are not of the same height, the voltage may be slowly raised, and the gain on the oscilloscope should be turned down to keep the tops of the pulses in the field of view. By varying the two controls, the voltage and gain, the student will learn the meaning of the concept "gas amplification."

When the unit is operating in the Geiger region, the source can be brought close and a large number of counts should fill the screen. With this arrangement, it is easy to see at a glance how nearly of the same size the pulses are. The pulses should cease immediately, except for the sporadic background when the source is removed.

Precautions: Do not run the voltage to excessive values. If the counter breaks into a discharge or glow, cut off the voltage at once. The voltage is high enough to cause painful shock; care should be taken not to touch any part of the high-voltage system. A current-limiting resistor, of 100,000 to 1,000,000 ohms, should be inserted inside the high-voltage supply for personnel safety.

2. To Demonstrate Proportional and Geiger Counting

Apparatus: A thin-window counter, a source of alpha particles, a voltage supply and an oscilloscope. Connect the counter and the voltage supply and oscilloscope as before.

Procedure: Turn the gain on the oscilloscope to maximum value. Place the alpha source immediately adjacent to the thin window of the counter. Slowly bring up the voltage. Counts should appear on the screen. When they do, remove the source. The counts should stop entirely, except for a very rare occasional background-alpha. Alpha particles have very little penetration and a thin piece of tinfoil placed between the source and the window should suffice to stop them. Backing the source away a few cm through air should have the same effect. The air-equivalent thickness of the thin window can be estimated by measuring how far the alpha source can be backed away with the counts still barely visible and subtracting this distance from the range, in cm of air, given for the alpha particles in question in the tables of radioactive substances.

As the voltage is further raised, counts produced by beta rays, gamma rays and cosmic rays will begin to appear. The alpha pulses will be much larger. Then, as the voltage is slowly raised, and the gain turned down to permit the tops of the pulses to be seen on the oscilloscope screen, the transition from the proportional to the Geiger operation can be observed. As the Geiger threshold voltage is approached, the pulses produced by the alpha particles will not grow as fast as do those produced by the gammas, and the pulses will all eventually approach the same size.

Precautions: Be careful with the high voltage. Do not touch the alpha source with the fingers, and do not permit fingers or the alpha source to touch the thin window of the counter.

3A. Characteristic Plateau Curves of Geiger Counters

Apparatus: Counter, voltage supply, scaling circuit, mechanical register and source of gamma radiation. Cathode ray oscilloscope is not required but may be left attached.

Procedure: Connect, as before, input of scaler replacing, or left in parallel with, oscilloscope. Bring source of radiation near counter. Slowly raise voltage until scaler starts counting. Determine counting rate, using stopwatch or electric timer and allowing about 1000 counts per point. Read the voltage. Leave the source at a fixed place with respect to the counter. Then vary the voltage in steps of 25 or 50 volts, noting the counting rate at each voltage. Plot the result. This is the plateau curve of the counter. Estimate the statistical fluctuations to be expected. Pass the best straight line through the points, and find the slope of the plateau curve, expressed in percent increase in counting rate per 100 volts' change in voltage.

Precautions: Do not raise the voltage beyond that value at which the counting rate begins to depart markedly from the plateau.

3B. Starting Potential Curve of a Counter

Apparatus: Leave the counter attached to the vacuum system. Arrange all the other apparatus as above in 3A. Note the voltage at which the scaler begins to operate. This is the starting potential, by definition.

Procedure: Start by admitting only 2 cm argon (or other vehicular gas) to the counter, the organic constituent being always present in fixed amount. Note the starting potential. Then admit 2 more cm argon, wait for diffusion to take place and again determine starting potential. In this manner, by varying the gas and pressure thereof, starting potential curves are obtained.

4. Zenith Angle Distribution of Cosmic Rays

Apparatus: Two counters (or more), a coincidence circuit, voltage supply, scaler, register and clock.

Procedure: Connect the counters to the coincidence circuit, the scaler and the voltage supply. Arrange the counters with their axes horizontal, and parallel, one above the other. Mount on a board, so that the board can be tilted and the counter separation and parallelism remain unchanged. The voltage is raised until the counters are about in the middle of their plateaus. The arrangement should now be counting cosmic rays which pass through both counters. Determine the coincidence counting rate. Then tilt the board through various angles with respect to the zenith, using 15-degree intervals. Find the counting rate in each position. Plot and fit with a cosine squared curve. Note that the counting rate is not zero when the counters are in a horizontal plane because of showers. Subtract this shower correction from all values (it will not be very different in amount when the counters are vertically above each other). If there are three counters in the coincidence arrangement, place the central counter out of line, just sideways enough so that no single straight line can be drawn through all three. The shower correction can be found in this way also. Estimate the flux of cosmic ray particles at sea level, per sq cm, per sec and per unit solid angle. Find the total number of particles per unit time crossing a horizontal sq cm from any direction.

5A. Absorption Coefficients of Various Substances

Apparatus: Gamma ray source, single counter, scaler, register and clock. Connect as in Experiment 2 to find counting rate. Adjust voltage to middle of plateau.

Procedure: Arrange gamma ray source at fixed distance from counter. Obtain convenient thicknesses, for example, centimeter or millimeter slabs, of various substances, such as paraffin, aluminum, copper, or lead. Determine counting rate with source at a fixed point, with zero, one, two and more slabs in place between source and counter. Plot data on semi-log paper, as counts per minute vs. thickness; express as exponential absorption. Find slope of line and evaluate absorption coefficient. Plot absorption coefficient as function of amount of matter and as function of atomic number.

5B. Absorption of Cosmic Ray Particles

Apparatus: Two or more counters, coincidence circuit, scaler, register, voltage supply and clock. Arrange counters vertically, and place slabs of absorber, as in 5A above, between the counters. Find counting rates with various thicknesses. Plot and evaluate data as above. Note that (a) cosmic rays have much more penetration than gamma rays; millimeter slabs of lead will reduce gamma rays appreciably, but centimeter slabs reduce cosmic rays only slightly; (b) continue the experiment up to 20 cm of lead. Try it with lead in front of and in between counters. Note the difference. With the lead in front, there will be an increase in counting rate for the first one or two cm lead, the so-called "Rossi maximum."

6. Measurement of Lifetime of Radioactive Silver

Apparatus: Single counter, scaler and register, voltage supply, clock, and a source of neutrons. Secure a piece of silver. (A half-dollar or silver dollar will do.)

Procedure: Place the silver close to the neutron source. If practicable surround source and silver with paraffin, to any thickness (it need not be regular) up to 30 or 40 cm. Even a single pound block of paraffin *behind* the silver helps a lot. If no paraffin is available use cans of water. (Do not use Pyrex beakers or containers.) Leave silver near source for half an hour. Take silver out and place next to the counter. Counter should detect radioactivity at once.

Starting as soon as possible after removing the silver, determine the counting rate at various intervals. The intervals may be progressively lengthened as the activity decays so that roughly constant total numbers of counts are secured. The first interval can be 10 or 15 sec if the silver activity is high. Plot the counting rate as a function of time on semi-log paper. Fit the data with the best possible straight line or two straight lines. Silver has two periods easily measurable in this manner, of 22 sec and 2.3 min. Each corresponds to the slope of the straight line through the portion of the data applicable.

CHAPTER 6

ERRORS AND CORRECTIONS IN COUNTING

A. Introduction

In the operation of counters, there are several possible sources of inefficiency which, if not recognized and taken into account, may lead to error in the interpretation of the results. First there is the efficiency of the counter itself to be considered. This we shall define as the probability that, when the ionizing event to be studied actually occurs, the counter discharges. The counter may fail to discharge for several possible reasons. The event to be detected may not produce an ion in the sensitive volume. Then the sensitivity of various portions of the counter's volume may be different. Finally, the event may occur before the counter has recovered from the previous count. Quite exact numerical estimates of accuracy are possible for each of these contingencies.

The second type of inefficiency is that encountered if the particle to be counted does not reach the sensitive volume, i.e., is absorbed in the wall of the counter. Third we shall discuss the case of coincidence counting and the efficiencies to be expected in this case and, fourth, the efficiency of proportional counters.

1. Probability that Ionization Will Take Place in the Sensitive Volume. The probability that an ionizing event will occur in the sensitive volume of a counter has been discussed in a preliminary manner under the heading of "efficiency" in Chapter 4. Specifically, the discussion presupposes that if one electron is formed in the sensitive volume, a count will be recorded. This is an extremely severe condition, and the failure to realize it in practice will lead to the production of spurious counts and unreliable data. We repeat, *it actually takes only one electron* to produce a count. If a single electron is produced anywhere within the sensitive volume by any agency other than the event to be studied, a spurious count will be produced.

The counter is assumed to be operating in the Geiger region. If a particle is to be counted, then the particle must produce one ion-pair in the sensitive volume. This may occur due to an ionizing collision, or due to an electron knocked out of the wall of the counter. In most cases the ionization is produced in the gas of the counter. If a non-ionizing photon or neutron is to be detected, this entity must produce a photoelectron in the gas or from the walls, the latter being the more usual, or a Compton electron or nuclear disintegration or a nuclear recoil due to a collision with a nucleus in the wall or gas. If the ionization is produced in the wall, the electron or nuclear particle must get out of the wall and into the gas of the counter. Wall recoils are therefore limited by the range of the recoiling particle in the material of the wall, a phenomenon which was discussed in the section on neutron counters, Chapter 3. The probability of a disintegration occurring is also discussed there.

If a counter is to count photons, a large surface, photosensitive to the radiation to be studied, is desirable. In addition, a window to admit the radiation must be provided. Since the photoelectric efficiency of most surfaces is low, many photons will strike the cathode for one photoelectron ejected. Alkali metals are commonly used for photoelectric surfaces. On the other hand, when particles are to be counted, photon counts are usually unwanted and therefore alkali metals should be avoided and radiation should be kept from reaching the inside of the cathode.

In counting particles, the efficiency G may be computed from eq. (4–3), which we repeat for convenience,

$$G = 1 - e^{-slp} \qquad (6-1)$$

where s is the specific ionization of the particle in the gas of the counter, l is the path length and p the pressure of the gas in atmospheres in the counter. To employ this equation presupposes that we know l, the effective path length which the particle travels through the sensitive volume. In the case of coincidence counting, where the path of the particle is determined by other counters, the values of l are known with some accuracy. In single counters, placed so as to be in a beam of particles, the path length may again be known. For single counters exposed to random radiation we must consider the average path length. It is evident that for a cylinder the longest path is diagonally down the length, i.e., $l_{max} = (d^2 + h^2)^{1/2}$ where d is the diameter and h the length. The minimum path is zero. The exact solution for the general case involves a difficult integration, so that simplifying assumptions or special cases are necessary.

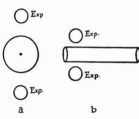

FIG. 6–1. Arrangements of exploring counters to study the distribution of sensitive volume.

Near the ends of the cylinder the field is distorted, and may in places drop below that value required to produce Geiger action. The efficiency of a counter as a function of its length or radius can be measured with the aid of exploring counters as shown in Fig. 6–1a and b, and the distribution of efficiency along its length for a typical counter is shown in Fig. 6–2.

It is evident that our condition, that a single electron will initiate an avalanche, may be vitiated if the electron is captured and does not reach the high field region where the avalanche occurs. Consider two possible causes of electron-removal, recombination and negative ion formation. Recombination may be neglected. The fields are comparatively high, the pressure low, and any electron will become so rapidly removed from the neighborhood of its positive ion that the number recombining will be negligible. As has been shown above, the recombination coefficient (eq. 2–3) and the numerical values cited indicate that recombination is highly improbable in counters.

The effect of negative ion formation may influence the operation of a counter. With gases such as oxygen, the halogens or water vapor present, the probability of electron capture and negative ion formation (see Table 4–2) is not negligible, as we have shown above. The negative ion will drift toward the center wire under the field, and near the wire may either lose the

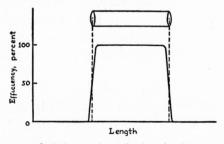

FIG. 6–2. Distribution of efficiency along the length of a typical counter. Data determined using arrangement in Fig. 6–1b.

electron or may acquire enough energy to produce ionization by collision, in other words may start an avalanche. In either case a count is observed. Hence the effect of negative ions is not to reduce the number of counts. What can happen, however, is that a count may be delayed because of the long time required for the negative ion to reach the wire, a time much longer than is needed by an electron. If delayed, then the count may occur (a) after the coincidence circuit has shut off, thereby decreasing the apparent efficiency for counting coincidences, or (b) after the counter has recovered from a count due to an avalanche initiated by some other electron produced in the same ionizing event but not captured, thus producing a spurious count. Either contingency is undesirable and hence gases permitting the formation of negative ions should be avoided.

2. Effects Due to Recovery Time and Statistical Fluctuations.

We assume that the events to be counted occur at random. They are thus assumed to be independent of each other. We may therefore discuss the statistics of random distributions. In this discussion we shall further assume that the intensity, or average number occurring per unit time, is constant. The extension to the special case of a source, the intensity of which varies with time, such as is encountered in measuring radioactive decay, is accomplished by applying the analysis which will follow to each interval of time selected during the variation.

For most practical work, the corrections are small enough to be given in terms of a single parameter called the resolving time t_r. This is the length of a time interval following the initiation of a first count in which a second count would be missed. The resolving time is approximately equal to what has previously been defined as the dead time, but it is slightly larger since, in practice, counts produced just as the counter starts to recover will be so small that they will not actuate the recording apparatus.

Let N_0 be the average observed number of counts per sec. We make the assumption, valid to a high degree for Geiger counters, that all counts arriving within a time interval t_r after an observed count are missed while all others are recorded. Then, on the average, the counter is insensitive for a total time $N_0 t_r$ out of each sec, and, on the average, in each sec the counter is sensitive for a time

$$t_s = 1 - N_0 t_r \qquad (6\text{--}2)$$

If N_t is the true number of counts per sec, the number missed per sec is $N_t N_0 t_r$. The true number is equal to the observed number plus the number missed. Therefore

$$N_t = N_0 + N_t N_0 t_r \qquad (6\text{--}2A)$$

We may solve eq. (6–2A) for the true number

$$N_t = N_0/(1 - N_0 t_r) \qquad (6\text{–}3)$$

If t_r has been determined, the corrected counting rate may be determined. Thus, for example, if the observed counting rate N_0 is 100 per sec, and the resolving time for this counter is 5×10^{-4} sec, the fraction missed $N_0 t_r$ is 5%, and the corrected counting rate is about 105 per sec.

Statistical errors. Consider now that counts occur at random. We mean by this that the counts are independent, that the initial ionizing events are independent, and that the occurrence of one event does not influence the next. In that case if we make a number of measurements each for a time t, because of statistical fluctuations we will observe a random variation in the number of counts observed. The observed numbers will be in accord with the Poisson distribution law which gives the probability P_n of observing n counts in a time t when the number of counts averaged over a large number of observations is $\bar{n}$ in a time t:

$$P_n = (\bar{n}^n/n!)e^{-\bar{n}t} \qquad (6\text{–}4)$$

The derivation of this law and a discussion of its application in various cases will be found in standard texts on statistics. The problem has been fully discussed by Bateman.[B5] It may be shown that, if the average number $\bar{n}$ becomes very large and if the mathematical device of allowing $\bar{n}$ to take on a continuous set of values is employed, this law approaches asymptotically the Gauss or "normal" error law. From this result it is possible to evaluate the root mean square deviation in the number of observed counts: that is, essentially the standard deviation in the quantity $(n - \bar{n})$. This deviation D is given by

$$D = \sqrt{\bar{n}} \qquad (6\text{–}5)$$

or the deviation is the square root of the average number of counts observed. The standard deviation in the counting rate, which is of more direct interest, is then

$$D_t = \frac{\sqrt{\bar{n}}}{t} \qquad (6\text{–}5\text{A})$$

The standard deviation either in the number of counts or in the counting rate, expressed as a percentage of the average value, is

$$D_f = \frac{100}{\sqrt{\bar{n}}} \qquad (6\text{–}5\text{B})$$

Thus the percentage deviation is inversely proportional to the square root of the number of counts. If a value as large as 10% can be tolerated, only 100 counts are required, but for 1% 10,000 are required, and for 0.1% one million counts must be used. Therefore, in general, for high precision data a large number of counts must be observed, and usually long observation times must be used. According to standard treatments of the theory of error, the probable error is 0.6745 of the standard deviation. The probable errors corresponding to the above quantities may be found by multiplying them respectively by this constant.

If a counting rate meter is used, the deviation will depend on the time constants of the tank circuit. The analysis has been carried out by Schiff and Evans [89] who showed that the standard deviation is given by $D = (2XRC)^{-\frac{1}{2}}$, where X is the rate of arrival of pulses, R and C being the resistance and capacity of the tank circuit respectively. Similar fluctuations will be observed in the case of integrating ionization chambers.

Usually counters have a background counting rate, and the counts observed must be distinguished from this background. The background will be due to cosmic radiation and natural radioactive contamination, plus such other stray radiation as may enter the counter. Near any accelerating device, such as a cyclotron, or Van de Graaff machine, there is usually a considerable amount of stray gamma-radiation causing background counts. Experimentally, the magnitude of the background is determined by observing the counting rate when no particles to be counted are entering the sensitive volume. This cannot always be done without changing the background, but the magnitude of the background should be determined, even if it be only approximately known. The procedures for applying the corrections we shall next consider.

Then if n_1 is the number of counts due to source-plus-background observed in a time t_1 and if n_β and t_β are the corresponding quantities due to the background, the counting rates are respectively

$$N_1 = n_1/t_1 \quad \text{and} \quad \beta = n_\beta/t_\beta \tag{6-6}$$

The counting rate due to the source alone is their difference

$$N = N_1 - \beta$$

The theory of error shows that the standard deviation in the difference in two quantities is equal to the square root of the sum of the squares of the standard deviations of the two quantities. Therefore, by the use of eqs. (6-5A) and (6-6) it may be seen that the standard deviation in the counting rate due to the source alone is

$$D_t = \left(\frac{N_1}{t_1} + \frac{\beta}{t_\beta}\right)^{1/2} \tag{6-7}$$

When the counting rate due to the source is large compared to the background, the term due to the background, the second on the right-hand side of eq. (6-7), is small and often may be neglected, but when the counting rate due to the source is comparable to the background, it becomes very important. In such a case, to prevent this term from becoming excessive a considerable portion of the available observation time must be devoted to the measurement of the background, that is, to increasing t_β. Under such conditions it is desirable to know the most efficient method of dividing the total observation time between the two measurements. It may be shown easily that subject to the condition that the total observation time $t_1 + t_\beta$ be a constant D_t, as given in eq. (6-7), is a minimum when

$$t_1/t_\beta = (N_1/\beta)^{1/2} \qquad (6-7A)$$

In other words, the observation times should be made proportional respectively to the square root of the corresponding counting rates.

The practical consequence of the existence of the background is to reduce the precision (or increase the standard deviation) as compared to what could have been obtained in the same total observation time if the background had been absent. For example, suppose the counting rate due to the source alone were equal to background (that is, $N = \beta$ or $N_1 = 2\beta$) and suppose measurements are made in accordance with eq. (6-7A). Then according to eq. (6-7), D_t will be 2.41 times as large as would have been the case if the background β had been zero and the same total time had been used in measuring the source. If the source is decreased still further, this ratio becomes larger very rapidly, and generally when the source is appreciably less than background, the error becomes so large that measurements generally become impractical.

The previous discussion has been based upon the assumption that the background counting rate β is constant. Loevinger and Berman [L17] have developed a procedure to be used when the background is not constant.

Further discussion of resolving time corrections and statistical considerations may be found later in this chapter in Sections 10, 11, and 12. The reader is also referred to the excellent general discussion of these topics contained in the paper of Rainwater and Wu.[R16]

3. Errors Due to the Particle Not Reaching the Sensitive Volume. Absorption of the entity being counted in the walls of the counter is the usual cause for the failure of particles to

TABLE 6–1. RELATIVE STOPPING POWER OF VARIOUS MATERIALS FOR
α-PARTICLES OF ABOUT 6 MV *

A. Thickness (in mg/cm^2) equivalent to 1 cm of air

Substance	Marsden and Richardson	Rosenblum
Al	1.62	1.51
Cu	2.26	2.09
Ag	3.86	2.71
Au	3.96	3.74
Mica	1.45 †	1.43 ‡

B. Atomic stopping power relative to air

Subst.	Geiger	Mano	Subst.	Geiger	Mano
½H$_2$	0.22	0.20	Cu	2.29	2.57
He	0.42	0.35	Kr	2.89	2.92
Li	0.53	0.50	Mo	2.75	3.20
½N$_2$	0.98	0.99	Ag	3.04	3.36
½O$_2$	1.10	1.07	Sn	3.19	3.59
Ne	1.24	1.23	Xe	3.94	3.76
Al	1.40	1.50	Au	4.02	4.50
A	1.92	1.94	Pb	4.25	4.43

C. Atomic stopping power for various velocities (semi-empirical, air = 1)

$v(10^9$ cm/sec)	1.0	1.5	2.0	2.5	3.0	4.0	5.0
$E\alpha$(mv)	2.07	4.66	8.3	12.95	18.6	33.2	51.9
E_H(mv)	0.52	1.17	2.09	3.26	4.70	8.36	13.06
½H$_2$	0.26	0.224	0.209	0.200	0.194	0.186	0.181
C	0.94	0.932	0.921	0.914	0.908	0.899	0.892
Al	1.45	1.51	1.53	1.54	1.55	1.57	1.59
Cu	(1.92)	2.41	2.62	2.73	2.80	2.89	2.95
Ag	(2.25)	3.08	3.43	3.64	3.76	3.93	4.04
Au	(2.42)	3.96	4.64	5.00	5.25	5.57	5.79

*Atomic stopping power for converting range in the given substance to
air equivalent. Data from Livingston and Bethe, *Rev. Mod. Phys.*, **9**, 272
(1937).   † Briggs.   ‡ Bennett

reach the sensitive volume. We must therefore consider the range of the particle in the material of which the counter wall (or window) is made. In counting alpha and beta particles, the range of the particle being counted can be obtained from the range curves, Fig. 4–4. The range in air can then be converted to the range in glass by dividing by a factor between 10^3 and 10^4, depending on the type of glass. When a metal window is used, the range can be computed by using the figures for atomic stopping power for the atoms of various elements, listed in Table 6–1. Knowing the thickness of the window, it is possible to estimate whether particles of the type to be counted will reach the interior or what fraction will be absorbed in the process.

When using glass envelope counters to detect neutrons, absorption of neutrons by boron in the glass must be considered. This occurs principally in Pyrex glass which has a high boron content. The fraction H of slow neutrons absorbed in a layer of glass of thickness t cm is given by

$$H = \sigma N \rho P t / \mu \qquad (6\text{--}8)$$

where σ is the capture cross section of boron for the neutrons in question (a function of neutron velocity; see Chapter 3), N is Avogadro's number, ρ is the density of the glass, P is the percentage of boron in the glass and μ is its average atomic weight.

Fast neutrons and cosmic ray mesons and gamma rays are not appreciably stopped in the material of which counters are made and may hence be considered as entering the sensitive volume regardless of the construction of the counter.

4. Efficiency of Coincidence Counting. When counters are counting in coincidence, there are two general phenomena which may alter the counting rate and which must be considered. The first is that a particle passing through the coincidence arrangement may not be detected because of an inefficiency in the system. The second is that some event othe' than that to be detected causes the counters to discharge simultaneously. For example, a large cosmic-ray shower may send particles simultaneously through many counters in various geometrical arrangements.

It is important to know the number of accidental coincidences to be expected when counters are connected for coincidence. If one counter is counting at an average rate of $\bar{n}_1$ per sec and if the coincidence resolving time is t, then the chance that a single count will occur during that time will be $\bar{n}_1 t$. If a second counter counts at a rate of $\bar{n}_2$ counts per sec, then the rate of occurrence of accidentals is

$$A_2 = 2\bar{n}_1\bar{n}_2 t \qquad (6\text{--}9)$$

The factor 2 occurs because of the overlapping of the lengths of time t. Similarly for the threefold coincidences, the accidental rate A_3 for triples will be

$$A_3 = 3\bar{n}_1\bar{n}_2\bar{n}_3 t^2 \qquad (6\text{--}10)$$

Usually the counters are similar in size and shape and counting rate, and hence we may write for m-fold accidentals

$$A_m = m\bar{n}^m t^{m-1} \qquad (6\text{--}11)$$

The computations for any special case, such as when one counter is much larger or smaller or counts at a different average rate from the others, is self-evident.

It is evident that the probability of accidental counts is extremely small when (a) the multiplicity m of counters is large, (b) the resolving time is short, and (c) the counters are each counting at a slow rate. Thus for five- or sixfold coincidences, even at high rates of counting such as are found when cosmic-ray counters are operated in the stratosphere, accidentals are almost entirely negligible, providing the resolving time t is small.

The accidental rate for coincidences may be verified experimentally by placing the counters out-of-line, in more or less of a horizontal plane, and far away from each other. In such an arrangement, if no straight line can be drawn through all of them, we will measure only accidentals plus such events as extensive showers which produce ionizing events over a wide area. Extensive showers are quite rare at sea level, occurring perhaps once per hour or even less, depending on the lateral extent. The further the counters are separated, the better is the test.

If only two counters are being tested, and these two are placed in a horizontal plane a considerable distance apart, there will still be a possibility that a single particle could cause both to discharge, causing a "true" coincidence. However, it is much more probable that a single particle will pass through one and will also, as it passes through nearby matter, produce secondaries which will set off the other counter. Thus the arrangement is sensitive to "showers of two" particles. Similarly, if three counters are arranged out-of-line, the arrangement is sensitive to "showers of three," or indeed to the less likely chance that one particle will pass through two and its secondary through the third. The number of "showers of two" greatly exceeds the number of "showers of three" and in general it may be said that the greater the multiplicity the less probable is the event. No general distribution formula can be given because the probability of shower formation is controlled by the distribution of matter in the vicinity of the counters. The number of "showers of two" is much greater in the basement of a building than it is on the roof, due to shower production in the walls and floors of the building.

In any given experiment, the shower correction should be determined. This number of showers will always provide a background which must be added to the random accidentals. Thus the accidental rate for triples is determined by the rate of real doubles occurring simultaneously with random singles, and is larger than eq. (6–10) implies. The shower corrections can be made smaller by two procedures: (a) the use of higher multiplicity coincidences, and (b) the use of suitably disposed anti-coincidence counters as "guard counters" (see Chapter 7). Anti-coincidence counters can be so arranged that showers reaching the main train of counters will have to pass through them and will therefore not be counted. If anti-coincidences are used, the total time that the circuit is insensitive due to the discharge of the anti-coincidence counters must be taken into account if the time-rate of the events being studied is to be determined.

To illustrate this technique, in measuring counter efficiencies it is customary to arrange the counters in a vertical line (see Figs. 6–1 and 6–2). The counting rate of the coincidences of the extreme counters with and without the central counter, whose efficiency is being studied, is then determined. As will be seen from eq. (6–12) below, the efficiency of the counter is the ratio of the counting rates with and without this counter in the circuit. This follows, since the number of counts recorded as double coincidences by the outside pair is $n_2 = nE_2$, where n is the true number of events and E_2 is the efficiency of the two counters in coincidence. The rate of counting triples will then be $n_3 = nE_2E_3$, where E_3 is the efficiency of the third counter. All particles counted by the outside counters must, by the geometry, pass through the middle one. Now this experiment is subject to a shower correction as a "shower of two" can give a false double coincidence. Hence if we use three counters to determine the path, instead of two, the shower correction will be much reduced. Thus we shall measure the ratio of triples to quadruples instead of the ratio of doubles to triples, and thus minimize effects due to "showers of two."

Ordinarily coincidence counting can be done only with penetrating ionizing radiation such as cosmic-ray mesons. Alpha and beta particles will not go through most counter-walls and, when electrons or protons are to be counted by coincidence technique, a very thin window must be provided between the counters. The advantage of using coincidence technique is that it helps to eliminate the background due to stray gamma radiation which is so abundantly present near most accelerating devices.

Due to the low efficiency of detection, gamma rays will practically never produce coincidences. It is evident that if the efficiency of a counter is E_1, of another E_2 and so on, then the efficiency of a combination will be

$$E_m = E_1 E_2 E_3 \qquad (6\text{--}12)$$

and, if the efficiencies are equal,

$$E_m = E^m$$

Since the efficiency of a gamma ray counter may be 10^{-4}, the occurrence even of double coincidences is rare. A similar argument holds for fast neutrons, since the recoil efficiency is so small (see Chapter 3).

Slow neutrons cannot be used in coincidence work since the neutron disappears in the act of producing the disintegration which is detected.

Coincidences between proportional counters and Geiger counters can be measured. The circuits are described in Chapter 7, and the efficiency of any arrangement, once the efficiency of the proportional counter is shown, is given by eq. (6–12).

5. Errors in Using Proportional Counters. In general, proportional counters will give pulses depending on the amount of energy liberated in ionization in the primary ionizing event, and also depending on the gas amplification A, as in eq. (3–1). The possible errors in interpreting the results may arise from (a) the range of the particle not lying entirely in the sensitive volume, or being interrupted by the particle striking the wall of the counter, (b) the background of large pulses due to alpha particles and giant showers, and (c) any effects such as electron capture which cause an apparent decrease in A.

The resolving time of proportional counters is also of the order of 10^{-4} sec. The travel time of the positive ions and the appropriate calculations of the effects of this time have already been given. There is, however, one feature which should be mentioned. That is that the avalanche in a proportional discharge is not as fully developed as that in a Geiger discharge. The avalanche may not spread down the entire length of the wire. Hence there may be portions of the wire which will be sensitive and may support another avalanche before the first is terminated. Consequently it is possible, if

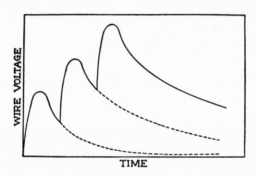

Fig. 6–3. Multiple counts in a proportional counter occurring within the recovery time of the counter. Normal pulse recovery indicated by dotted line.

the RC time of the central wire of the counter is short (say 10^{-5} to 10^{-6} sec), to have pulses superposed on one another and pulses occurring with spacings less than the resolving time needed to complete a pulse. Since proportional counters are usually operated at comparatively slow counting rates, this problem does not often arise, but at fast rates the potential of the wire may show various spurts in quick succession superposed on one another. The true "dead time" of a proportional counter is therefore less than that of a Geiger counter. The fact that the changing potential of the wire will cause A to vary for counts which overlap, should be borne in mind if pulse size distributions obtained at fast counting rates are to be interpreted with precision. The graph of the voltage variation of the wire is shown in Fig. 6–3. Because of the functioning of the space charge sheath, this phenomenon takes place only with proportional counters and not in the Geiger region.

The amount of ionization produced in the primary ionizing event must be formed in the sensitive volume to be effective. A particle which passes entirely through the counter or which collides with one of the walls will produce a correspondingly smaller pulse. The heaviest amount of ionization is produced near the end of the range. Consequently it is important to know not only the geometrical length of the range of the particle in the gas of the counter, but what portion (i.e., whether beginning, middle or end) of the range lies within the sensitive volume. Thus, for example, an alpha particle gives up 1.9 Mev in ionization in the last centimeter of its range, but only 0.7 Mev in 1 cm, 5 to 6 cm from the end of the range. If the counter is filled to 0.1 atm pressure with a gas whose stopping power is about the equivalent of that of air, and has a 10 cm average path through the sensitive volume, then the amount of energy in ionization produced in 1 cm of range in air (at STP) will appear in the counter. The expected pulse size can be computed now if we know what portion of the range is involved. Thus the expected pulse size depends on the nature and pressure of the gas and on the geometry of the path through the counter, and each case should be computed separately.

Proportional counters will exhibit a background of large pulses, which must be considered in interpreting the results. There are two chief agencies producing such large pulses. The first is the natural radioactive contamination of all substances. This contamination manifests itself by the emission of alpha particles into the sensitive volume. Most of these originate in the walls of the counter, as reasonably pure gas has a comparatively low radioactive content. A well cleaned surface, which has not had undue exposure to contamination, should show of the order of 10^{-4} alpha particle per sq cm per minute. Normal variations are large and may differ from the figure stated by a factor of ten in either direction. If the material of which the counter is made has been left around in some of the older laboratories in which radium or its products have at one time been used, the contamination is likely to be much greater. Similarly, some elements acquire long period radioactivities by prolonged exposure to neutrons and, for example, copper which has been stored in a room adjoining a cyclotron may have undesirable activity. The insides of ionization chambers are often painted with very pure carbon black to reduce the alpha background, and this can be done in counters although it is not often worth while.

The other cause of large pulses is cosmic radiation. Occasionally the core of a giant shower will strike a measuring device, and literally many thousands of electrons will traverse the sensitive volume simultaneously. Large amounts of ionization are thus liberated and a big pulse appears on the wire. This effect is not very large at sea level, usually only a few per day, but increases rapidly with elevation. In general no shielding is effective in reducing these showers. The number of such giant showers is, however, constant at any one place and can hence be determined and allowed for. Similarly, the alpha background is constant and need but be determined once for each instrument.

The expected value of A is not realized in every case. Suppose that an ionizing event takes place at some distance from the wire, and that electron-capture to form negative ions takes place. If some of the electrons are withdrawn and do not reach the region in which the avalanche is started, the total avalanche size will be smaller. Any negative ions formed will reach the wire or will shed their electrons near the wire long after the first avalanche due to electrons is over, and consequently will not contribute to the size of the initial pulse. Since the halogens are sufficiently electronegative to exhibit appreciable electron capture, we might expect that this phenomenon would manifest itself in BF_3 neutron counters. Indeed, Brubaker and Pollard [B6] found that the size of a pulse produced by a primary ionizing event of constant size depended on how far out from the wire the event occurred. They attribute the effect to electron capture. That this is probably not the only factor involved is seen from the fact that they find appreciable dependence on the radius also for some gases in which electron capture may be supposed negligible such as argon and hydrogen.

Another cause of an apparently lower A is the phenomenon of partial paralysis exhibited by proportional counters when operating with a very high beta or gamma ray background. Since in these circumstances numerous small avalanches will continuously be taking place, numerous positive ion groups will be migrating out toward the cylinder, and the result will be a lowering of the field in the counter. The value of A will therefore be reduced. The Montgomerys [M7] have observed a reduction in the number of large counts which are recorded under these conditions.

It may be well to repeat here that, in BF_3 counters when the disintegration produced by slow neutrons takes place, two particles are formed. One is an alpha, the other a recoiling lithium nucleus. They travel in opposite directions. Thus if one hits the wall, the other goes out into the gas. The pulse produced will of course be larger if both particles end their range in the gas, but even if only one component is effective, the amount of ionization produced is still considerably larger than that produced by beta particles.

6. Procedures To Insure Short Recovery Times. The analysis which we have given above presupposes that only one recovery time need be considered. If the mechanical recorder has a much longer recovery time than the counter, it will miss counts to which the counter responds. It is therefore important that the recovery time of the counter be the longest time constant in the entire arrangement.

In the case of non-selfquenching counters, the recovery time is determined by the RC of the quenching resistance if the counter is resistance quenched, or by that of the circuit if electronic quenching is used. As has been indicated elsewhere, RC quenching times are usually of the order of 10^{-2} to 10^{-3} sec. An electronic quenching circuit can operate satisfactorily in 10^{-4} sec but not much less, the limitation being attributable to the discharge mechanism. If the electronic quenching circuit is made with too short a time constant, the counter will not be completely quenched and the entire arrangement may indeed break into oscillation. We specifically except from this discussion the potential reversing circuits which are treated separately.

Selfquenching counters recover in the time determined by the ion-sheath mobility. This again is of the order of 10^{-3} to 10^{-4} sec. The amplifiers connected to any counter can easily be given time constants of 10^{-5} sec or so by choosing appropriate coupling RC values. The recovery times of amplifiers so designed may be neglected as they are smaller than that of the counter and do not affect the result.

Mechanical recorders are usually the slowest element in a counter circuit. Some will follow a 60 cycle AC wave, and have time constants of the order of 10^{-2} sec, but few are faster. Therefore scaling circuits (see Chapter 7) are recommended, and must be used for fast counting. A scaling circuit not only slows down the average counting rate to an interval which the recorder can follow but also improves the statistics in that the output pulses are more regularly spaced and hence the probability of close doubles is decreased. Since the recovery time of a scaling circuit can also be made short compared to that of the counter, this time also may be neglected. In ionization chambers, where the ion-collecting time is sometimes long, the fundamental limitation may be in the chamber and the recovery time of even a slow recorder may be neglected.

To summarize, for minimum errors in fast counting: (1) the recovery time of the amplifier must be short and (2) a scaling circuit should precede the mechanical recorder. The recovery time of the entire arrangement will then be determined by that of the counter, and the appropriate corrections may be made.

7. Interpretation of Counting Rate Data *a. Statistical tests.* The discussion of statistics which we have given above may be made the basis for ascertaining whether a counter is behaving properly. Suppose, for example, a counter is suspected of having spurious counts. The following simple procedure will throw light on its operation.

First the counter is adjusted to detect the radiation desired. Then the number of counts occurring in each minute is recorded. This observation is continued for about half an hour, thus giving some thirty numbers. If the counting rate is high, a time interval shorter than a minute may be used. The results are then tabulated. The average counting rate is determined. The standard deviation is next computed from the data. The standard deviation should, by eq. (6–5), be the square root of the number of counts. If the standard deviation differs appreciably from this figure, the presumption is strong that the events being counted are not at random. For example, spurious counts such as would be produced by negative ions would follow the true count at short intervals. The resulting standard deviation calculated from the data would then be less than that obtained by taking the square root of the number of counts.

b. Significance of counting rate curves. Any given recording circuit, unless it is provided with a special arrangement to eliminate large pulses, will count all pulses greater than a certain minimum size. This minimum size is determined by the characteristics of the circuit (see Chapter 7) or by the "bias" or "cutoff" of the amplifier used. The curve of counting rate as a function of voltage is therefore an integral curve and continually increases. Should the counting rate decrease beyond a certain voltage, it is an indication that some sort of paralysis or saturation is taking place in the counter or in the attached electronic circuit. The data obtained on such a curve above the point where it starts to decrease should be interpreted with caution. A counter should not be operated in the region where the characteristic has a negative slope, in ordinary circumstances, as this can be due to excessive overvoltage, which may damage the counter.

The characteristic curve of counting rate as a function of voltage determines the total number of counts, N, greater than a certain size (E_{min}), as indicated by

$$N \left| \begin{array}{c} E_{max} \\ E_{min} \end{array} \right. = \int_{E_{min}}^{E_{max}} N(E)dE \qquad (6\text{--}13)$$

where the upper limit E_{max} is usually practically infinite. The pulse size distribution is then given by

$$N(E)dE \qquad (6\text{--}14)$$

which may be defined as the number of counts of size (or energy) lying between E and $E + dE$. This pulse size distribution may therefore be determined by differentiation, with respect to energy, of the integral counting rate curve. Thus, for example, two groups of particles of different sizes (say a few contamination alpha particles and a lot of electrons) would give rise to a curve of counting rate as a function of voltage which would have two "steps" in it. Another illustration is the normal "plateau" curve of a Geiger counter which, if flat, means that all the pulses are of the same size at any one voltage and that no new or spurious counts occur as the voltage is raised. Either the differentiation or the integration may be done graphically. The accuracy usually decreases in such graphical operations. For a discussion of procedures, the reader is referred to the standard texts on statistics, such as *Treatment of Experimental Data*, by Worthing and Geffner, Wiley, 1943.

B. Recent Developments

8. Geometrical Corrections. The increased use of counters for purposes of precision measurements in recent years has led to a number of articles in the literature in which the errors produced both by geometry and by fast counting are discussed for various cases. Geometrical calculations for single end-window counters have been carried out by Berne [B23] who has computed the integrals and an entire set of curves applicable to this case. The geometrical factors for coincidence counting have been considered by Newell,[N7] who gives the families of curves for both radiation incident isotropically and incident according to the usual cosine squared distribution exhibited by cosmic rays at sea level.

Cockcroft and Curran [C19] have considered the procedures to eliminate end effects and have pointed out that a guard ring or sleeve covering the wire, extending in from each end a distance equal to the radius, will achieve this purpose. The potential of the sleeve is adjusted to equal that which is normally present at that radius in the counter. This limits the sensitive volume of the counter to that volume defined by the exposed wire, and the sleeve insures that the field in this region shall be uniform. Error calculations for ionization chambers without guard rings have been published by Tellez-Plasencia.[T4]

9. Fast Counting Procedures. Three procedures have been developed that speed up the operation of counters. These are: (1) the use of beads on the wire; (2) the operation of the counter in the proportional region; and (3) the use of potential reversing circuits. The last of these, being an electronic technique, is discussed elsewhere.

In earlier chapters we saw that one of the factors operative in a counter in which time lags had been reduced to a minimum was the travel time of the sheath along the central wire. Hence it is clear that, if a bead on the wire terminates the spread of the avalanche, the spread time can be limited to the time required to cover the free length. The use of several beads will permit the spread time to be much shortened. Counters of this type have been built by Nonaka and Shimazu.[N8]

Other features of beaded wire counters should again be mentioned. In a selfquenching counter, since each section operates independently, if two sections become activated, the pulse size will be double. Hence coincidence measurements can be made by observing pulses which are two or three or n times as large as the single-section pulse.

The operation of counters in the proportional region has also been used to speed up counting. As we have pointed out above, the dead time and resolving time in this region are much shorter than that in the Geiger region. Making use of this, Muelhause and Friedman[M20] have operated counters successfully at far faster rates than would be possible by the same counters in the Geiger region. Higher gain in the vacuum-tube circuits is a necessary corollary. Factors with a gain of up to 100 in the speed of operation of counters seem possible.

10. Correction for Dead and Recovery Time Losses.* There are two principal methods for securing data for making corrections for these losses. One of these is to use the single sweep oscilloscope or "synchroscope" according to the method of Stever to measure the dead and recovery times as described in Section B2 of Chapter 4. The second method is the multiple-source method,[D8] in which the counting rates due to several sources are measured separately, and then counting rates due to combinations of these are measured. Since the fractional counting loss increases as the counting rate increases, the measured counting rate of any combination is less than the sum of the counting rates of the separate sources. From determining these differences it is possible to make corrections in a manner to be described. Of course, it is necessary to repro-

* Sections 10, 11, and 12 have been written by Y. Beers.

duce the positions of the sources with high precision. Also it is desirable if the sources employ gamma rays to use "dummy" sources of the same scattering characteristics to replace any actual sources not in use to prevent any real difference in the counting rates as a result of scattering. If only two sources are employed, the method becomes considerably simplified since there is no need to provide special means for reproducing the positions of the sources with use of the following procedure: (1) measure the counting rate of the first source; (2) with the first source unmoved place the second source in position and measure the combined counting rate; and (3) without moving the second source, remove the first source and measure the counting rate due to the second source.

The data obtained by the Stever method are more significant in terms of the fundamental theory of Geiger counter mechanism, but such information is not as useful for practical corrections as that obtained by the multiple source method. In practice the number of counts lost depends upon the minimum pulse size which is required to actuate the scaling circuit. If a second particle enters a counter a short time after the close of the dead time but before the counter has fully recovered, it produces a pulse of sub-normal size. If the scaling circuit can operate from pulses considerably smaller than the normal ones, most of these sub-normal pulses are counted; whereas if the scaling circuit requires minimum pulses almost as large as the normal ones, hardly any are counted. In addition there may be errors in the scaling circuit which need correction. On the one hand, counts may be lost due to the finite resolving time of the scaling circuit. On the other hand, some scaling circuits do not operate correctly for a range of pulse heights near their threshold. In such cases the first scale-of-two fails to "flip over," but it may supply an amplified signal to the second scale-of-two causing it to operate, and thus the equivalent of spurious counts may be recorded. Approximate correction for these effects is obtained automatically by the multiple source method. Generally, however, all of these effects are relatively small, and unless the counting rate is very large, reasonable accuracy also may be obtained by using data obtained by the Stever method.

In eq. (6–3) there was given a relation between the true counting rate N_t and the observed counting rate N_0. In the derivations [S26, R17] it was assumed that a particle entering the counter while it is responding to a previous particle neither is counted nor does it disturb the mechanism in any way. Hence the possibility of detecting a third particle a brief instant after the dead period is not altered. In other words the existence of a "dead" time is assumed, but the existence of a "recovery" time is neglected. This kind of device has sometimes been called a Type II Recorder. Such an assumption for a Geiger counter is largely justified by the fact that the major portion of the total time required for its mechanism to operate is occupied by the discharge, and during this time the few ions produced by a second particle have very little influence on the mechanism.

On the other hand, this assumption is not always valid. If the second particle enters a brief instant after the end of the dead time but before the avalanche of ions has been collected and the voltage across the counter has fully recovered, this second particle gives rise to a second discharge together with a pulse which may or may not be recorded, depending upon the pulse size required by the scaling circuit. In either case a third particle entering shortly after, that is, during this second discharge, is not counted. Thus, in this case, the presence of the second particle eliminates the possibility of detecting the third one. Under these conditions the Geiger counter acts very nearly like another idealized type of instrument, the so-called Type I Recorder, which requires for the observation of a given particle that no particles enter the counter within a time t_r previous. In other words, a Type I Recorder, in a sense, counts the number of intervals greater than t_r rather than the number of particles.

A theoretical formula relating the true counting rate N_t to the observed counting rate N_0 and t_r may be derived as follows: [V3,S27]

The probability of the arrival of a particle within the interval t, $t + dt$ is $N_t\,dt$. It is assumed that dt is small compared to $1/N_t$. Therefore the probability that no particle will arrive in this interval is $1 - N_t\,dt$. Let $f(t)$ be the probability that no particle will arrive before the elapse of a time t. Then

$$f(t + dt) = f(t)(1 - N_t\,dt)$$

$$df(t) = f(t + dt) - f(t) = -f(t)N_t\,dt$$

This last equation may be integrated by elementary methods to yield the result:

$$f(t) = Ce^{-N_t t} \tag{6-15}$$

Since there is no probability of getting a particle in the time $t = 0$, or, in other words, since the probability of getting no counts in the time $t = 0$ is unity, $f(0) = 1$, and the constant of integration in eq. (6–15) $C = 1$. As such an instrument records only intervals greater than t_r, the number of observed counts per unit time is equal to the true number of particles multiplied by the probability of obtaining an interval greater than t_r, which is found by substituting $t = t_r$ in eq. (6–15). Therefore the result is that

$$N_0 = N_t e^{-N_t t_r} \tag{6-16}$$

At low and moderate counting rates eqs. (6–3) and (6–16) give essentially the same numerical result. Eq. (6–3) may be expressed in series form by solving for N_t in terms of N_0 and by replacing the quantity $1 + N_0 t_r$ in the denominator by the same quantity in the numerator raised to the minus first power and expanding by the binomial theorem; eq. (6–16) may be expressed in series form by making use of the well-known series expansion of the exponential factor. The first two terms are identical respectively in the two series, while the third terms differ by the amount $\frac{1}{2}N_0{}^3t_r{}^2$ or by the fractional amount $\frac{1}{2}N_0{}^2t_r{}^2$. Since both series have terms which alternate in sign, this quantity may be taken as the upper limit of the discrepancy between the two formulas.

It will be noted that, when eq. (6–3) is solved for N_0, N_0 approaches asymptotically a maximum value $\dfrac{1}{t_r}$ as N_t increases, while from eq. (6–16) N_0 is seen to reach a true maximum value $\dfrac{1}{et_r}$ and then decreases, a result differing from the first by a factor "e." These facts suggest a method for determining t_r by measuring the maximum observable counting rate. Aside from uncertainty in the theory, such a method is not very reliable, since at the very large counting rates involved the losses in the circuit and register and the effects of circuit non-linearities may be appreciable. Also in some cases the counter may be damaged by the use of very high counting rates.

As has been pointed out, eq. (6–3) is more valid when applied to Geiger counters than eq. (6–16), but neither is exact. More exact theories may be developed but generally they are too cumbersome for practical work.[L18, G12, K18, K19] Such theories give results which approach eq. (6–3) asymptotically. One practical procedure is to avoid uncertainties in the simple theory by limiting the counting to rates low enough to cause the discrepancy in the formulas to be negligible. On the other hand, if very large counting rates must be used, it is convenient to adopt an empirical point of view: to suppose that the true counting rate is expressible in terms of the observed counting rate by means of a power series [K20] with unknown coefficients and then evaluate the coefficients by means of data obtained from the multiple source method and by applying in generalized form the reasoning which will be described later in Section 11.

For the sake of definiteness the previous discussion has assumed the use of a Geiger counter. However, almost the entire discussion applies to other instruments such as scintillation counters, proportional counters and single-particle ionization chambers if these are used with particles which give pulses of uniform height. In such a case these instruments should conform with the Type II Recorder formula, eq. (6–3). On the other hand, if a continuous distribution of pulse heights is present, the near coincidence of two particles gives rise to a pulse proportional to the sum of their ionizations. If the ionizations are both large, the result is one lost count. However, if the device is used with a scaling circuit requiring a minimum pulse height for operation, the coincidence of two particles having separate ionizations slightly less than the threshold gives a total ionization great enough to cause the recording of one count which would not have been recorded if the particles had been separated. If the multiple-source method is used to measure t_r (which, with these instruments, should be called logically the "resolving" time), the value obtained depends upon the distribution of pulse heights involved, and it is possible in some cases that a negative value may be obtained. Nevertheless if the distribution is held constant and if the counting rates are not excessive, it should be possible to obtain reliable corrections by obtaining a value of t_r by the multiple-source method and employing this in eq. (6–3).

Frequently these various proportional instruments are employed to measure the distribution in pulse heights arising from a group of particles. The previously mentioned effect of the coincidence of two particles to give a pulse equivalent to the sum of their ionizations may be seen to result in a distortion of the observed distribution giving too large a number of big pulses. If the objective of the measurement is to determine the distribution, a much more convenient correction procedure is to observe the distribution at several different average counting rates and then to extrapolate the observed distributions to the one which would be obtained at small average counting rates.

11. Theory of the Two-Source Method. In the previous section the multiple-source method of measuring dead or resolving times was described briefly, and its advantages were discussed. Also it was pointed out that this method becomes especially convenient when only two sources are used. In this section a detailed theory of the two-source method will be given.

In practice all sources are measured in the presence of background, and therefore the counting rate due to the source alone requires subtraction of the background counting rate from the counting rate measured with the source present. If it is assumed that, with a reasonable accuracy, the Type II Recorder formula, eq. (6–3), is valid, the counting rate due to the first source corrected for both background and for dead time losses is

$$N_1' = \frac{N_1}{1 - N_1 t_r} - \frac{\beta}{1 - \beta t_r}$$

$$= \frac{N_1 - \beta}{(1 - N_1 t_r)(1 - \beta t_r)} \tag{6–17}$$

where N_1 is the observed counting rate due to the first source plus background, and β is the observed counting rate due to background.

Similar expressions may be written for the corrected counting rate of the second source, denoted by the subscript 2, and for the combined source, denoted by the subscript 12. From the conditions of the experiment, the corrected counting rate due to the combined source must be equal to the sum of the corrected counting rates of the two separate sources, or

$$N_{12}' = N_1' + N_2' \tag{6–18}$$

If the quantities in eq. (6–18) are expressed in terms of measured counting rates by means of eq. (6–17), the resulting equation may be solved for t_r. The exact solution, however, is not convenient for numerical calculation mainly because of a radical which is hard to evaluate. A more convenient form is obtained by expanding this quantity by the binomial theorem and obtaining a power series. The first two terms are:

$$t_r = \frac{\Delta}{2(N_1 - \beta)(N_2 - \beta)} + \frac{1}{8(N_{12} + \beta)} \left[\frac{\Delta(N_{12} - \beta)}{(N_1 - \beta)(N_2 - \beta)} \right]^2$$

(6–19)

where $\Delta = N_1 + N_2 - N_{12} - \beta$.

In eq. (6–19) the quantity $\dfrac{\beta^2 \Delta}{(N_1 - \beta)(N_2 - \beta)}$ has been neglected in comparison to the quantity $N_{12} - \beta$. In practice, the second term on the right side of eq. (6–19) is small compared to the first term, and usually it may be neglected.

The quantity Δ is generally only a few percent of N_{12}. It is apparent from symmetry considerations that, for a given combined counting rate N_{12}, Δ is the largest when the two separate counting rates N_1 and N_2 are made equal. Furthermore these counting rates must be determined with a small statistical error if Δ is to be significant. Therefore, the total observation time must be comparatively long, and it is desirable to apportion the total observation time among the various measurements in the most efficient manner.

Since the second term in eq. (6–19) is small, it may be neglected for the purpose of calculating error. Moreover, since Δ is only a few percent of N_{12} and also of N_1 and N_2, it may be supposed that the entire error in t_r is essentially that resulting from the error in Δ. By application of the material of Section 2 it may be shown that the standard deviation in Δ is

$$\delta\Delta = \sqrt{\frac{N_{12}}{t_{12}} + \frac{N_2}{t_2} + \frac{N_1}{t_1} + \frac{\beta}{t_\beta}}$$

(6–20)

where t_{12}, t_2, t_1, and t_β are respectively the times involved in the measurement of N_{12}, N_2, N_1, and β. It may be shown that this quantity is a minimum, provided that the total time is a constant, if these times are made proportional to the square root of their respective counting rates.

The standard deviation in t_r is approximately

$$\delta t_r = \frac{\sqrt{\dfrac{N_{12}}{t_{12}} + \dfrac{N_2}{t_2} + \dfrac{N_1}{t_1} + \dfrac{\beta}{t_\beta}}}{2(N_1 - \beta)(N_2 - \beta)} \tag{6-21}$$

If these data are used to correct some other measured counting rate N_3, the corrected counting rate may be calculated by inserting the measured value of t_r into eq. (6–17) and by replacing N_1 and N_1' by N_3 and N_3' respectively. The contribution to the error in the corrected counting rate N_3' resulting from the error in t_r may be shown by simple differentiation to be

$$\delta N_3' = N_3'\left(\frac{N_3}{1 - N_3 t_r} + \frac{\beta}{1 - \beta t_r}\right)\delta t_r \tag{6-22}$$

where δt_r is evaluated from eq. (6–21).

12. Counting Losses in the Electrical Circuit and Register. Counts may be lost because of the finite response time required by the various electrical circuits and by the register. With the large scaling ratios now generally used these losses are generally very small and in many cases are identically zero. When they are small but not zero, correction is, to a large extent, made automatically if the multiple-source method is used. It is sometimes desirable and, when the Stever method is used, necessary to evaluate these losses separately.

The greatest source of these losses is the register, which generally employs an armature actuated by a solenoid. This armature is connected to a pawl and rachet device which turns a mechanical counter. Such an apparatus conforms more nearly to a Type I Recorder correction formula, eq. (6–16), than to eq. (6–3), because if a pulse enters just as the mechanism has nearly completed a cycle of operation, the armature reverses its direction and starts a new cycle of motion. However, since the rachet was not left in its normal position due to the incompletion of the first cycle, the pawl is unable to engage the next tooth of the rachet and it falls back against the first tooth and finally brings it into its normal end position. Thus the second pulse is not recorded and also this action makes it impossible to count a third pulse if the latter should come very shortly after the close of the first cycle of operations.

As may be readily shown by connecting a variable frequency signal to the register, its resolving time t_r' is usually about 0.01 sec or larger, while the dead time of Geiger counters is usually about 10^{-4} sec, and those of other counting instruments are usually still shorter. Therefore, it is customary to employ a scaling circuit to reduce the number of pulses supplied to the register by some known factor S. The counting losses decrease much more rapidly than in direct proportion to S for a given input counting rate, because the pulses at the output not only are reduced in number but they become less random since S particles are required to give one output pulse. According to the results given in Section 2, the standard deviation in the interval between output pulses decreases inversely proportionally to the square root of S.

It is easy to determine when losses in the register are identically zero. The most unfavorable situation, assuming that the response time of the input amplifiers is negligible or its effect is included in the dead time of the counter t_r, would be to have S particles arrive at successive intervals just barely larger than t_r. In that case two output pulses will be produced at an interval slightly larger than St_r. If this is larger than t_r', or if, in other words,

$$S > \frac{t_r'}{t_r}$$

no counts are lost in the register.

The exact theoretical treatment of the situation when the losses are not zero is very difficult because the pulses are neither perfectly random nor perfectly periodic. Such a theory has been developed,[A3] but it is generally not very convenient to apply, since it requires an evaluation of the incomplete gamma function.

Alternatively, the losses in the register may be estimated by numerical summation of the Poisson distribution law, eq. (6–4). We may assume that, if the Geiger counter makes more than S discharges within the time t_r', some are lost. The fraction of the counts lost is the probability that n counts occur, P_n summed from $n = S$ to $n = \infty$. In this calculation employing eq. (6–4) we place $\bar{n} = N_0 t_r'$, where N_0 is the number of discharges per second of the Geiger counter.

Neither method is convenient to use for the correction of individual measurements. However, these calculations are highly useful for determining what scaling ratio is required to make the losses negligible in any given experiment. Due to recent technological developments in scaling circuits and due to the wide commercial availability of circuits of high scaling ratio, it is generally practical to employ circuits such that this objective is achieved.

CHAPTER 7

AUXILIARY ELECTRONIC CIRCUITS

A. Introduction

The counter discharge produces a voltage pulse on the central wire system, and it is the purpose of the auxiliary electronic circuits to measure, record or control this pulse. As we have mentioned before, the pulse is of about 10^{-4} sec duration and is therefore too short to operate many of the currently available recording devices. On the other hand, the pulse produced by a Geiger counter is often of considerable size, being in general of the order of the overvoltage in amplitude. A pulse of 100 to 200 volts amplitude is not uncommon. It is evident, therefore, that such pulses are sufficiently large to operate most vacuum tubes and do not require further amplification, but may require broadening or lengthening. The pulses formed by a proportional counter, on the other hand, may be quite small and may require considerable amplification. A pulse of 10^{-4} volt from such a counter is not unusual, and high gain circuits are required to render such a pulse capable of operating recording equipment.

Almost without exception, counters are operated with the central wire positive and the cylinder negative. The voltage sources supplying such a counter may have either the positive or the negative side grounded, depending entirely upon convenience. The circuits appropriate to operation with either the central wire system or the cylinder of the counter at ground potential are shown in Fig. 7–1A and B. In the case of counters in which the cylinder also serves as the external envelope, it is desirable to operate the cylinder at ground potential (Fig. 7–1B). In these circumstances the cylinder may be safely handled while the high voltage is on. In addition the central wire system is electrostatically shielded. In those counters employing an outer envelope of glass or other insulating ma-

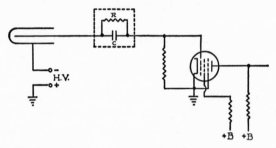

FIG. 7–1A. Fundamental counter circuit for negative high voltages. Wire at ground potential. Dotted condenser and quenching resistor omitted with selfquenching counters.

terial, it is often useful to have the central wire system at essentially ground potential (Fig. 7–1A). The cylinder, in the latter case, is operated at a high negative potential with respect to ground. The advantage of the latter system is that it eliminates the necessity for the blocking condenser which must be a good insulator and must have a high leakage resistance.

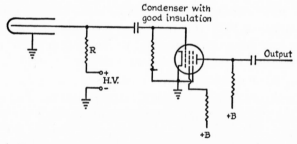

FIG. 7–1B. Fundamental counter circuit for positive high voltages. Cylinder at ground potential.

Some of the circuit diagrams shown below are in schematic form, without constants. This is done since the constants depend on the characteristics of the particular tubes used. The justification of particular values lies outside the scope of this text. As anyone familiar with such circuits knows, a few of the constants are critical, but most may be widely varied without interfering with the operation of the circuit. One laboratory may have available powerpacks producing 400 volts; another may have similar sets producing 325 or 250 volts. The resistances in scaling circuits, integrating circuits and other devices will have to be adapted accordingly. It would be erroneous to imply that a given circuit will work only on one set of voltages and circuit constants. Usually, if specific voltages are available, or if particular vacuum tubes are at hand, the constants can readily be modified to suit the circumstances. Similarly, wide variations in tube types are usually possible. When substituting new tube types, the "resistance-coupled amplifier" section of the standard receiving tube manuals will be found helpful. British experimenters may prefer to use Mullard or Osram triodes instead of RCA pentodes in several of the circuits shown below. Conversely, pentodes may be substituted for triodes with good results in other cases. Such constants as are given in the diagrams should be regarded, not as the only possible values, but rather as the starting point for testing. Any new circuit should be built the first time on a "breadboard" so that various circuit constants and experimental rearrangements can be readily tried. Experimentation and trial of various values and arrangements is to be preferred to rigid insistence on unnecessarily detailed "cookbook" specifications.

B. QUENCHING CIRCUITS

Non-selfquenching counters require the use of a quenching arrangement which may be either a high resistance or an electronic circuit. These circuits may be dispensed with in the case of the selfquenching counters. The objection to using a high resistance is, as we have pointed out above, that a long time constant is introduced into the circuit. Since it is not practical to reduce the value of the resistance sufficiently to provide a short time constant, it is therefore customary to employ an electronic circuit which performs this function. Several such circuits are shown in Fig. 7–2.

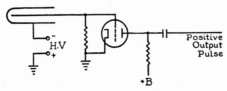

FIG. 7–2A(1). Modified Neher and Pickering quenching circuit to give positive output pulse.

It must be recalled that the fundamental limitation on the time of recovery of a non-selfquenching counter is determined by the mobilities of the positive ions in the counter itself. The several quenching circuits therefore are also governed by this limit. If the time constants of the circuits are made much less than 10^{-4} sec, the counter itself will not have ceased to discharge and the entire arrangement will not operate satisfactorily. Thus these circuits may reduce the quenching time from, say, 10^{-2} second for a resistance-quenched counter

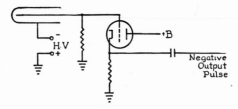

FIG. 7–2A(2). Modified Neher and Pickering quenching circuit to give negative output pulse.

($R = 10^9$ ohms, $C = 10^{-11}$ farad) to a figure near 10^{-4} sec, but will not operate at still shorter times.

Fig. 7–2A(1) shows a quenching circuit devised by Neher and Pickering.[N1] In this circuit, a negative pulse from the counter wire arrives on the grid of the tube. Since the grid of the tube is connected through a resistance to the cathode, the tube is normally in a conducting state and the grid and counter wire are approximately at cathode potential. The arrival of a negative pulse on the grid causes the tube to become non-conducting, and the grid is effectively isolated for an instant. Thus the high potential is, in effect, removed from the counter during this time. The counter wire and grid recover with a *RC* time constant characterized by the resistance of the grid leak and the distributed capacity of the counter wire and grid

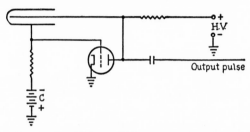

Fig. 7–2B. Neher and Harper quenching circuit.

system. If we take this distributed capacity to be of the order of 10^{-11} farad and use a 10 megohm grid leak, the counter will recover in 10^{-4} sec. It is evident that a positive pulse will appear in the plate circuit of the tube as indicated. This pulse may then be fed into the subsequent scaling or recording circuits. If it is desired to have a negative pulse to feed into the next stage, this may be accomplished by the modification shown in Fig. 7–2A(2). In this circuit the load resistance of the tube is placed in the cathode line instead of in the plate circuit, and the sign of the pulse therefore reverses. The chief disadvantage of this circuit is that, since the tube is conducting, a constant drain is put on the high voltage supply.

The second type of quenching circuit was devised by Wynn-Williams [W3] and later independently developed by Neher and Harper.[N2] This arrangement is shown in Fig. 7–2B. In this circuit it will be observed that the grid is held at a negative

potential by the C battery, and that therefore the tube is normally in a non-conducting state. When the counter counts,
the cylinder of the counter swings to a positive value. This
causes the tube to conduct, and the plate current passing
through the plate resistor R_p produces a voltage drop which
is effectively subtracted from the high voltage. Thus the
vacuum tube partially short-circuits the counter, or in other
words removes part of its potential. If the gain of the tube is
μ then the effective resistance of the tube is μR_g when the

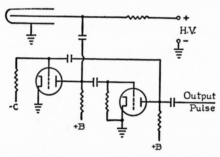

Fɪɢ. 7–2C.   Multivibrator quenching circuit devised by Getting.

tube is conducting. The recovery of the system is again controlled by the RC time constant of the grid circuit and may
be made of the order of 10^{-4} sec as in the previous case. The
disadvantage of this system is that the entire high voltage is
connected across the vacuum tube. Most receiving tubes are
sufficiently well insulated so that they will not break down,
but the useful life of the tube is often short and occasionally
flash-overs occur.

The third type of circuit is the multivibrator arrangement
devised by Getting [G7] and shown in Fig. 7–2C. In this circuit
one tube of a multivibrator is biased negatively so that it is
normally in a stable state with one tube conducting and the
other cut off by the bias. The arrival of a negative pulse from
the central wire of the counter system causes the multivibrator to go through one cycle of its oscillation. The final act in

this oscillation is the arrival of a considerable charge from the plate of the second tube through the condenser onto the grid and counter wire system. The counter wire is thus driven to a potential below its normal operating voltage, and the discharge consequently ceases. The recovery of this system depends on the time constants of the multivibrator and in particular on the grid condensers and resistors. Again, this system can be made to operate in about 10^{-4} sec, the fundamental limit being again not in the circuit but in the positive ion collection time in the counter.

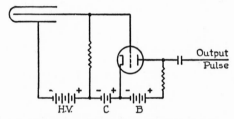

FIG. 7–2D. Modification of circuits shown in Figs. 7–2A and B to be completely floating or grounded at any one desired point.

A modification of these circuits (Fig. 7–2D) has been found useful in connection with radiosonde cosmic-ray balloon observations. This circuit was devised by Johnson,[J1] and was used by Johnson and Korff [J2] in a series of balloon flights. In these flights economy of battery weight was essential. In this circuit the plate voltage of the quenching tube is added to the high voltage supply. The plate battery is thus made to perform a double function. The operation of the circuit is essentially identical with that described above in the circuit in Fig. 7–2A.

Still further modification of this circuit is that made by Wynn-Williams,[W4] in which a single thyratron performs the dual function of extinguishing the discharges and causing a recording counter to record. This circuit is shown in Fig. 7–2E. In this circuit, the thyratron grid is normally held at a negative potential by the C battery, and the thyratron is normally non-conducting. The potential across the counter is therefore the sum of the voltages of the high voltage battery plus the B battery plus the C battery. When a count occurs, the cylinder of the counter swings to a more positive value and the grid of the thyratron becomes positive, thus permitting the thyratron to conduct. The flow of plate current causes the recorder relay to open, thus simultaneously recording a count and extinguishing the discharge in the thyratron by breaking

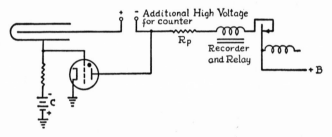

FIG. 7–2E.   Combined quenching and recording circuit using a thyratron.

its plate circuit and permitting the negative grid to resume control. This same break effectively removes the potential from the counter, which then recovers. The recovery time of this circuit is controlled by the speed of the recording unit. The chief objection to this type of circuit is that, as with the Neher-Pickering circuit, the counter cylinder is floating, and further, that the entire high voltage supply must be kept at some potential above ground.

C. Coincidence Circuits

One of the most important uses of counters has been made possible through coincidence technique. Coincidence circuits permit imposition, on an arrangement of counters, of the condition that the counters must discharge simultaneously or within an assignable time interval of each other. Thus it is possible to determine the direction in which a particle is travel-ing by the use of two or more counters connected in coinci-dence and arranged in line.* Multiple coincidences permit an-alysis of the complex ionizing events encountered in cosmic radiation and nuclear physics in which an ionizing ray may be followed as it traverses matter and generates secondary parti-cles with various characteristics. The part played by non-ionizing radiation may also be studied by the aid of anti-coincidence devices.

1. Normal Coincidence Arrangements. The simplest type of coincidence circuit is that devised by Rossi in 1929.[R2] With this circuit it is possible to record coincidence due to any num-ber of counters, triples and quadruples being commonly re-corded, but the circuit will operate satisfactorily on tenfold or even greater coincidences. The circuit is shown for triple co-incidences in Fig. 7–3A. If additional identical branches are desired, all plates are connected together. The circuit is shown connected for resistance-quenched, non-selfquenching counters. For selfquenching counters the resistance R and condenser C are omitted. The essential feature of this circuit is that all of the plates of the tube are tied together, and connected through a common resistor to the B supply. The grids of all the tubes are connected to the cathodes so that the tubes are conducting. When a negative pulse arrives on the grid of any tube, it ceases to conduct and the tube therefore becomes a high resistance, whereas it was a much lower resistance while it was conducting. The potential of the common plate circuit is therefore deter-mined by the equivalent of a system of parallel resistances. If all the tubes but one become non-conducting, or in other words become high resistances because of the arrival of negative pulses on their respective grids, we will have a circuit in which

* Another method of obtaining directional indication has been devised by B. Rajewski (*Zeits. f. Phys.* **120**, 627 (1943)) who made use of asymmetric electron emission first reported by Bragg & Madsen (*Phil. Mag.* **16**, 918 (1908)). Thus if a counter cylinder is made half of lead and half of aluminum, more electrons are ejected by gamma rays entering lead, and leaving aluminum.

there will be several high resistances in parallel with one low resistance. Since most of the current will flow through the low resistance, the change in potential of the plate circuit will be small. If on the other hand all tubes cease to conduct, the change in potential of this plate circuit becomes considerable. A large pulse therefore occurs in the output only when all tubes simultaneously cease to conduct. The circuit can therefore re-

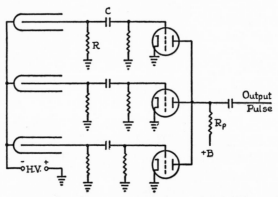

FIG. 7–3A.   The conventional Rossi coincidence circuit.   With selfquenching counters, R and C are omitted.

cord coincidences between the discharges of any number of counters. For example, the resistance of a 6C6, when it is conducting, may be 10^5 ohms, whereas it may exceed 10^8 when it is not conducting. Let R_p in Fig. 7–3A be 10^6 ohms, and let the B potential be 200 volts. The potential of the common plates will therefore be $+6.6$ volts when the three tubes are conducting, i.e., when no counts have taken place. Let two tubes but not the third count, and the potential becomes $+22$ volts; but let all three count and the potential becomes $+198$ volts. Thus we have a pulse of only 14 volts for an incomplete, as compared to 192 volts for a complete, coincidence.

The resolving time of the circuit is determined by the RC time constants of the coupling condensers and plate and grid resistors. Short resolving times are often desired to minimize accidentals. Times of the order of five microseconds may be obtained by using condensers of 0.00005 microfarad and resistors of 10^5 ohms. This time is shorter than that required by the counter to recover, and only the sharp initial "break" of the counter discharge curve is used. However, accidentals are greatly reduced by this procedure. The ultimate limit on resolving times is caused by the intrinsic time-lags of the counters themselves.

Another system for recording coincidences is also possible through the use of a multiple grid tube. Such a circuit is

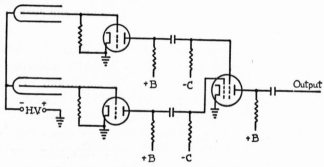

Fig. 7–3B.   Mixing circuit for multiple grid tubes.

shown in Fig. 7–3B. Here the several grids are held at a negative potential by a C battery, and the tube becomes conducting only when a positive pulse is applied simultaneously to all of the grids. Such positive pulses may be obtained either directly from the cylinders of the counters or through an intermediate stage of vacuum tubes, as shown in the diagram. The intermediate tubes may be quenching tubes, and thus non-self-quenching counters may be used with this arrangement. The multiplicity of the coincidences is limited by the number of nearly electrically identical grids in the mixing tube.

2. Anti-Coincidence Circuits. It is sometimes important to impose upon an arrangement of counters the condition that one or more tubes shall not count while other tubes are counting. This arrangement adds one degree of flexibility to counter circuits and permits important advances in the analyses which can be made therewith, since it is possible to establish that when one thing happens something else does not happen. Thus, for example, it is sometimes desirable to know that a ray traversing an arrangement of counters is a single ray and is not a portion of a multiple-ray shower. An illustration of an arrangement of counters in coincidence (C) and anti-coincidence (A) is shown in Fig. 7–3E(1). Here we see that the counters C define a path through the absorber. Any simultaneous shower rays or non-collimated particles will trip the guard counters in anti-coincidence A at the side and the event would not be recorded.

Also, for example, it may be desirable to ascertain whether a given ray has stopped in an absorber. The arrangement shown in Fig. 7–3E(2) will insure the above condition. Here the three counters C determine that a particle has passed into the absorber, and the fact that the anti-coincidence counter A does not count proves that the particle did not come out in the downward direction. The importance of high efficiency in the anti-coincidence counters is self-evident, for even a 98% efficiency might render the interpretation of such an experiment ambiguous.

If we consider the operation of a simple coincidence circuit, the electrical requirement of the anti-coincidence circuit becomes evident. In general, negative pulses are fed into a set of Rossi coincidence tubes, and the swing in the plate circuit will be large if all of the tubes receive a negative pulse simultaneously. If a pulse of the opposite sign arrives simultaneously in the plate circuit of the mixing stage, then no coincidence will be registered. All that is necessary to introduce such a pulse is the addition of one vacuum tube which reverses the sign of the pulse going through it. Anti-coincidence circuits were used by Swann and Ramsey in the equipment carried aloft during the stratosphere flight of the balloon "Explorer II" in 1936. Similar circuits have been published by Herzog [H2] and have been used by many observers. A simple schematic arrangement for this type of device is shown in Fig. 7–3C, in which it will be seen that the counter which operates as an anti-coincidence counter has one more vacuum tube in its control circuit. The pulse produced by this counter is therefore fed into the mixing stage reversed in sign as compared to those produced by the other counters, and the large plate swing

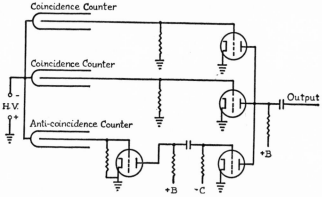

FIG. 7–3C. Anti-coincidence circuit, selfquenching counter shown.

which causes the Rossi circuit to record coincidence is thereby nullified. It should be added that, since a positive pulse must be introduced into the grid of the mixing tube to record anti-coincidences, therefore the grid of this tube must have a negative bias rendering it non-conducting. If no pulse appears on its grid, the remainder of the circuit functions to give normal coincidences. In general, the arrangement can be adapted to an indefinite number of tubes, and it is possible to have many tubes in coincidence and many in anti-coincidence.

3. Coincidences between Proportional Counters and Geiger Counters. In certain investigations it is desirable to measure the coincident discharge of Geiger counters and proportional counters. Thus, for example, it is possible to measure the specific ionization of a given ray by the arrangement shown in Fig. 7–3F(1). In this arrangement a coincident discharge of the three Geiger counters and the proportional counter proves that a ray has passed through the proportional counter P along a definite and well collimated path. The size of the pulse in the proportional counter may be measured simultaneously and independently by an additional circuit (see below), thus mak-

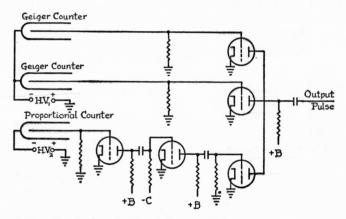

Fig. 7–3D. Circuit for coincidences between Geiger counters and proportional counter. Separate high voltage supplies are shown as the operating potentials are often different.

ing use of condition of coincidence as well as recording the amplitude of the pulse which produces that coincidence.

Another arrangement in which the proportional counter and Geiger counters are used in coincidence was employed to study the association between neutron and showers.[K10] The neutron counter was a proportional counter of the boron-trifluoride type described in Chapter 3, and was adjusted so as not to be sensitive to electrons. A tray of Geiger counters was arranged below it. Thus, the simultaneous discharge of the Geiger and neutron counters established that (a) shower took place and (b) a large ionizing event such as produced by a neutron occurred in the neutron counter. The counter arrangement is shown in Fig. 7–3F(2), where N represents the (proportional) neutron counter and the horizontal array of Geiger counters C below it represent the shower-detecting arrangement. Since the neutron may be slowed down to a velocity at which it can be detected more efficiently in perhaps 10^{-4} sec, it is desirable not to have the resolving time of the circuit (Fig. 7–3D) too short. This is readily accomplished by making the RC times of the grid-plate coupling resistors and condensers of the desired values. For example, a 10^6 ohm resistor and a 0.0001 microfarad condenser will serve the purpose.

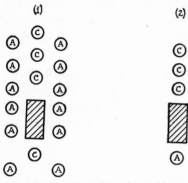

FIG. 7–3E. Typical anti-coincidence arrangements. (1) Employs anti-coincidence counters A as guard counters to assure that the counters C are not set off by showers from the side. (2) Insures that a particle having passed through C is absorbed and does not emerge in the direction determined by C.

The electrical procedure employed to determine coincidences between Geiger counters and proportional counters must take account of the fact that the pulses due to the proportional counters are usually much smaller than those due to Geiger

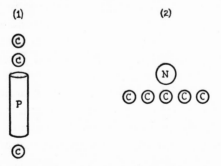

FIG. 7–3F. Typical counter arrangements using counters in coincidence with proportional counters. (1) The counters C define a path for particles through the proportional counter P. (2) Coincidences between neutrons (N) and showers C are counted.

counters. It is therefore usually desirable to have additional stages of amplification preceding the mixing stage. Since negative pulses are added in the mixing stage, and since the proportional counter gives a negative pulse, an even number of additional stages of amplification must be used. For most problems, two stages suffice. The suitable circuit arrangement in this case is shown in Fig. 7–3D. The counters are shown supplied by a common high voltage source but independent supplies are used if the proportional and Geiger counters operate at different voltages. Selfquenching Geiger counters are assumed in the circuit as shown.

D. Scaling Circuits

In many experiments with counters it is important to use scaling circuits for the purpose of scaling the impulses down to slower counting rates. This procedure is useful when the counting rate of the counter exceeds the rate which the mechanical recorder can follow and, further, it improves the statistics. The occurrence of closely spaced double counts is highly probable on statistical grounds even in the case of comparatively slow counting rates. These close doubles would be registered as a single count by a comparatively slow mechanical recorder even though the circuit appeared to be counting properly.

1. Vacuum Tube Scaling Circuits. The general principle of scaling circuits in use at the present time is that embodied in the trigger circuit developed by Eccles and Jordan in 1918.[E1] An arrangement of two triodes is possible, which has a characteristic curve in which a portion exhibits a negative slope. Since the negative slope portion of the curve is unstable, the circuit is able to change suddenly from one stable state to the other. A typical circuit diagram employing an arrangement of this sort is shown in Fig. 7–4. If the potentials and resistances are correctly chosen, one of the tubes will be conducting and the other non-conducting. The plate current of the tube which is conducting flows through its plate resistance and also through the grid resistor of the other tube. The IR drop through this resistance is such as to keep the grid of the second tube negative and thus to render it non-conducting. It is evident that this state is stable and that the tubes will remain in this state indefinitely. If now a positive pulse is applied through the two condensers to both grids, the positive pulse will not affect the tube which is conducting, since it cannot render it appreciably more conducting. The second tube which

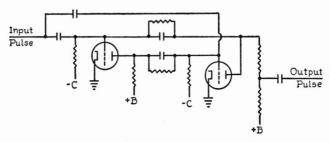

Fig. 7–4. Eccles and Jordan trigger pair.

is non-conducting, on the other hand, will become conducting and a negative pulse appearing in the plate circuit will be transmitted to the grid of the first tube, causing it to shut off. The circuit will now remain in this new stable condition, which is the inverse of the former state, until the arrival of the next pulse, at which time it will execute one more cycle and return to the initial state. Thus the two tubes alternately conduct and do not conduct. A stage following this unit will therefore receive alternate positive and negative pulses as the tubes fluctuate back and forth between their two states. It is evident that an indefinite number of stages of this type may be built, and many units employing nine stages, in other words, a scale of 512, are in common use at the present time.

In many of the present designs, in-between-stage tubes are used between each trigger pair for the purpose of transmitting pulses of only one sign, and also for the purpose of amplifying the pulse. These interstage tubes may be either triodes or pentodes. Several complete diagrams of multiple scale [L3] counters appear in the literature. A typical unit is shown in Figs. 7–5A and 7–5B.

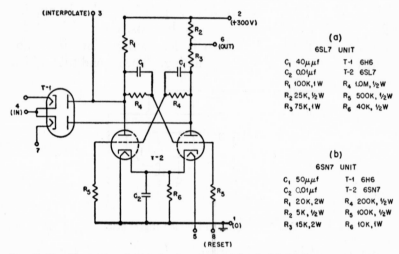

Fig. 7–5A. The scales of two plug-in units used in the Model 200 counter. (*Electronics*, W. C. Elmore and M. Sands, McGraw-Hill, New York (1949))

E. Voltage Supply and Regulating Circuits

Since most laboratories are equipped with a 110-volt, 60-cycle alternating current line, it is customary to operate most of the laboratory equipment on this line. Various types of battery eliminators have consequently been designed. A typical power supply is shown in Fig. 7–6A. It will be seen that this consists of two condensers and one choke. Further condensers and inductances may be added if necessary to smooth out the residual ripple still further. A voltage dividing resistance is shown in the output, and various taps will then provide the potentials required in the several parts of the circuits to be supplied.

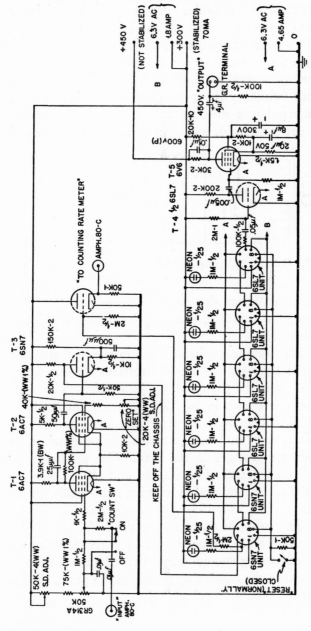

FIG. 7–5B. The Model 200 counter which has a resolving time of 5 microseconds and can be adjusted for input pulses varying in amplitude from 10 to 100 volts. (*Electronics*, W. C. Elmore and M. Sands, McGraw-Hill, New York (1949))

The principal difficulties encountered with this type of circuit are (1) that variations in the input voltage are magnified and affect the output voltage, and (2) that the output voltage depends on the load. In order to secure constant output voltages, one of several arrangements are normally employed. If the input frequency is constant, one of the several types of AC voltage regulators may precede the B eliminator. This arrangement is desirable wherever it can be used as it will largely

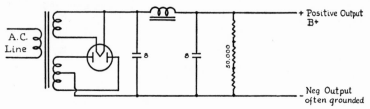

Fig. 7–6A. Ordinary DC power supply or "battery eliminator." Resistances in ohms, capacitances in microfarads.

eliminate fluctuation due to line voltage variations. Such devices are, for example, the Raytheon and the Sola voltage regulators.

Fluctuations due to the changes in the load may be largely eliminated through the use of electronic circuits and devices. One of these is the gas-filled regulator tube. The operation of this device is shown in Fig. 7–6B. Such gas discharge tubes have a flat operating characteristic curve and will in effect maintain a constant voltage across the terminals of the tube for moderate changes in the load. Gas discharge tubes are available for voltages of 75, 90, 105 and 150. These tubes may be used in series, and stabilization may be secured at any voltage such as 165, 180, 195, 450, or other combination sums of these. The tubes in question are the RCA types VR75, 874, VR105 and VR150, respectively. The series resistor must be capable of passing enough current to take care of the load plus the current in the regulating tube, and the power dissipation of this resistor should be calculated.

Electronic voltage regulators are also available and give extremely stable output characteristics. As Hunt and Hickman [H3] have shown, all of these devices may be classified in three categories. The first of these is the transconductance bridge circuit, the second is the amplification factor bridge circuit, and the third is the simple degenerative amplifier. In addition, combination of these three arrangements is possible. Schematic diagrams for the three types of regulators are shown in Fig. 7–6C.

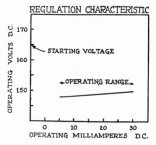

In general, no single circuit may be considered as ideal to be used in all circumstances, but the individual arrangements will depend on the problems encountered. Thus, for example, a circuit may be designed to stabilize a high voltage at a low current output, or it may stabilize a comparative low voltage but high current drain. The first and second types of circuits would be quite different. One typical arrangement is shown in Fig. 7–6D. This is a high voltage stabilized supply, capable of producing 10,000 volts for counter potentials. It is impor-

FIG. 7–6B. Characteristic curve of RCA-VR150 voltage-regulating tube. (*R.C.A. Vacuum Tube Handbook*)

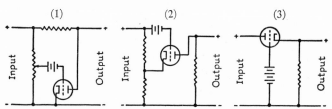

FIG. 7–6C. Schematic voltage-stabilizing circuits. (1) Transconductance bridge. (2) Amplification factor bridge. (3) Degenerative amplifier.

tant that this voltage should not fluctuate, but at the same time the current capacity required of such a device is extremely small. The circuit shown employs a high gain pentode as the stabilizing tube and is designed to be entirely floating. Either

the positive or the negative may be at high potential with respect to ground, although the operation is usually much easier
for the high negative and grounded positive. In this case, the
cathode of the regulating tube is grounded and the only potential across it is the amount of the regulation. Thus, for example, a 10,000 volt supply can be quite adequately regulated,
while the plate of the regulating tube need not be more than

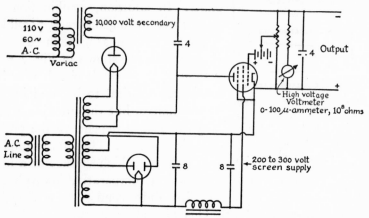

Fig. 7–6D.   Complete circuit for producing 10,000 volts DC, regulated, stabilized,
adjustable and fully floating.   Resistances in ohms, capacitances in microfarads.

a few hundred volts above ground. On the other hand, if the
counter is to be operated with the cylinder grounded, the regulating tube will float at a high potential, and the tube as well
as its filament and screen voltages must be insulated accordingly. A transformer with a one-to-one ratio, insulated to
withstand 10,000 volts, is provided to isolate the regulator
system from the 110 volt input line which is customarily
grounded on one side.

Another circuit, suitable for regulating a comparative low
voltage but high current, is that used in certain commercial
regulators. The circuit is shown in Fig. 7–6E. In these devices, a high gain pentode picks up the variations in voltage,
its own cathode being held at a constant potential by a gaseous

voltage regulating tube. The fluctuations in the potential of its plate are directly connected to the grid of a triode capable of transmitting comparatively large currents. This triode in

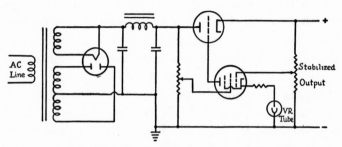

FIG. 7–6E.   Voltage-regulating circuit for controlling relatively large currents.

turn regulates the voltage. Thus, for example, if the voltage should increase, the grid of the pentode will become more negative, and the triode in turn will be rendered less conducting. The output will therefore tend to be stable.

In measuring the high potentials for counters, a vacuum tube voltmeter which draws practically no current is desirable.

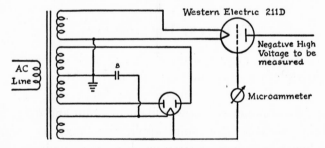

FIG. 7–6F.   Vacuum tube voltmeter having high resistance suitable for measuring high negative voltage. The scale can be changed by shunts across the microammeter. This microammeter should also have a variable shunt of 250,000 ohms or so for zero adjustment.

Such a meter, suitable for measuring high negative voltages, is shown in Fig. 7–6F. A triode is operated with its grid positive, and the high negative potential to be measured is applied to its plate.[K12] The application of this voltage produces a field which in turn decreases the grid current. The meter is calibrated by applying known voltages. The grid-current microammeter will read backwards, i.e., it will show a lower current as the voltage applied to the plate increases. A voltmeter of this type can have a resistance of more than 10^9 ohms and will therefore only drain a few microamperes from a several thousand volt supply.

Conclusion. It would be possible to describe an almost indefinite number of auxiliary electronic circuits. Discussion has been confined to those which in the author's opinion are most generally useful. Recent developments are discussed in the following section. References appended to the end of this chapter can be consulted for further discussion. This list is not complete, and the reader will find many more in the literature. The subject is expanding rapidly and, as new tubes become available, the reader may enjoy working out new modifications. Detailed discussions of circuits may be found in the standard texts on electronics.

F. Recent Developments

An enormous amount of development work on new circuits has taken place during the past few years. Many new tubes have appeared. These often render previous models obsolete, as they have smaller size, lower filament drain and other characteristics which for particular applications may be desirable. Entire books have been written on electronic circuitry. Many laboratories now employ professional electronic technicians, who do nothing except build and service circuits. It appears completely impractical to attempt to cover this vast field in a chapter. We shall therefore indicate a few points of departure and give almost no specialized references, confining ourselves to the general discussions, summaries and treatises.

G. Modern Scaling Circuits and Amplifiers

The newer designs of scaling circuits and linear amplifiers have rendered the older designs obsolete. Tubes of the types 6C6 and 80, described in the first edition of this book, are no longer used and indeed are, in many cases, hard to obtain. For the benefit of those persons who do not have texts on electronics available, we include brief descriptions of two circuits considered successful today. The first is the Higinbotham scaler [H21] shown in Fig. 7–7A. While this differs only in detail from the fundamental trigger-pair arrangement mentioned previously, the differences are important in that they contribute to stability. One of these important distinctions is the use of a double-diode input stage, preceding the trigger-pair. The diode passes pulses of one sign only, which helps the stability of operation. Complete circuit constants are given. Each scale-of-two unit can be built up into a small plug-in unit, for ease in changing.

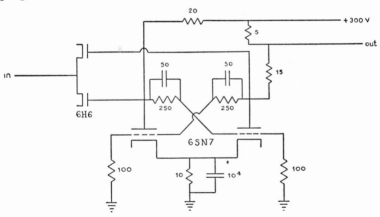

Fig. 7–7A. Higinbotham scale-of-two. Resistance in thousands of ohms, capacities in micromicrofarads. [H21]

The Bell-Jordan [J4] amplifier is today well considered. It too has many characteristics of stability and low noise which ren-

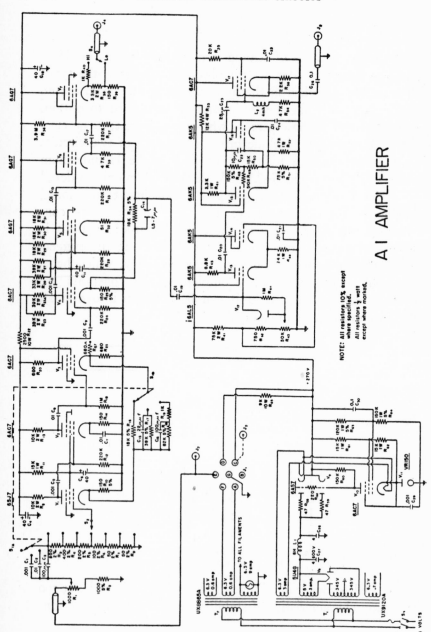

A I AMPLIFIER

NOTE: All resistors 10% except
where specified.
All resistors ½ watt
except where marked.

Fig. 7-7B.   Jordan-Bell amplifier with negative feedback, discriminator, and other adjustments.[J4]

der previous designs obsolete. A diagram of this amplifier is shown in Fig. 7-7B. This amplifier is very stable and flexible. It is ideally suited to almost any counting problem and will work on Geiger counters, scintillation counters, proportional counters, or amplifiers. It has a variable band-width control, so that it can be adapted to devices having varying response speed characteristics. It is fast enough to follow scintillation counts; and it has a variable gain enabling it to be used for proportional counting and discrimination.

REFERENCES

"Interval Selector." A. Roberts, *R.S.I.* **12**, 71 (1941)

"Ionization Chamber Circuit." S. W. Barnes, *R.S.I.* **10**, 1 (1939)

"Linear Amplifier." C. E. Wynn-Williams and F. A. B. Ward, *P.R.S.* **131**, 391 (1931)

R. C. Waddell, *R.S.I.* **10**, 311 (1939)

A. A. Petruskas and C. A. Van Atta, *R.S.I.* **11**, 103 (1940)

G. P. Harnwell and L. N. Ridenour, *R.S.I.* **11**, 346 (1940)

"D.C. Amplifiers." D. B. Pennick, *Rev. Sci. Inst.* **6**, 117 (1935); A. W. Vance, *Rev. Sci. Inst.* **7**, 490 (1936)

"Triode Scaler." D. DeVault, *R.S.I.* **12**, 83 (1941)

"Double Pulse Generator." A. Roberts, *R.S.I.* **10**, 316 (1939)

"Pulse Amplitude Selector." A. Roberts, *R.S.I.* **11**, 44 (1940)

"Electron Multiplier as Counter." Z. Bay, *R.S.I.* **12**, 127 (1941)

"Resolving Time Measurement." Y. Beers, *R.S.I.* **13**, 72 (1942)

N. F. Moody, W. J. Battell, W. D. Howell and R. H. Taplin, *Rev. Sci. Inst.* **22**, 551 (1951)

Comprehensive circuits for counting:

G. C. Scarrott, *Progress in Nuclear Physics*, Butterworth, London (1950). Review of circuitry.

N. F. Moody, *Rev. Sci. Inst.* **22**, 236 (1951). D-c amplifiers.

Z. Bay, *Rev. Sci. Inst.* **22**, 397 (1951). High-speed coincidence circuits.

C. E. Nielsen, *Rev. Sci. Inst.* **18**, 44 (1947). Characteristic curves for tubes of type 38, 954, 959, used as electrometer tubes.

D. E. Hudson, *Rev. Sci. Inst.* **22**, 850 (1951). Quenching circuit for parallel plate counters.

G. F. Pieper, *Science* **112**, 377 (1950). Instrumentation for radio-activity. Review with bibliography.

Books recently issued:

Counting Tubes, S. C. Curran and S. D. Craggs, Academic Press, Butterworth, London (1949)

Ionization Chambers and Counters, B. Rossi and H. Staub, McGraw-Hill, New York (1949); National Nuclear Energy Series.

Electronics, W. C. Elmore and M. Sands, McGraw-Hill, New York (1949)

Electronic Tube Circuits, S. Seely, McGraw-Hill, New York (1950)

Millimicrosecond Pulse Techniques, I. A. D. Lewis and F. H. Wells, McGraw-Hill, New York (1954)

Electrical Breakdown of Gases, J. M. Meek and J. I. Craggs, Oxford, Clarendon Press (1953)

The following texts on electronics contain much useful material on circuits and circuit analysis methods:

Theory and Application of Electron Tubes, H. S. Reich, McGraw-Hill, New York (1939)

Electronics, J. Millman and S. Seely, McGraw-Hill, New York (1941)

The following books are often found useful in connection with counter problems:

Electrical Phenomena in Gases, K. K. Darrow, Williams & Wilkins, Baltimore (1932)

Radiations from Radioactive Substances, E. Rutherford, J. Chadwick and C. D. Ellis, Cambridge, England (1930)

Procedures in Experimental Physics, J. Strong, Prentice-Hall, New York (1938)

Electrical Counting, W. B. Lewis, Cambridge, England (1942)

Fundamental Processes of Electrical Discharges in Gases, L. Loeb, Wiley, New York (1938)

CHAPTER 8

SCINTILLATION COUNTERS *

I. BASIC PRINCIPLES OF THE SCINTILLATION COUNTER

A. INTRODUCTION

The basic principle of the scintillation counter is analogous to that of the ionization chamber. In the latter the ions produced in the gas by high-energy particles or gamma radiation are collected at an electrode where they are measured by an electrometer or some equivalent instrument; in the scintillation counter the high-energy particle excites a luminescent material and the photons created in this process are collected at the electrode of a photocell, where they are converted into electrons.

In order to make the comparison more quantitative let us consider an actual situation. In an air-filled ionization chamber a 3-Mev alpha particle is completely absorbed and produces roughly 10^5 ion pairs along its path. These are rapidly collected with very little loss at an electrode, providing a pulse which can be measured with proper amplification. For a high-energy electron or any other light particle, the situation is quite different. Because of the smaller stopping power of the gas for light particles these are not completely stopped within the dimensions of the ordinary chamber. They therefore trans-

* This chapter was written by H. Kallmann, Professor of Physics, New York University. The author wishes to express his thanks to Grace Marmor Spruch for her aid in the revision and preparation of the manuscript for this chapter.

mit only a part of their energy to the gas and this part is usually not sufficient to produce the number of ion pairs necessary
for a detectable pulse.

In the case of the scintillation counter a 3-Mev alpha particle
produces approximately 2×10^5 photons in a highly luminescent material and if half of these are collected at the electrode
of a photocell a pulse consisting of 10^4 electrons is obtained,
since even the best photocathode has a photoelectron conversion factor of only 0.1. It would seem, then, that the
scintillation counter is inferior to the ionization chamber by a
factor of ten except for the fact that when the scintillation
counter is in actual use one does not employ a photocell but
rather a photomultiplier. This is essentially a photocell with
internal multiplication provided by causing each electron released from the photocathode to impinge upon a series of
surfaces called dynodes where they release secondary electrons.
The end result is that about 10^6 electrons are produced at the
output of the photomultiplier for each primary electron released from the photocathode. Consequently, a 3-Mev alpha
particle produces close to 10^{10} electrons at the output of a
scintillation counter equipped with a photomultiplier. Therefore, with respect to the number of electrons delivered at the
output for a given energy absorbed in the counter, the scintillation counter is superior to the ionization chamber by orders
of magnitude. The present-day scintillation counter can produce an output pulse of 50 volts at a capacity of 10 $\mu\mu f$ for
each incoming alpha particle.

One might inquire why the scintillation counter is so recent
an instrument in view of this high sensitivity and the fact that
it was known as early as 1930 from the experiments of Riehl
and Wolf that in a good luminescent material, such as ZnS,
roughly 50% of the energy transferred by an alpha particle
to the material is converted into visible light. The answer is
that actually the scintillation counter as such is not so recent,
but was introduced almost half a century ago as an aid in

nuclear research by Rutherford and by Regner who used it to count alpha particles. They used the human eye as the optical receiver, however, since no instruments were available to record the light flashes which could easily be seen with the aid of a small magnifying glass. This only served to render the scintillation method obsolete in a short time, because by the time photomultipliers were developed other methods for detecting alpha particles, such as the proportional counter and ionization chamber, had long since been in use and had proved satisfactory for most purposes. In addition, it was believed that the scintillation counter could not be used to count any but alpha particles because these highly efficient luminescent materials could be used only in thin layers, and light particles and gamma rays are not stopped in thin layers. Thus the matter was left pretty much at the stage it had been in at the time of Rutherford's experiments until 1947 when Broser and Kallmann re-examined the situation and came up with the scintillation counter in its present form.

They attempted to apply the scintillation method to the detection of fast electrons. To produce light flashes from electrons comparable in size to those obtained from alpha particles two conditions had to be fulfilled. One was that the luminescent material have a high light output, i.e., the number of photons emitted for a given absorbed energy, and the second was that the material be highly transparent in order to permit the emergence of the light produced along the rather long path an electron traverses in matter. The first condition was met by the then familiar luminescent materials such as ZnS, but the second was not. These ZnS phosphors were available in powder form only, and this granular structure gives rise to a great deal of internal scattering which lengthens the path of the photon produced in the interior of the powder to such an extent that it is often absorbed before it reaches the surface. Thus light generated inside the powder half a millimeter away from the surface has only a moderate chance to emerge. Since

fast electrons hitting a luminescent powder lose only a relatively small amount of energy in a distance of half a millimeter, these substances are hardly suitable for producing large
light flashes from fast electrons. Therefore, Broser and Kallmann proposed to use large, single crystals of high luminescent
efficiency which are transparent to their own radiation. They
were able to demonstrate the validity of their idea with a large
piece of transparent naphthalene placed on the window of a
photomultiplier. With this arrangement they were able to
record on an oscilloscope the light flashes produced by single
gamma quanta. Naphthalene was used because it was the
only substance available to them (in the rather unscientific
form of moth balls) for which on theoretical grounds they
predicted a high luminescent efficiency under high energy
bombardment.

B. Performance of the Scintillation Counter

A scintillation counter consists as shown in Fig. 8-1 of the
luminescent material (a transparent crystal or liquid), an
optical device to facilitate the collection of light (usually a

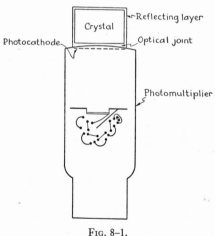

Fig. 8-1.

reflecting layer such as aluminum foil enclosing the luminescent substance), an optical joint between the luminescent material and the photomultiplier to minimize reflection at this surface (Canada Balsam or an oil), the photomultiplier tube, and an electrical circuit to record the pulses appearing at the output of the photomultiplier. A variety of circuits may be used similar to those described earlier for use with Geiger counters.

Before the performance of the scintillation counter is considered in its entirety, it might be well to examine the behavior of some of its components.

The Photomultiplier. The performance of the photomultiplier may be described in terms of its characteristics. The multiplication factor, G, gives the number of electrons appearing at the output for each primary electron released from the photocathode. It increases sharply with the total applied voltage, which is divided almost equally among the various dynodes, and with a potential of -1000 volts between the cathode and ground G exceeds 10^6. Details and curves showing this voltage dependence appear in the various tube handbooks.

Another characteristic of the photomultiplier is its cathode sensitivity, E_c, the number of electrons released per incident photon. The highest values thus far obtained are about 10% for the 1P21 tubes and 5% for the end-window tubes of the 5819 type. E_c depends upon the wave length of the incident light. Curves showing the variation of E_c with wavelength are also given in the tube manuals.

The photomultiplier affects scintillation counting in two ways. The product of the cathode sensitivity and the multiplication factor, $E_c \times G$, determines the size of the pulse produced by a given light flash, and the dark current, the number of pulses occurring without illumination (noise pulses), determines the lowest amount of radiation which can be detected. Actually one should make a distinction between dark current and number of noise pulses. Noise pulses are due to the thermal release of primary electrons from the photocathode, each producing an avalanche of G electrons at the output. The total current due to these noise pulses is $n_0 Ge$ if n_0 is the average number of noise pulses per second and e the electronic charge. But this often accounts for only a small part of the dark current, of the order of several percent. The total dark current is larger due to various sources of leakage in the tube. It consists of a large number of pulses each very much smaller than the noise pulse due to a single primary electron. Both the total dark current, I_0, and the number of noise pulses are important limiting factors for a scintillation measurement; which one is of greater importance depends upon how the unit is employed.

It should be noted that a single primary electron does not always create the same number of electrons, G, at the output. If G is the average multiplication factor, the size of the output pulses fluctuates about G. About 10% of all pulses are larger than $2G$ or smaller than $G/2$, and only a small number are larger than $3G$ or smaller than $G/3$. This lack of uniformity in pulse size is a major consideration in energy determinations using the counter and will be discussed in detail in a later section.

Optical Coupling. Another factor affecting the pulse height produced by a light flash is the optical coupling, C_{op}, between the scintillator and the multiplier. If n is the number of photons emitted by the scintillator, $C_{op} \times n$ gives the number of photons that hit the photocathode. C_{op} is ordinarily less than unity. It can be made to approach unity in multipliers with an end-window and whose photosensitive layer is deposited directly on the inside of the window as in the 5819. Here the geometrical losses are least. The 1P21 type has a side window where considerable losses due to unfavorable geometry are unavoidable. With the end-window photomultiplier the crystal should be cemented to the multiplier with a material of index of refraction close to that of the glass, and the remaining faces of the crystal should be covered with a highly reflecting layer such as metal or a white powder. With this arrangement C_{op} can assume a value as high as 0.8, but a value of 0.5 is considered to be a rather good achievement. When it is not feasible to cement the crystal to the multiplier directly, a light guide may be used. This consists of a rod of highly transparent material such as lucite mounted on the photomultiplier. The crystal is then cemented to the other end of the lucite. The light emanating from the crystal is channeled in the guide in either of two ways, one being total internal reflections at the uncovered side walls of the lucite rod, the other being reflections at a metallic surface surrounding the side walls. In the first case the losses amount to about 50% and are virtually independent of the length of the lucite rod, provided that it is clear; in the second, the losses are only 20% for small rod lengths, but they increase with length due to continuous reflection losses at the metallic surface. For good optical contact between scintillator and photomultiplier or light guide, liquid scintillators are decidedly advantageous.

Luminescent Efficiency. The last factor affecting the pulse size is the luminescent efficiency ϵ of the scintillator. If a high-energy particle loses an energy E in traversing a scintillator, k photons are emitted, where k is given by $\epsilon \dfrac{E}{h\nu}$, ν being the average frequency of the fluorescent light emitted by the scintillator. ϵ gives the percentage of absorbed energy which is transformed into light. Values of ϵ for the more important luminescent materials are given in Table 8–1. These values are most often obtained by measuring the total light output from a luminescent material under the bombardment of a beam of electrons, alpha particles, or gamma-rays of known energy, rather than by observing single light flashes. It is important, therefore, to know accurately the amount of energy absorbed in the material. Because of the difficulties inherent in such measurements the absolute values in Table 8–1 are not very accurate in some cases. The relative efficiencies of

TABLE 8–1. FLUORESCENT EFFICIENCIES FOR VARIOUS EXCITATIONS

| Phosphor | Activator | Efficiency | | Slow Electrons or Soft X-Rays |
		Alpha	Fast Electrons	
ZnS	Ag	0.28	0.135	0.20
ZnS	Cu	.25	.22	.30
CdS	Ag	.23	.23	.15
ZnS/CdS	Cu	.12	.18	.12
CaWO$_4$	—	.017	.08	.04
KBr	Tl	.017	.07	—
CsBr	Tl	—	.23	—
CsI	Tl	—	.06–.16	—
KI	Tl	—	.02–.09	—
LiF	AgCl	—	.0055	—
NaCl	AgCl	—	.126	—
NaI	Tl	—	.08–.22	—
Anthracene Crystal	—	.011	.10 *	—
Anthracene Powder	—	.006	.09	—
Diphenyl	—	.0027	.031	—
Terphenyl (3 gm/l) in Phenylcyclohexane	—	—	.05 †	—

* Some investigators give values of .04 or lower. The differences are very likely due to differences in crystal size and purity. The value of .10 was obtained with a single thin crystal.

† This is the value for the concentration which gives the maximum intensity; the actual physical efficiency extrapolated to zero selfquenching would be .07.

these materials are very much more accurate, but here again deviation from the true values occurs because of the different purities and sizes of the samples.

It may be noted that ϵ is not independent of the energy or, better, of the velocity of the incident particle. This is due to the fact that greater specific ionization is associated with smaller velocity, and it is known that in some scintillators

highly ionizing particles exhibit a smaller ϵ than do weakly ionizing particles.   This is especially true of organic scintillators.

If all the above-mentioned effects are considered together,
the number of electrons appearing at the output of the photomultiplier is given by

$$P = GE_c C_{op}\epsilon \frac{E}{h\nu} = GZ \qquad (8\text{--}1)$$

where Z is the number of primary electrons released.   If the
output capacity is C, the voltage pulse appearing at the output of the photomultiplier is given by

$$V = \frac{e}{C} GE_c C_{op}\epsilon \frac{E}{h\nu} = \frac{eGZ}{C} \qquad (8\text{--}2)$$

where e is the charge on the electron.

The values given by (8–1) and (8–2) are mean values which
are subject to fluctuation, as has already been mentioned, fluctuation which can be described approximately by a Gaussian
distribution of width η.   Examination of η^2 shows that it is
composed of two parts, one stemming from the fluctuation in
the number of primary electrons released from the photo-
cathode, Z, and which is given by $(\overline{\Delta Z})^2 = \overline{Z}$, and the other
from the fluctuation in the multiplication of a single primary
electron in its passage through the multiplier.   The latter
fluctuation decreases with increasing number of primary electrons contained in a single pulse since the result of superim-
posing a large number of small effects of different sign is for
the many small effects to cancel.   It is proportional to
$Z\left(\dfrac{\sigma}{\sigma - 1}\right)$ where σ is the multiplication factor of a single
stage of the multiplier.

Another point which must be considered when applying
eqs. (8–1) and (8–2) concerns the time during which the pulse
appears at the output.   Up to now we have been concerned
only with the total number of photons emitted by the scintil-

lator, the number of electrons released from the photocathode, and the number of electrons collected at the output. We have not considered the fact that the photons are not emitted instantaneously. The time required for the exciting particle to traverse the scintillator in all ordinary nuclear events is of the order of 10^{-10} sec, since the dimensions of the scintillator are usually several centimeters and the velocity of the particle is of the order of 10^{10} cm per sec. The interval of time during which the light emission occurs is much longer, however, ranging from 3×10^{-9} sec for some substances to times of the order of hours for others. For convenience one may describe the emission of photons by an exponential law $N = N_0 e^{-\frac{t}{\tau}}$ where N is the number of photons emitted per second, τ is defined as the decay time of the light pulse, and $N_0 = \frac{\epsilon}{\tau} \frac{E}{h\nu}$. This law is by no means valid for all known materials, but the main portion of the light emitted by many of the more important materials can be described, at least to a first approximation, in this way. The important ZnCdS phosphors constitute a major exception.

If the output of the photomultiplier is connected to ground through a resistance R, we have an electrical circuit with a time constant $\tau_c = RC$, where C is the capacity of the photomultiplier and the circuit connected to it. Then the output voltage as a function of time is given by the following equation $V = V_0 \frac{\tau_c}{\tau_c - \tau} (e^{-\frac{t}{\tau_c}} - e^{-\frac{t}{\tau}})$, which can be obtained from straightforward application of Kirchhoff's laws to an RC circuit with an exponentially decaying input current. V_0 is the total charge appearing at the output of the photomultiplier divided by C. The maximum output voltage V_m is given by

$$V_m = V_0 \left(\frac{\tau}{\tau_c}\right)^{\frac{\tau}{\tau_c - \tau}}$$

The rise time of this pulse is essentially given by the smaller of the two time constants (see Fig. 8–2). The observed maximum, V_m, is always smaller than V_0 and only approaches V_0 for $\tau_c \gg \tau$. For $\tau_c \ll \tau$, $V_m \rightarrow V_0 \frac{\tau_c}{\tau}$ and is only a small fraction of V_0 in this case. To obtain large pulses, τ_c should be

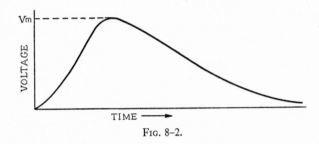

FIG. 8–2.

made large compared to τ. But even with $\tau_c = 10\tau$, V_m is only $0.8V_0$. Therefore, the loss in pulse height incurred when τ_c is not much larger than τ can be considerable. When the apparatus is used for fast counting, it is desirable to make the pulse width small in order to avoid overlapping of pulses. This can be done only by making τ_c small, for the width of the pulse is essentially determined by τ_c as long as $\tau_c > \tau$. Very often τ_c is chosen to be less than 10^{-6} sec, which is still large enough to keep the pulse height high for organic but not for inorganic scintillators.

It may be noted that the pulse depicted in Fig. 8–2 is actually not a smooth curve but consists of numerous small pulses or jumps corresponding to the bursts produced by the single primary electrons which compose the entire pulse. These single small pulses can be seen on an oscilloscope screen when the time axis is sufficiently extended.

The time constants for some important materials are given in Table 8–2.

TABLE 8–2. FLUORESCENT DECAY TIMES

Gamma Excitation

Phosphor	Decay Time $\times 10^{-9}$ Sec
Naphthalene	57–87
Anthracene	23–35
Phenanthrene	8–12
Terphenyl	4–12
Stilbene	4.4–12
NaI (Tl)	250 *
KI (Tl)	>1000 *
CsI (Tl)	>1000 *
LiI (Tl)	>1000 *
CaWO$_4$	∼500 *

Alpha Excitation

ZnS (Ag)	<1000 *

* For many inorganic substances the decay of the light flash can be described only crudely by an exponential function. The figures given above imply that the major portion of the light has been emitted in this interval, but there is a very noticeable tail extending over longer periods of time. This is very apparent in ZnS, particularly when excited by gamma radiation.

Let us now consider an actual situation. Suppose that a fast particle of 1-Mev energy has been absorbed by the scintillator. Assuming $C_{op} = 0.5$, $E_c = 0.05$, $\epsilon = 0.2$ (the value for NaI), $h\nu \sim 3$ ev, and assuming $\dfrac{V_m}{V_0} = \dfrac{2}{3}$, then Z, the number of primary electrons emitted would be 1000. Or, to produce one primary electron, about 1000 ev must be absorbed in a good scintillator under favorable conditions. Different authors give somewhat different figures, but the smallest reported up to now is 710 volts for a particular phosphor, which is in fair agreement with the expected value. The maximum potential appearing at the output of the photomultiplier for 1 Mev absorbed energy, assuming a capacity of 10 $\mu\mu$f, would be 15 volts with a multiplier gain of 10^6. Since a multiplication factor of 10^6 is easily obtained, considerable pulse voltages are produced even by particles of low energy.

These calculations show that there is no difficulty associated with the detection of particles or quanta with energies above 10 kev even when they occur much more infrequently than noise pulses, since under favorable conditions the absorption of 10 kev should produce an average pulse of 10 primary photoelectrons, which can be distinguished from noise pulses. Only for particles with smaller energies does discrimination against noise present a serious problem. To minimize the number of noise pulses, the multiplier can be cooled, reducing in this manner the thermal emission of primary electrons from the photocathode. A reduction in temperature of $10°$ C reduces the number of noise pulses by a factor of 2, roughly.

Three different methods have been developed in order to detect high energy radiation with the aid of scintillators.

1. The counting method, where the individual pulses induced by the absorption of single particles or quanta in the scintillator are recorded.

2. The integrated intensity method, where the total change in electric current $\Delta I = nPe$ appearing at the output of the multiplier as a consequence of the absorption of radiation is measured; n is the number of pulses per second and e the elementary charge. When the incident radiation does not furnish pulses of uniform size but a distribution in pulse size, as is the case when Compton electrons are produced within the scintillator, one must substitute $\overline{P}$ (average P) for P, and if the incident radiation is not homogeneous but consists of different particles or quanta, the total induced current change is given by

$$\Delta I = e \sum_i n_i \overline{P}_i$$

where n_i is the number of particles or quanta of a particular type, and $\overline{P}_i$ is the average pulse height due to this type. In any case n, or n_i, is proportional to the intensity of the incident radiation; thus the change in current is a measure of that intensity.

3. The storage method, where a special type of luminescent material is used, the so-called storage phosphors. These have the ability to store for long periods of time a considerable portion of the energy of the radiation they absorb. This stored energy may be released at any time later by illuminating the phosphor with visible or infrared light. The release of stored energy is accompanied by the emission of light, this light being of the same wave length as the fluorescent light and of shorter wave length than the light which releases it. It is essential that the light which releases the stored energy does not itself excite the phosphor; hence light of long wave length must be used. To investigate unknown radiation, a storage phosphor is exposed to this radiation for a given length of time. Later the phosphor is placed in front of a photomultiplier and the total amount of light which can be released from it determined. The phosphor emits light only when it has previously been excited, and the amount of light which can be released is a measure of the energy which has been stored. This method determines the total energy dose that the phosphor has received rather than the intensity of the radiation with which it was excited. The amount of energy released does not depend upon the total energy dose alone, however. It is also a function of the length of time between irradiation and stimulation. But this presents no difficulty since it can easily be taken into account by calibrating the decay of the storage energy as a function of time.

The range of application of the foregoing methods is the following.

The counting method is the most sensitive. All charged particles and gamma rays produce pulses, even hard gamma rays when a sufficiently thick scintillator is used. It is particularly useful in nuclear investigations since not only the number of particles impinging upon the crystal can be determined but, to a certain extent, the type of radiation can also be determined from the height of the pulses produced. The outstanding feature of the scintillation method in any of its forms is its high detection efficiency, i.e., the ratio of the number of particles detected to the number of incident particles. Where previously gamma radiation could be detected with an efficiency of only several percent, with a scintillation counter the detection efficiency approaches 100% due to the availability of thick transparent scintillator materials. The lower limit of detectable radiation intensity is determined by contamination of the scintillator material and by cosmic radiation, the latter producing pulses which are easily detectable. The noise of the multiplier is not of any great consequence once the height of the desired pulse is sufficiently great. That is, the detection of radiation which transfers more than 10 kev to the scintillator in a single process is not impeded by noise pulses. For the detection of events which transfer only small amounts of energy to the scintillator it is essential to keep the factors in eq. (8–1) as favorable as possible, especially E_c, C_{op}, and ϵ. The efficiency of the photomultiplier cathode should really have the high value claimed for it by the manufacturer since a drop in E_c does not reduce the height of the noise pulses but only their number, if anything, while it does reduce the height of the pulse produced by the light flash. Thus a drop in E_c may make the desired pulse disappear into the noise region. If detection is to be accomplished at the minimum level, it is essential to know the number of noise pulses occurring per second.

The integrated intensity method has the advantage of simplicity since no counting equipment is needed. A simple arrangement consisting of an electrometer tube whose grid resistance is connected to the output of the photomultiplier is sufficient to just detect radiation which gives about the same excitation as cosmic radiation at sea level. In other words, radiation of the order of 10^{-5} roentgen per hour or

10^{-6} erg/sec cm^2 can be detected in this simple manner. Another advantage of this method is that the time constant for light emission is of no importance, provided that it is shorter than the period of observation. The latter is usually of the order of seconds. Therefore, one is not restricted to scintillators with fast decay times as was the case with the counting method in order to avoid overlapping of consecutive

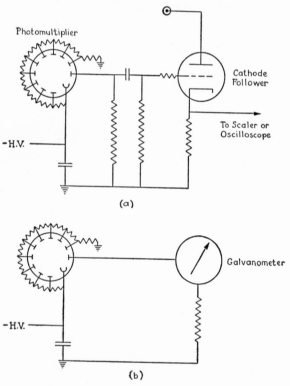

FIG. 8-3.   (a) Circuit used for scintillation pulse counting.   (b) Circuit used for measuring integrated intensities.

pulses. The disadvantage of the integrated intensity method is that it does not discriminate as easily as the counting method between pulses produced by different types of radiation. The lower limit of detectable intensity is determined by the magnitude of the dark current of the multiplier and by its steadiness. With a good tube a change in output current which amounts to 0.1% of the dark current is just detectable. A circuit diagram of the apparatus used in this method is given in Fig. 8–3.

The outstanding feature of the storage method is that the measurement of the radiation, i.e., the excitation of the luminescent material, can be carried out far from the photomultiplier and associated equipment, in a place which may be difficult to reach with that equipment. A radiation dose of 10 mr can easily be detected.

II. APPLICATIONS OF THE SCINTILLATION METHOD

A. Detection of Particles and Quanta

As has already been stated, the detection of electromagnetic radiation and charged particles is possible with an efficiency of almost 100% throughout a wide range of energies. Only for very high and very low energies is any decrease in detection efficiency encountered. The difficulty encountered in the quantitative detection of particles and quanta of low energy stems from the fact that low energy radiation produces light flashes so faint that not every flash releases a primary electron from the photocathode of the multiplier. For 100% detection the lower limit of energy for any one particle is about 1 or 2 kev, when the best geometry, multiplier, and luminescent material are used. Radiation of this type can be measured only by comparing the readings with and without incident radiation because the pulses cannot be distinguished from noise pulses.

In the high energy range deviations from 100% detection efficiency occur only for gamma radiation. Most scintillators have a thickness of about 2 inches. If NaI is used, it being a heavy material, at least 70% of hard gamma radiation is absorbed in this thickness. To bring the absorption up to 90%

the crystal thickness must be doubled. In order to achieve the same detection efficiency as NaI an organic crystal must be roughly four times larger. The use, however, of large scintillators involves several difficulties. First, the size itself may be awkward to use. Then, such large crystals are costly and difficult to obtain. This obstacle is often surmounted by the use of long liquid columns. The use of long scintillators entails another difficulty, however, and that is that the light generated in parts remote from the photomultiplier window does not reach the photocathode as well as does light from nearer sections because of absorption and reflection losses at the surface. This causes the light flashes produced by monochromatic gamma radiation to vary in size far more than they would in a small crystal. If this can be tolerated, close to 100% efficiency can be obtained. Usually one is satisfied with a detection efficiency of 70%, this being extremely high compared to other detection devices. Solid solutions of fluorescent molecules in plastic have also been used as scintillators with success.

a. Electromagnetic Radiation: While charged particles are detected by means of their direct interaction with the luminescent material, electromagnetic radiation is detected by means of the secondary electrons produced in matter. Electromagnetic radiation produces light flashes in a scintillator as a consequence of three elementary processes: (1) photoelectric absorption; (2) Compton scattering; and (3) production of electron position pairs. The first process produces electrons of an energy $h(\nu_0 - \nu_{K,L,M}...)$, where ν_0 is the frequency of the incident radiation, and $\nu_{K,L,M}...$ denotes the absorption frequency of the atom in the different electronic shells $K, L, M...$. Since the absorption in the K shell, or in the lowest shell excitable, is always predominant, the photoelectric process produces pulses which are almost uniform in size. In heavy luminescent materials such as NaI it is the photoelectric process which is most prevalent for an incident energy up to several hundred kev. In organic materials the Compton process is more probable even in the X-ray region because of the small probability of photoelectric absorption in carbon and oxygen atoms. Recently, however, liquid organic luminescent materials containing somewhat heavier atoms have been developed; here the photoelectric process may play an important rôle. The Compton process results in a whole range of energies being transferred to the scintillator by a monochromatic incident gamma ray beam, since the end products of the process are an electron and a gamma of lower frequency than the original with the original energy divided between the two. The maximum energy transferred to the crystal is

$$\Delta E_{max} = \frac{2(h\nu_0)^2}{mc^2}\left(\frac{1}{1 + \frac{2h\nu_0}{mc^2}}\right)$$

where $h\nu_0$ is the energy of the incident gamma and mc^2 is the rest energy of the electron. All energies from zero to this maximum energy occur. The majority of the electrons produced in the Compton process take on an energy rather close to the maximum energy; thus the distribution curve of the light flashes exhibits a definite maximum at the position corresponding to the largest energy imparted to the scintillator.

The third process, that of pair production, is important only at very high gamma ray energies, of the order of several Mev, and in heavy materials. The probability of producing a pair increases with increasing $h\nu_0$ and increasing atomic number of the scintillator, as opposed to the probability of the Compton process which decreases with increasing $h\nu_0$. The energy transmitted to the crystal is always $h\nu_0 - 2mc^2$; thus light flashes of uniform size are produced.

The scintillator which has proved most useful for the detection of gamma radiation is NaI because of its high atomic number which enables it to stop even hard gamma radiation in a thickness of several centimeters, its high luminescent efficiency, and the fact that this efficiency is not dependent upon the energy of the incident radiation (it is nearly the same for strongly ionizing as for weakly ionizing particles as contrasted with the organic crystals whose luminescent efficiencies decrease with increasing specific ionization). Its disadvantages are: it is affected by air and must therefore be used in a sealed protective enclosure if it is not to become cloudy and less efficient; and the time constant for the decay of the light flash is longer than that of the organic phosphors (see Table 8–2), a factor which is of considerable importance in coincidence work.

Because of their short decay times, organic materials, liquid and solid, are also used for gamma radiation. Their disadvantage, as has already been mentioned, is the dependence of luminescent efficiency upon the specific ionization of the incident particle. For the same amount of energy transferred to the crystal, the light flash produced by a 1-Mev electron is almost twenty times larger than that produced by a 1-Mev alpha particle. This decrease in efficiency with higher density of excitation is also noticeable with electromagnetic radiation. X-rays of 100 kev display a higher density of ionization and excitation than gamma radiation of more than 0.5 Mev of energy, and the luminescent efficiency of organic materials is less for the X-rays than for the gamma radiation. For soft X-rays the effect is quite pronounced. Because of the high specific ionization of 10-kev electrons, the response in organic crystals is rather small.

b. Charged particles produce light by the direct ionization and excitation they produce in luminescent materials. In those materials which display a luminescent efficiency almost independent of the specific ionization of the particle the amount of light emitted is proportional to the energy transferred to the material along each segment of the path. For those materials which do not exhibit this independence the amount of light emitted for equal amounts of absorbed energy varies along the path and decreases strongly at the end of the path where the velocity is least and, hence, where the ionization and excitation are greatest.   In spite of this, the total amount of light produced by a fast electron is very nearly proportional to the total energy of the particle if it is stopped in the phosphor, because the decrease in luminescent efficiency sets in only at low energies and thus only a relatively small part of the total energy is affected by the decrease.   In general, the choice of a suitable scintillator for charged particles is governed by similar considerations as that for gamma radiation.   For highly ioniz⁻ ing particles luminescent substances of the ZnCdS group are most effective, but they exhibit nonuniformity of pulse height even for monoenergetic particles when used in powder form; only single crystals of this material produce uniform pulses.

c. Neutrons are detected by means of secondary reactions. Fast neutrons of greater than 1-Mev energy are detected by the light flashes produced by recoil protons in luminescent matter containing hydrogen, i.e., organic substances.   These protons display a smaller light efficiency in the crystal than electrons of corresponding energy because of their higher specific ionization.   Thus the pulse heights produced by moderately fast neutrons are, on the average, very much smaller than those of electrons of equal energy.   Protons of several hundred kev produce light flashes which, in turn, produce electrical pulses in the photomultiplier which are larger than noise pulses.   The situation becomes worse with decreasing neutron energy and is aggravated by the fact that the average energy imparted to the recoil proton is considerably less than the energy of the original neutron because the protons assume a continuous distribution of energies.   Organic substances have, however, a high efficiency for the detection of neutrons.   In a scintillator several inches thick as many as one third of the neutrons penetrating the substance react with protons.

For the detection of neutrons of moderate energy any reaction which produces charged particles or gamma radiation as an end product could be used, but the efficiency of a device employing these reactions would, of necessity, be very low because of their small cross sections. Detection becomes particularly difficult when the weak neutron intensities are present together with other radiation from which the neutrons must be distinguished.

The following reactions with boron and lithium are the ones most often used in the detection of neutrons of low or moderate energy:

$$_0n^1 + {_3}Li^6 \rightarrow {_1}H^3 + {_2}He^4 + 4.78 \text{ Mev}$$

$$_0n^1 + {_5}B^{10} \rightarrow {_2}He^4 + {_3}Li^7 + 2.79 \text{ Mev}$$

The resulting charged particles give rise to light flashes. Liquid scintillators containing boron, and crystals of LiI activated with europium are used. In both cases the resulting light flashes are not very large; in the liquid case this is due again to the low luminescent efficiency for highly ionizing particles. Since the cross section for thermal neutrons is rather high in boron and lithium, a high detection efficiency for these neutrons can be obtained, using luminescent materials containing only small amounts of lithium or boron. If the detector is to be used for neutrons of greater than thermal energies also, then it is of importance to have scintillators with rather high lithium and boron concentrations, for the reaction cross section decreases in proportion to the increase in neutron velocity. Another possible detector is the combination of ZnCdS with boron or lithium in order to utilize the high luminescent efficiency of the former for heavy particles. Arrangements of this type have rather low detection efficiencies.

B. Discrimination Between Different Types of Radiation

A more complex problem than the mere detection of radiation is the discrimination between different types of radiation, especially when they occur together. Discrimination is made possible by utilizing the characteristic responses of various luminescent materials to different types of radiation. If, in addition to the number of pulses appearing at the photomultiplier output, their distribution in size is also recorded, some conclusions may be drawn as to the nature of the radiation, since each particle or quantum of definite energy produces a characteristic pulse height distribution in a given scintillator. The ideal situation would be one in which there would be different scintillators for each type of radiation which would respond to that radiation and no other. This is partially the case when one distinguishes charged particles from gamma radiation by selecting thin layers of material of low atomic number for use as phosphors. These have a high detection efficiency for charged particles and a low one for gamma radiation because of the small probability that a gamma ray will be absorbed in a thin layer of light material. The problem of distinguishing charged particles from gamma radiation is actually not a serious one, for there are methods other than observation of the pulse distribution which can easily perform the discrimination. A problem which is important, however, is the detection of weak neutron intensities in the presence of gamma radiation. A boron- or lithium-lined alpha detector, containing ZnS for example, would achieve this purpose, and such a detector was actually used in early experiments when luminescent screens were employed in neutron detection. The effects of the alpha or $_1H^3$ particle produced in the neutron reaction with boron or lithium are predominant if the ZnS layer is made only thick enough to absorb the charged particles completely. The effects of gamma radiation in so thin a layer will be exceedingly small. The disadvantage of this method is that only a small number of neutrons are recorded, only those which are absorbed in the thin layer of boron or lithium from which the alpha or $_1H^3$ particles can emerge and penetrate the ZnS layer. Those which react with the lithium or boron at a distance from the ZnS greater than the range of the charged particles are not recorded.

The liquid boron counter accomplishes the discrimination between gammas and neutrons in a manner opposite to that described above. Here a liquid containing boron is used in large thicknesses. Gamma rays therefore produce a great number of large pulses and only a few small ones. The alpha pulses released from boron by the neutrons, however, are always small. Therefore, if this counter is equipped with a device such as a pulse height analyzer which is set to record only the small pulses, it will overwhelmingly favor the counting of neutron pulses. This arrangement works as long as the gamma intensity does not exceed the neutron intensity by a great deal.

C. Energy Determination with the Scintillation Counter

As was stated earlier, it is possible to determine the energy of the incident radiation by observing the distribution in height of the pulses induced in the photomultiplier of the scintillation unit, because for a given type of radiation the size of the light flash emitted is a direct function of the energy transferred to the luminescent material. In materials whose luminescent efficiency is independent of the specific ionization of the particle absorbed the pulse height is directly proportional to the absorbed energy. In materials which do exhibit this dependence the pulse height can be calibrated as a function of the energy absorbed for each type of particle; then the energy of the incident radiation may be determined by comparing the observed height distribution with the calibration.

If the particle is completely absorbed in the scintillator, the pulse height is a measure of the total energy of the particle. The energy of alpha particles and electrons can be determined relatively easily if the range of these particles is smaller than the dimensions of the scintillator. For gamma radiation the situation is somewhat more complex because the energy imparted to the scintillator is not equal to the energy of the incident gamma ray $h\nu_0$. The light flash is produced either by a photoelectron process, where the energy given to the scintillator is $E_s = E_{h\nu_0} - E_{K,L,M}\cdots$ ($E_{K,L,M}\cdots$ is the absorption energy of the various electronic levels in the scintillator), or by pair production, where $E_s = E_{h\nu_0} - 2m_0c^2$, or by a Compton process, where the energy given to the scintillator takes on a whole spectrum of values as has been discussed in Section A. But since the Compton distribution produces a sharp maximum at the value given on page 311, from the position of this maximum the energy of the original gamma ray can be determined. Because three processes are induced by gamma radiation it is possible that, with a single energy, $h\nu_0$, three different maxima may appear in the pulse height distribution curve, one for each process. Knowledge of the relationship existing between these maxima enables one to attribute all three to the one $h\nu_0$, however, even when several gamma rays of different energies are present. The foregoing considerations indicate the necessity for having an apparatus which not only counts the pulses appearing at the output of the multiplier but which, in addition, assorts them according to size. An instrument that accomplishes this in a somewhat primitive manner is a scaler which records only those pulses above a certain adjustable level. If a series of readings are taken for different settings of this level, the total number of pulses above a certain pulse height is obtained as a function of the pulse height. Then, by differentiating this curve, the true pulse height distribution is obtained, i.e., the number of pulses occurring in each pulse height interval. This is a somewhat tedious and inaccurate method since the number of pulses in the interval between V_i and V_{i+1} is given by $N_i - N_{i+1}$, where N_i and N_{i+1} are the total number of pulses with heights larger than V_i and V_{i+1} respectively. Both N_i and N_{i+1} are large numbers; therefore the accuracy of the difference between them will not be very great unless N_i and N_{i+1} are determined with a great deal of precision, i.e., by counting a large number of pulses.

The differentiation can be obtained automatically by the use of a multichannel pulse height analyzer. This is a scaler which counts the pulses occurring in ten or more channels, each channel counting only pulses between certain adjustable voltages. The instrument gives the desired pulse height distribution in one run, thereby reducing the measuring time considerably. The accuracy in the number of pulses in a particular interval is not given by the accuracy of the difference between two large numbers, but by the accuracy in the number of pulses in a particular channel, which is decidedly greater.

A multichannel pulse height analyzer is a rather complicated instrument. A much simpler but less accurate means for determining the pulse height distribution consists of observing the height of the pulses appearing at the screen of an oscilloscope.

The accuracy with which an energy measurement can be made depends both upon the accuracy with which the position of the maximum can be determined, i.e., the counting accuracy, and upon the resolving power of the entire apparatus. The resolving power determines the width of the maximum and hence the ability to distinguish between neighboring peaks which are due to different energies. Contributions to the width of the maxima have three sources: one is the fluctuation in the number of primary electrons released from the photocathode of the multiplier for a given amount of energy absorbed in the scintillator; the second is the fluctuation in the multiplication of a single primary electron (see page 301); and the third is the fluctuation due to geometrical factors, such as the exciting particle not being completely absorbed in the scintillator, or its exciting the scintillator in a section remote from the multiplier so that less light proceeds to the photocathode than from other sections, or the intensity of the light flash not being uniformly distributed over the multiplier window coupled with the photocathode not being uniformly sensitive over its entire area, or inhomogeneities in the light efficiency of the crystal itself.   The first fluctuation, ΔZ, is given by $\sqrt{\overline{Z}}$ where $\overline{Z}$ is the average number of primary electrons released.   The percentage fluctuation due to this source is $\dfrac{\Delta Z}{\overline{Z}} \times 100$, which decreases with increasing size of the light flash.   The percentage fluctuation due to the fluctuation in multiplication likewise decreases with increasing size of the light flash.   These fluctuations are inherent to the scintillator and multiplier and can only be minimized by making the factors of eq. (8–1) as high as possible.   This can be accomplished by using luminescent materials and photocathodes of high efficiency and avoiding loss of light between the scintillator and the multiplier.   As for the fluctuations due to geometrical factors, this can be reduced by a suitable choice of scintillator material.   Large, clear transparent scintillators are essential in this type of work, the size being limited only by the losses suffered through absorption of light inside the scintillator, or losses incurred through repeated reflections at the surfaces.   A further reduction of fluctuation can be effected by selecting a rather narrow beam of the radiation under investigation, making the path of different light flashes as uniform as possible.   With all these precautions, measurements can be made to have rather high accuracy, and a resolution of several percent can be obtained.

One of the first experiments to determine the energy of particles with a scintillation counter was performed by Broser and Kallmann using alpha particles.   They found that ZnS powder excited by monoenergetic alpha particles did not emit pulses of a definite size but a rather wide band of pulses of different sizes.   This distribution was attributed to the strong scattering of the light inside the luminescent powder at the grain boundaries.   When the powder was replaced by a single CdS crystal they obtained pulses of nearly equal height which could be used to determine the energy of the incident alpha particle.

The problem of energy determination for gamma radiation, more difficult because of the several reactions induced (see page 310), is further complicated by the fact that, although alpha particles can easily be restricted to a small region of the scintillator, gamma radiation excites the scintillator over a large area and thus the electrons produced in the scintillator travel through a large part of the crystal. Gamma energy spectroscopy was carefully accomplished by Hofstadter and McIntyre, using techniques which increase the accuracy of such determinations considerably. They will be considered in greater detail in the next section.

D. Coincidence Measurements

Another realm in which the scintillation counter has proved to be of great use concerns the investigation of correlated single events such as the scattering of several particles, or the emission of an electron from a nucleus and the subsequent emission of a gamma ray or internal conversion electron, or the angular correlation between particles and quanta emitted in different directions, to mention only a few. Progress in these fields has been made possible by the circumstance that the light flash in the scintillator decays in a very short time, of the order of 3×10^{-9} sec in organic liquids. For all correlation work it is important to establish the coincidence of the events and to discriminate between true coincidences and those occurring accidentally. This is done by making the resolution time T during which two events are considered to be coincident as short as possible. For a given external radiation the number of accidental coincidences decreases with T, while the number of true coincidences remains constant. Thus, by using scintillation coincidence circuits in which events are recorded as coincident only if one follows the other in less than 10^{-8} sec, the number of accidental coincidences is sharply reduced, enabling one to record even those true coincidences which occur relatively infrequently.

Another advantage of the scintillation counter in this type of work stems from its high detection efficiency. If a gamma ray is involved in the coincident process and detectors other than a scintillator are employed, many true coincidences escape detection because of the low detection efficiency for gamma rays. If, however, a scintillator with high detection efficiency for gamma radiation is used, a large number of true coincidences will be recorded, and hence even the rare event will not escape detection. The scintillation coincidence circuit is the same as other coincidence circuits, the only difference being that the detector is a scintillator coupled to a photomultiplier. The resolving time of the circuit, the time during which two unrelated events one following the other are not recorded as a coincidence, depends upon the time required by the scintillator and multiplier to decay to a value of $1/e$ of the maximum excitation. That the de-excitation time of the multiplier, as well as that of the scintillator, is a determining factor of the resolution time is due to the finite time of flight of the electrons in the multiplier or, more accurately, to the spread in the time of flight of an avalanche of electrons. Usually the multiplier response is faster than that of the scintillator, but with some tubes (5819) the flight time is comparable with the decay time of the fastest scintillators.

One might mention here that the high time resolution of scintillation coincidence detectors can also be used to determine the small time differences which exist between correlated events.

Scintillation coincidence counters were used by Hofstadter and McIntyre to determine gamma-ray energies. Making use of the Compton effect, they measured the size of the light flash produced by the recoil electron in one scintillator, while another scintillator in coincidence with the first recorded the associated scattered gamma photon. From the size of the pulse in the first scintillator they determined the energy of the recoil electron. The angle made by the second scintillator with the incident direction gives the angle through which the incident gamma was scattered. These two pieces of information are sufficient to determine the energy of the original photon. In an analogous manner triple scintillation coincidences have been used by others to determine the energy of electron pairs.

Still another application of scintillation coincidences is the study of radioactive decay schemes.

III. THE PHYSICS OF LIGHT EMISSION FROM SCINTILLATORS EXCITED BY HIGH ENERGY RADIATION

We turn now to the physics of luminescence in solid and liquid matter. The problems in this field are so varied that it is beyond the scope of this article to deal with them in any great detail. We shall restrict our discussion, therefore, to three of the more important questions raised by a study of the scintillation counter. The first is the fundamental question of why only certain materials are highly fluorescent whereas others do not fluoresce at all. The second is the question of how it is possible that a large amount of energy, several percent of the total energy absorbed, is emitted in only a relatively small spectral band when matter is excited by high energy radiation, a process in which practically all energy levels of a system are excited. The third question is concerned with how a large amount of light is emitted in some cases by only a relatively small number of "special" molecules (activators, impurities, or solute molecules) when the energy imparted to the substance is absorbed by the molecules of the bulk material.

The elementary processes of fluorescence can be described in the following way: if a certain energy level, usually the lowest excited state of the system, is excited, there are various ways for the excited electron to return to the ground state. We shall divide these into radiationless transitions and transitions accompanied by the emission of light. The probability of a radiationless transition is given by $1/\tau_{RL}$ and that for an emission transition by $1/\tau_R$, where τ_{RL} and τ_R are the lifetimes of the system when the specified transition occurs alone. The fluorescent efficiency ϵ is then given by

$$\epsilon = \frac{(1/\tau_R)}{(1/\tau_R) + (1/\tau_{RL})} = \frac{\tau_{RL}}{\tau_{RL} + \tau_R}$$

One sees, then, that there is a competition between two processes. If the probability of radiationless transitions is large relative to the probability of emission transitions, the fluorescent efficiency will be low even when the absolute probability of emission transitions is not small. The probability of emission transitions can be determined, at least to some extent, from absorption measurements since a correlation between emission and absorption exists. It has been found that in many systems the probability of radiationless transitions depends greatly upon the structure of the light-emitting atom or molecule and, in some cases, upon the surroundings of these molecules. Small changes in the structure of a molecule can affect the probability of radiationless transitions considerably, without affecting the probability of emission transitions. This can be seen from the little change which occurs in the absorption spectrum of the system. Therefore, an effective calculation of the fluorescent efficiency depends largely upon our knowledge of the probability of radiationless transitions, a knowledge which has remained incomplete up to the present.

There is, however, another relationship which is of use in the investigation of fluorescent efficiencies. The probabilities of emission and radiationless transitions determine not only the efficiency of a fluorescent process but also the lifetime of the excited states, which is the observed decay time of the fluorescent molecule. If τ is the lifetime of these states, then the following relationship exists:

$$\frac{1}{\tau} = \frac{1}{\tau_R} + \frac{1}{\tau_{RL}} \quad \text{or} \quad \tau = \frac{\tau_R \tau_{RL}}{\tau_R + \tau_{RL}}$$

Therefore, from a measurement of τ, knowledge concerning the probability of radiationless transitions can be obtained. The reverse is also true. If τ_R is known from absorption measurements, for instance, and if the fluorescent light output is known, one can determine τ. It can be seen, then, that the lifetimes of the scintillators as given in Table 8–2 are intimately connected with the probability of radiationless transitions. The work in this field is not sufficiently advanced, however, to give a full account of these probabilities and lifetimes for each scintillator material.

Before proceeding further it must be emphasized that the simple description given above holds in the main only for systems in which one kind of transition occurs. In systems where more than one transition must be taken into account the energy which can be emitted as light is not only used to excite one kind of molecule or atom but may also excite other atoms which are present as impurities, for example. It was found that in such cases the excitation energy itself, or the excited electrons, may be trapped by these impurities for relatively long periods of time without their returning to the ground state. One speaks then of the trapping of the excitation energy and its storage. In some instances years can elapse before the energy is finally released in the emission of light. This trapping of excitation energy by impurities is the explanation for the storage phenomena described at the end of Section IB.

There is still another condition which must generally be fulfilled in order for strong fluorescence to be observed. The fluorescent light must not be absorbed to any great extent in the bulk material of the scintillator. If the fluorescent light is reabsorbed, an excited molecule is produced anew and once more radiationless transitions have the opportunity to occur. Thus each reabsorption increases the probability of occurrence of radiationless transitions and leads to a decrease in fluorescent light output. The fact that the emission spectra of all fluorescent materials are displaced to the longer wave lengths with respect to the absorption band of the bulk material gives credence to these considerations. This shift of the fluorescent spectrum comes about in two ways. Each transition which leads to light emission is related to an absorption transition. In atomic gases the emission transition usually takes place between the same levels as the absorption transition, and so the absorption and emission spectra are coincident. But very often with molecules, especially in solids and liquids, the emission spectrum is shifted somewhat to the longer wave-length part of the spectrum because of the strong coupling between electron motion and atomic vibration. The electronic absorption occurs with considerable probability only when there is simultaneous excitation of atomic vibration (Franck-Condon principle). Thus the excited state created by absorption is an excited electronic state plus atomic vibration of the molecule or the lattice of the bulk material or even the surrounding solvent molecules. These atomic vibrations are dissipated very rapidly, and only the excited electronic state remains. The light emitted from this state has a longer wave length than the absorption wave length, and so the emission spectrum is displaced with respect to the absorption spectrum, preventing reabsorption of the emitted light. This shift to longer wave lengths becomes more pronounced due to the fact that the transition from the excited electronic state is not to the unexcited ground state but to the ground state with atomic vibration. If there is only a small overlap of the absorption and emission spectra, the emitted light can still be absorbed by the bulk material, but only to a small extent. The fluorescence of most organic substances in solid and liquid form can be described in this way. This mechanism also plays an important rôle in the description of some inorganic luminescent materials.

The shift of the spectrum of the fluorescent light to longer wave lengths is still more accentuated when the light is emitted from activators. Only those activators are effective whose emission spectra are much more in the longer wave-length region than the absorption band of the bulk material. Since the activators are present in only small concentrations their emitted light is certainly absorbed far less than if they were as numerous as the atoms of the bulk material, but even in the concentrations ordinarily used one would expect a noticeable absorption if the emission and absorption spectra of the activators coincided. That this absorption is not very noticeable in the scintillator thicknesses normally used indicates that in all probability the emission spectrum of the activators is also shifted to longer wave lengths.

How important absorption effects can be is shown in Fig. 8–4 in which the intensity of fluorescent radiation of a powdered inorganic material is given as a function of the sample thickness. The excitation was furnished by alpha particles, fast electrons, and hard gamma radiation. The gamma energy was barely attenuated along the path through the sample. One would expect, therefore, that the amount of light emitted would be proportional to the thickness of the sample, since the amount of absorbed energy increases with the sample thickness. The curves show, however, that even at relatively small thicknesses there is a saturation in the amount of light emitted. With alpha and electron excitation the curves actually show a decrease. The saturation does not occur if single crystals are used instead of powdered samples except at much greater thicknesses. The reason for the saturation is that in a powdered sample the path of the light produced in the interior becomes so long as a consequence of repeated scattering at the grain boundaries that when the thickness becomes too great (>100 mgm/cm²) the light is absorbed before it reaches the

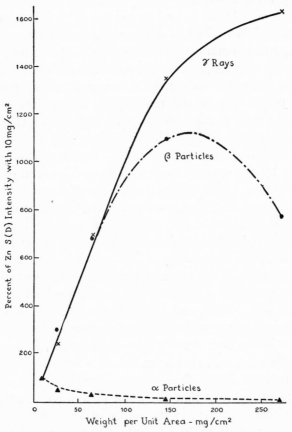

FIG. 8–4. Response of ZnS (D) powder to high energy radiation.

surface. It was found further that the shorter wave lengths of the emitted light are more strongly attenuated than the longer wave lengths, the reason being that the absorption spectrum lies at shorter wave lengths than the emission spectrum, and thus absorption increases with decreasing wave length. It is this absorption of their own fluorescent light which makes powdered samples such inefficient scintillators for high energy radiation which requires large thicknesses from which light can emerge.

We turn now to the second question. How is it possible for a material when excited by high energy radiation to emit all its light, which amounts to a considerable percentage of the total energy absorbed, within a relatively small spectral band, when the radiation excites the different electrons with comparable probability to different higher excited states? The energy of a fast particle in its path through matter is constantly dissipated, and its initially high energy (in the case of gamma radiation it is the energy of the secondary electron produced by the gamma quantum) is divided into numerous smaller quanta which excite the different electrons to many excitation levels and may even ionize the atoms or molecules. Some of the electrons can receive rather large amounts of energy; this occurs, however, with only small probability, and when it happens, this energy is further dissipated in the same manner as that of the primary particle. The excitation and ionization energy is then converted either into heat or directly into radiation. Since the probability of interaction of the higher excited states with the atomic vibration levels is rather high, one infers that considerable conversion of energy into atomic vibration, i.e., into heat, occurs when the excited electrons return to lower electronic excitation levels. There is also some probability that radiation of a wave length in the far ultraviolet is emitted in the course of these processes. But if this were to happen, the radiation would be quickly reabsorbed by the material and eventually converted into heat. It has been observed that the fluorescent spectrum of a material excited by high energy radiation is practically the same as that excited by light, in which case only the lowest state is excited. This can be explained by the process described above of the electrons returning to lower states converting their excitation energy constantly into heat until they reach the lowest excitation level where again radiationless transitions can occur with considerable probability. For these states of lowest excitation energy, however, the probability of light emission is not always small compared to the probability of radiationless transition and hence light emission can occur. Thus light emission from luminescent materials is due practically only to electronic transitions from the lowest excited state to the ground state, and this is the reason for the small region of the spectrum occupied by the emission band.

One might assume that the light observed from one particular transition in the molecule is just that portion of the total energy with which a particular electron (in an organic molecule, for instance, the electron which constitutes the double bond) was excited during the passage of the high energy particle. What actually happens, however, is that the excitation energy of many other electrons (for instance, those of the single bonds) will contribute at least in part to the excitation of the lowest excited state of the molecule or lattice in the following manner. A particular electron which has been excited becomes de-excited by transferring its energy to atomic vibrations. In making its final transition, that to the unexcited level, a rather large amount of energy is available for conversion into atomic vibration. Instead, this energy may be used to excite another electron in the same molecule through direct interaction, and only the excess energy between these two electronic transitions is converted into atomic vibration. Thus the excitation energy of different electrons may be "collected" in the state of lowest excitation of the molecule or lattice, from which light emission takes place.

The third question, that of how emission takes place from the small number of activators when the entire material is excited, can be answered if the process of energy transfer inside the bulk material and from the bulk material to the light-emitting molecule is considered. Two means for this transfer of energy are known. One occurs when the excitation of a material consists of the production of electrons and positive charges (holes), both free to move independently, the former in the conduction band and the latter in the valence band. The holes migrate through the bulk material until they are trapped by the activators, the activator atom losing an electron and becoming ionized in the trapping process. Meanwhile the free electron moving in the conduction band of the bulk material collides with an activator which has previously been ionized, recombines with it, and emits light in the recombination process. Here the transfer of excitation energy takes place by the independent free motion of the positive and negative charges. This mechanism was first proposed for the ZnCdS type of luminescent material by Riehl and Schön. It was corroborated by experiments which showed that the ZnCdS type phosphors exhibit electrical conductivity under both light and high energy excitation. The other method for transferring energy in activator emission proceeds by the migration of the excitation energy as such (excitons) through the bulk material. The excitation energy moves from molecule to molecule in a kind of diffusion until it collides with an activator or a solute molecule and is trapped. The trapping comes about when the excitation energy of the emitting solute or activator molecule is smaller than that of the bulk material. When an excited bulk molecule transfers its energy to the activator molecule, it produces an excited electronic state in the activator as well as atomic vibrations. The vibrations are dissipated very rapidly and the purely electronic excited state of the activator molecule remains, the energy of which is too small to re-excite the bulk material. This type of energy transport was first considered by Franck and Teller and its existence demonstrated for organic molecules by Bowen, who used light excitation. Kallmann and Furst assume the same kind of energy transport to be responsible for the excitation to strong fluorescence of dilute solutions under high energy radiation. Curves of the type of those in Fig. 8–5 can be explained in the following way: At low solute concentrations, no transfer of energy from the bulk material to the solute occurs and the energy is dissipated in the solvent without light emission. With increasing solute concentration the probability of collision between excited molecules and solute molecules becomes greater and

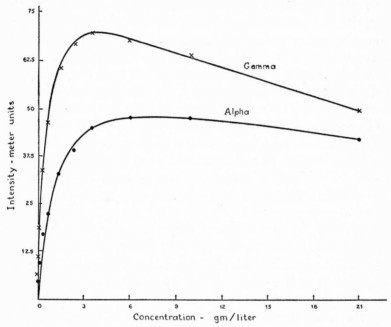

FIG. 8–5. Variation of emitted light intensity for various concentrations of phenyl alpha-naphthylamine in xylene for both gamma and alpha excitation.

therefore the amount of energy transferred to the solute increases. Now it is known from measurements of Vavilov that under light excitation the fluorescent efficiency of dilute solutions decreases with increasing concentration, a process called "selfquenching" taking place which diminishes the amount of energy emitted in the form of light. Because of this decrease in the probability of light emission with increasing concentration the amount of light emitted by a solution under high energy excitation does not continually increase until it reaches a saturation value where all the energy of the bulk material is transferred to the solute; instead the amount of light emitted reaches a maximum and then decreases with further increase in concentration. The energy transfer from the bulk material to the activator could also take place by means of absorption of radiation instead of by collision. Energy transfer by absorption has been studied by Kallmann and Furst and has been found to occur between solute molecules of different types. Here various solutes are dissolved in one solvent. A solute molecule of type 1 emits light which is in turn absorbed by a solute molecule of type 2. This is re-emitted as light of longer wave length. This type of energy transfer has been made use of in order to shift the spectral distribution of the fluorescent light more to the visible, where photomultipliers are more sensitive. Kallmann and Furst used a terphenyl solution which emits in the near ultraviolet. The addition of very small amounts of diphenylhexatriene caused the terphenyl radiation to be absorbed and re-emitted as blue light. They also investigated whether energy transfer by absorption of light could take place between the bulk material and the solute molecule. For such a process to occur it would be necessary for the bulk material to emit a large amount of radiation which is much more highly absorbed by the few solute molecules than by the large number of bulk molecules. Since no radiation other than that emitted by the solute molecules was detected, rather than attribute the transfer of energy to a "hidden" radiation, Kallmann and Furst concluded that the energy transport occurs by means of collision. Some investigators still assume, however, that the energy is transported by means of the absorption of this "hidden" radiation of rather short wave length which is produced by the high energy radiation. Other experiments performed by Kallmann and Furst tend to invalidate the assumption of transfer by absorption. These experiments showed that the same type of energy transport as is observed for high energy excitation also occurs when the excitation is produced by light of rather long wave length, and in the latter case the possibility of existence of hidden radiation of short wave length is excluded.

Finally, an experiment may be described which conclusively demonstrates the important rôle of energy transport in the production of fluorescent light when the excitation is produced by high energy radiation. Two solutions of one solute, diphenylanthracene in xylene and in hexane, for example, exhibit nearly equal fluorescent efficiencies under light excitation, while under high energy excitation the fluorescent efficiency of the hexane solution is much lower than that of xylene. The reason for this is that under high energy excitation the fluorescence comes about by energy transfer from the bulk material to the solute, while under light excitation the solute molecules are directly excited, the solvent not being affected at all. In hexane and xylene the fluorescent efficiencies of diphenylanthracene is roughly the same. Therefore, under light excitation, where the diphenylanthracene is excited directly, both solutions give the same light intensity. Under high energy excitation, however, energy transfer from the solvent to the solute is necessary. In hexane the probability of energy transfer is rather small because of the short lifetimes of the excited states of the hexane molecules, while in xylene the probability of transfer is high. Therefore, less energy is transferred from the hexane to the solute than from the xylene, and so the amount of light emitted is smaller in the former case than in the latter.

References

Section I

P. R. Bell, *Phys. Rev.* **73,** 1405 (1948)

A. Bril and H. A. Klasens, *Philips Research Report 7,* 401 (1952)

I. Broser and H. Kallmann, *Zeits. f. Naturforsch.* **2a,** 439 (1947)

I. Broser and H. Kallmann, *Zeits. f. Naturforsch.* **2a,** 642 (1947)

Broser, Herforth, Kallmann, and Martius, *Zeits. f. Naturforsch.* **3a,** 6 (1948)

G. B. Collins, *Phys. Rev.* **74**, 1543 (1948)

G. B. Collins and R. C. Hoyt, *Phys. Rev.* **73**, 1259 (1948)

J. W. Coltman and F. H. Marshall, *Phys. Rev.* **72**, 528 (1947)

S. C. Curran, *Luminescence and the Scintillation Counter*, Academic Press, New York (1953)

M. Deutsch, *Nucleonics* **2**, 58 (1948)

Garlick and Wright, *Proc. Phys. Soc. (Lond.)* **B65**, 415 (1952)

R. Hofstadter, *Phys. Rev.* **74**, 100 (1948)

Hofstadter, Liebson, and Elliot, *Phys. Rev.* **78**, 81 (1950)

W. H. Jordan and P. R. Bell, *Nucleonics* **5/4**, 30 (1949)

H. Kallmann, *Natur. & Technik*, July (1947)

A. Lundby, *Phys. Rev.* **80**, 477 (1950)

R. J. Moon, *Phys. Rev.* **73**, 1210 (1948)

G. A. Morton, *RCA Rev.* **10**, 523 (1949)

G. A. Morton and J. A. Mitchell, *RCA Rev.* **9**, 632 (1948)

R. F. Post, *Phys. Rev.* **79**, 735 (1950)

R. C. Sangster, *Tech. Rep. Electron.* Mass. Inst. Tech. No. 55 (1952)

R. Sherr, *Rev. Sci. Inst.* **18**, 767 (1947)

Taylor, Jentschke, Remley, Eby and Kruger, *Phys. Rev.* **84**, 1034 (1951)

Section II

Ageno, Chiozzetto, and Querzoli, *R. C. Accad. Lincei* **6**, 626 (1949)

I. Broser and H. Kallmann, *Annalen der Physik* **6**, 21 (1948)

Broser, Kallmann, and Warminsky, *Research* **2**, 87 (1949)

W. C. Elmore, *Nucleonics* **6**, 24 (1950)

Franzen, Peelle, and Sherr, *Phys. Rev.* **79**, 742 (1950)

G. F. J. Garlick and R. A. Fatehally, *Phys. Rev.* **75**, 1446 (1949)

Greenblatt, Green, Davidson, and Morton, *Nucleonics* **10/3**, 32 (1952)

L. Herforth and H. Kallmann, *Annalen der Physik* **6**, 231 (1949)

R. Hofstadter and J. A. McIntyre, *Phys. Rev.* **78**, 619 (1950)

H. Kallmann, *Phys. Rev.* **78**, 621 (1950)

R. M. Kloepper, *Rev. Sci. Inst.* **23**, 446 (1952)

C. O. Muehlhouse and G. E. Thomas, Jr., *Nucleonics* **11**, 44 (1953)

R. F. Post and L. I. Schiff, *Phys. Rev.* **80**, 1113L (1950)

Reynolds, Harrison, and Salvini, *Phys. Rev.* **78**, 488 (1950)

M. G. Schorr and F. L. Torney, *Phys. Rev.* **80**, 474 (1950)

R. K. Swank and W. L. Buck, *Phys. Rev.* **91**, 927 (1953)

Section III

Ageno, Chiozzetto, and Querzoli, *Phys. Rev.* **79**, 720 (1950)

Birks, *Scintillation Counters*, McGraw-Hill, New York (1953)

Bowen, *Chemical Aspects of Light*, Clarendon Press, Oxford (1946)
E. J. Bowen and A. H. Williams, *Trans. Faraday Soc.* **35**, 765 (1939)
Bowen, Mikiewicz, and Smith, *Proc. Phys. Soc.* **A62**, 26 (1949)
T. Förster, *Ann. d. Physik* **2**, 55 (1948)
J. Franck and E. Teller, *J. Chem. Phys.* **6**, 816 (1938)
J. Franck and R. Livingston, *Rev. Mod. Phys.* **21**, 505 (1949)
J. Frenkel, *Phys. Rev.* **37**, 17, 1276 (1931)
Furst and Kallmann, *Phys. Rev.* **85**, 816 (1950)
R. Hilsch, *Zeits. f. Physik* **44**, 860 (1927)
Kallmann and Furst, *Phys. Rev.* **79**, 857 (1950)
G. G. Kelley and M. Goodrich, *Phys. Rev.* **77**, 138 (1950)
Leverenz, *An Introduction to Luminescence of Solids*, Wiley, New York
    (1950)
S. H. Liebson, *Nucleonics* **10/3**, 35 (1952); **10/7**, 41 (1952)
S. H. Liebson and J. O. Elliot, *Phys. Rev.* **78**, 65 (1950)
W. von Meyeren, *Zeits. f. Physik* **61**, 329 (1930)
R. F. Post and N. S. Shiren, *Phys. Rev.* **78**, 80 (1950)
P. Pringsheim, *Fluorescence and Phosphorescence*, Interscience, New
    York (1949)
Riehl, *Physik und technische Anwendungen der Luminescenz*, Berlin
    (1941)
Riehl and Schön, *Zeit. f. Phys.* **114**, 682 (1939)
S. I. Vavilov, *Acta phys. pol.* **5**, 417 (1936)

APPENDIX A

CRYSTAL CONDUCTIVITY COUNTERS

Consider a crystal of any nonconducting solid substance, placed between two parallel plane electrodes, between which a difference of potential is maintained. The sides of the crystal are ground flat, so that good contact is established with the electrodes. Further, a current-sensitive device is assumed to be connected in the circuit with one of the electrodes. Ordinarily, such an arrangement shows little or no electrical conduction through the crystal. But if radiation is now allowed to impinge upon the crystal, "conductivity pulses" are observed.

In terms of our usual conceptions of solid matter, the conduction electrons inside the solid are held in local energy levels and are not free to migrate throughout a dielectric. However, if energy is supplied to them, they can be "kicked upstairs" into a conduction band and can then travel for relatively greater distances through the dielectric. Such energy can be supplied by the radiation which is allowed to impinge upon the crystal. The radiation may be electromagnetic quanta, or it may be charged particles, or in some cases even neutrons. In certain instances, electron avalanches may be formed.

The conductivity pulses are measurable by the same types of electronic circuits as are used in conventional gas-filled counters; they are found to be quite fast, often less than a microsecond in rise-time. The efficiency for gamma-detection is high, since the number of available electrons per cc is high. Many different kinds of dielectric crystals will serve, diamonds, CdS, Ag and Th halides and others having been tried successfully.

In some crystals, traps for electrons exist. In a diamond, for example, there are traps 0.25 to 0.75 volt in depth, into which the conductivity electrons will fall. In these traps, the electrons will constitute a space charge, and the crystal will polarize and be unable to detect further radiation. In certain cases, irradiating the crystal with light, the quantum energy of which is equal to or just slightly greater than the trap depth, will keep the electrons in the conduction bands and will tend to allow the space charge to dissipate rapidly.

The disadvantages of crystal counters are the comparatively small volume (often crystals are 2 mm thick and 5 × 5 mm in area); the cost (as in the case of diamonds); the experimental clumsiness (some crystals must be operated at liquid air temperatures to keep noise substantially below signal levels); and the slow counting rates due to crystal polarization. Against this is balanced the advantage of high gamma ray efficiency. Ideal applications therefore consist of measurements in narrow beams of gamma or X radiation of quite low intensity.

Since this type of counter is different in kind from gas-filled counters, and since an adequate discussion leads to extensive solid-state physics studies, and since counters of this kind lie somewhat outside of the scope of this book, we shall here merely list a few of the references, which any investigator interested in pursuing this subject can use as a starting point.

REFERENCES

A. J. Ahearn, *Phys. Rev.* **73,** 1113 (1948). Alpha and gamma pulses in diamonds.

A. G. Chynoweth, *Phys. Rev.* **76,** 310 (1949) and **83,** 254 (1951). Removal of space charge in diamonds.

L. F. Curtiss and B. W. Brown, *Phys. Rev.* **72,** 643 (1947). Diamonds.

H. Friedman, L. S. Birks and H. P. Gauvin, *Phys. Rev.* **73,** 186 (1948). Diamonds; ultraviolet transmission, etc.

G. J. Goldsmith and K. Lark-Horowitz, *Phys. Rev.* **75,** 526 (1949). Cadmium sulfide crystals; electrodes evap. gold; voltages 30 to

200; rise-time 0.2 microsec, studied pulses of alphas, betas and gammas.

R. Hofstadter, *Phys. Rev.* **73**, 631 (1948).   Diamonds of type II.

———, *Phys. Rev.* **72**, 1120 (1947).   TlBr or I.

———, J. C. D. Milton and S. L. Ridgeway, *Phys. Rev.* **72**, 977 (1947).   AgCl crystals.

———, *Nucleonics* **4**, 2, 29 (1949).   Review and summary.

J. R. Haynes, *Rev. Sci. Inst.* **19**, 51 (1948).   Prep. of AgCl crystals.

K. G. McKay, *Phys. Rev.* **76**, 1537 (1949).   Fast rise in germanium.

F. Seitz, *Phys. Rev.* **73**, 549 (1948).   Calc. of electron mobilities in nonpolar media; finds in diamond at room temp. about 156 cm^2/v sec.

K. A. Yamakawa, *Phys. Rev.* **82**, 522 (1951).   AgBr crystals.

APPENDIX B

REFERENCES

A1 R. K. Adair, *Revs. Mod. Phys.* **22**, 249 (1950)

A2 E. C. Anderson, W. F. Libby, S. Wienhouse, A. F. Reid, A. D. Kirschenbaum, and A. V. Crosse, *Phys. Rev.* **72**, 931 (1947)

A3 L. Alaoglu and N. M. Smith, Jr., *Phys. Rev.* **53**, 832 (1937)

B1 W. Bothe and H. Kolhorster, *Zeits. f. Phys.* **56**, 571 (1929)

B2 H. A. Bethe, *Revs. Mod. Phys.* **9**, 69 (1937)

B3 S. C. Brown, *Phys. Rev.* **62**, 244 (1942)

B4 S. C. Brown, L. A. Elliott and R. D. Evans, *Rev. Sci. Inst.* **13**, 147 (1942)

B5 H. Bateman, *Phil. Mag.* **20**, 704 (1910)

B6 G. Brubaker and E. Pollard, *Rev. Sci. Inst.* **8**, 254 (1937)

B7 J. G. Barry, *Rev. Sci. Inst.* **12**, 136 (1941)

B8 N. M. Blackman, *Rev. Sci. Inst.* **20**, 477 (1949)

B9 L. E. Beghian and H. H. Halban, *Proc. Phys. Soc. London* **A62**, 395 (1949)

B10 H. A. Bethe, *Revs. Mod. Phys.* **22**, 216 (1950)

B11 J. A. Bistline, *Rev. Sci. Inst.* **19**, 842 (1949)

B12 H. H. Barschall and H. A. Bethe, *Rev. Sci. Inst.* **18**, 147 (1948)

B13 W. Bernstein and R. Ballantine, *Rev. Sci. Inst.* **20**, 347 (1949)

B14 S. C. Brown and C. Maroni, *Rev. Sci. Inst.* **21**, 241 (1950)

B15 P. Bassi and E. Beretta, *Nuovo Cim.* **6**, 585 (1949)

B16 E. Beretta and A. Rostagni, *Nuovo Cim.* **6**, 391 (1949)

B17 H. Bradt *et al.*, *Helv. Phys. Acta* **19**, 77 (1946)

B18 G. Barrere, *J. Phys. Radium* **12**, 107 (1951)

B19 S. C. Brown and J. J. McCarthy, *Rev. Sci. Inst.* **19**, 851 (1948)

B20 D. Blanc and M. Scherer, *Comptes Rendus* **228**, 2018 (1949)

B21 S. C. Brown, W. M. Good, and R. D. Evans, *Rev. Sci. Inst.* **16**, 125 (1945)

B22 G. Borgren, *Ark. Math. Astr. Fys.* **36A**, 18 (1949)

B23 E. Berne, *Rev. Sci. Inst.* **22**, 509 (1951)

B24 Y. Beers, *Rev. Sci. Inst.* **13**, 72 (1942)

C1   A. H. Compton, E. O. Wollan and R. D. Bennett, *Rev. Sci. Inst.* **5**, 415 (1934)

C2   K. T. Compton and I. Langmuir, *Revs. Mod. Phys.* **2**, 191 (1930)

C3   M. Cosyns, *Bull. Tech. Ing. Ecole Polytech. Brux.* (1936)

C4   D. B. Cowie, *Phys. Rev.* **48**, 883 (1935)

C5   L. F. Curtiss, *Bur. of Stds. J. of Res.* **10**, 229 (1932)

C6   L. Colli, U. Faccini and E. Gatti, *Phys. Rev.* **80**, 92 (1950)

C7   J. H. Coon and R. A. Nobles, *Rev. Sci. Inst.* **18**, 44 (1947)

C8   J. H. Carter and G. K. White, *Nature* **163**, 526 (1949)

C9   B. Collinge, *Nature* **162**, 853 (1948)

C10   H. R. Crane, *Phys. Rev.* **75**, 985, 1268 (1949)

C11   M. Chaudhri, A. G. Fenton, and E. W. Fuller, *Proc. Phys. Soc.* **60**, 183 (1948); **62**, 32 (1949)

C12   R. Caillat, C. Lallement and G. Valdas, *J. Phys. Radium* **12**, 74 (1951)

C13   B. Collinge, *Proc. Phys. Soc. London* **B63**, 15 (1950)

C14   S. C. Curran and E. R. Rae, *Rev. Sci. Inst.* **18**, 871 (1947); *J. Sci. Inst.* **24**, 233 (1947)

C15   L. Colli, U. Faccini and E. Gatti, *Phys. Rev.* **84**, 606 (1951)

C16   J. D. Craggs and A. A. Jaffe, *Phys. Rev.* **72**, 784 (1947)

C17   S. C. Curran and J. M. Reid, *Rev. Sci. Inst.* **19**, 67 (1948)

C18   W. H. Chambers, *Rev. Sci. Inst.* **19**, 467 (1948)

C19   A. L. Cockroft and S. C. Curran, *Rev. Sci. Inst.* **22**, 37 (1951)

D1   K. K. Darrow, *Electrical Phenomena in Gases*, Williams and Wilkins (1932)

D2   W. E. Danforth, *Phys. Rev.* **46**, 1026 (1934)

D3   W. E. Danforth and W. E. Ramsey, *Phys. Rev.* **49**, 854 (1936)

D4   N. Davidson and A. E. Larsh, *Phys. Rev.* **74**, 220 (1948)

D5   M. J. Druyvesteyn and F. M. Penning, *Revs. Mod. Phys.* **12**, 87 (1940)

D6   P. J. G. de Vos and S. J. du Toit, *Rev. Sci. Inst.* **16**, 270 (1945)

D7   P. E. Damon, *Rev. Sci. Inst.* **22**, 587 (1951)

D8   O. S. Duffendack, H. Lifshutz, and M. Slawsky, *Phys. Rev.* **52**, 1231 (1937)

E1   W. H. Eccles and F. W. Jordan, *Radio Rev.* **1**, 143 (1919)

E2   R. D. Evans and R. E. Meagher, *Rev. Sci. Inst.* **10**, 339 (1939)

E3   L. G. Elliott and R. G. Bell, *Phys. Rev.* **74**, 1869 (1948)

E4   G. Ensell and S. D. Chatterjee, *Rev. Sci. Inst.* **22**, 700 (1951)

E5   A. G. Engelkemeier, W. H. Hamill, M. G. Inghram, and W. F. Libby, *Phys. Rev.* **75**, 1825 (1949)

E6   M. L. Eidinoff, *J. Am. Chem. Soc.* **69**, 2504 (1947)

F1 P. Frey, *Helv. Phys. Acta* **19**, 41 (1946)
F2 I. L. Fowler and P. R. Tunnicliffe, *Rev. Sci. Inst.* **21**, 734 (1950)
F3 S. S. Friedland, *Phys. Rev.* **74**, 898 (1948)
F4 E. C. Farmer and S. C. Brown, *Phys. Rev.* **74**, 902 (1948)
F5 S. S. Friedland and H. Katzenstein, *Phys. Rev.* **84**, 591 (1951)
F6 S. G. F. Frank, *Phil. Mag.* **42**, 612 (1951)

G1 H. Geiger, *Verh. d. D. Phys. Ges.* **15**, 534 (1913); *Phys. Zeits.* **14**, 1129 (1913)
G2 H. Geiger and E. Rutherford, *Phil. Mag.* **24**, 618 (1912)
G3 H. Geiger and W. Muller, *Phys. Zeits.* **29**, 839 (1928); **30**, 489 (1929)
G4 H. Geiger and O. Klemperer, *Zeits. f. Phys.* **49**, 753 (1928)
G5 K. Greisen and N. Nereson, *Phys. Rev.* **62**, 326 (1942)
G6 G. Glockler, *Proc. Nat. Acad. Sci.* **11**, 74 (1925)
G7 I. A. Getting, *Phys. Rev.* **53**, 103 (1938)
G8 H. H. Goldsmith, H. W. Ibser and B. T. Feld, *Revs. Mod. Phys.* **19**, 259 (1947)
G9 J. Geerk and H. Neuert, *Z. Naturforschung* **5**, 502 (1950)
G10 W. M. Good, *Rev. Sci. Inst.* **18**, 133 (1947)
G11 T. Graf, *Rev. Sci. Inst.* **21**, 285 (1950)
G12 J. Gittay, *Physica* **10**, 725 (1943)

H1 V. F. Hess and R. W. Lawson, *Wiener Ber.* **127**, 599 (1918)
H2 G. Herzog, *Rev. Sci. Inst.* **11**, 84 (1940)
H3 F. V. Hunt and R. W. Hickman, *Rev. Sci. Inst.* **10**, 6 (1939)
H4 R. D. Huntoon and L. J. Strohmeyer, *Rev. Sci. Inst.* **12**, 35 (1941)
H5 R. D. Huntoon, *Rev. Sci. Inst.* **10**, 176 (1939)
H6 W. E. Hazen, *Phys. Rev.* **63**, 107 (1943)
H7 F. L. Hereford, *Phys. Rev.* **77**, 559 (1950)
H8 C. G. Hanna, D. H. W. Kirkwood and B. Pontecorvo, *Phys. Rev.* **75**, 985 (1949)
H9 A. O. Hanson and J. L. McKibben, *Phys. Rev.* **72**, 673 (1947)
H10 H. den Hartog, F. A. Muller and N. F. Verster, *Physica* **13**, 521 (1947)
H11 P. Huber and F. Alder, *Helv. Phys. Acta* **18**, 232 (1945)
H12 D. E. Hull, *Rev. Sci. Inst.* **22**, 338 (1951)
H13 A. L. Hodson, A. Loria and N. V. Ryder, *Phil. Mag.* **41**, 826 (1950)

H14   P. Huber, F. Alder and E. Baldinger, *Helv. Phys. Acta* **19,** 207 (1946); **20,** 73 (1947)

H15   J. E. Hill and J. V. Dunworth, *Nature* **158,** 833 (1946)

H16   D. E. Hudson, *Rev. Sci. Inst.* **22,** 849 (1951)

H17   R. J. Hart, K. Russell and R. M. Steffen, *Phys. Rev.* **81,** 460 (1951)

H18   G. E. Hagen and D. H. Loughridge, *Phys. Rev.* **73,** 1131 (1948)

H19   K. Hashimoto, *J. Phys. Soc. Jap.* **3,** 151 (1948)

H20   C. P. Haigh, *Nature* **168,** 246 (1951)

H21   W. A. Higinbotham, J. Gallagher, and M. Sands, *Rev. Sci. Inst.* **18,** 706 (1947)

J1   T. H. Johnson, *Rev. Sci. Inst.* **9,** 218 (1938)

J2   T. H. Johnson and S. A. Korff, *Terr. Mag. & Atm. Elec.* **44,** 23 (1939)

J3   E. T. Jurney and F. Maienschien, *Rev. Sci. Inst.* **20,** 932 (1949)

J4   W. H. Jordan and P. R. Bell, *Rev. Sci. Inst.* **18,** 703 (1947)

K1   C. Kenty, *Phys. Rev.* **32,** 624 (1928)

K2   W. R. Kanne and J. A. Bearden, *Phys. Rev.* **50,** 935 (1936)

K3   S. A. Korff and W. E. Danforth, *Phys. Rev.* **55,** 980 (1939)

K4   S. A. Korff, *Revs. Mod. Phys.* **14,** 1 (1942)

K5   S. A. Korff and E. T. Clarke, *Phys. Rev.* **61,** 422 (1942)

K6   S. A. Korff and W. E. Danforth, *J. Franklin Inst.* **228,** 159 (1939)

K7   S. A. Korff and R. D. Present, *Phys. Rev.* **65,** 274 (1944)

K8   H. Kallmann and B. Rosen, *Zeits. f. Phys.* **61,** 61 (1930)

K9   S. A. Korff, W. Spatz and N. Hilberry, *Rev. Sci. Inst.* **13,** 127 (1942)

K10   S. A. Korff, *Proc. Am. Philos. Soc.* **84,** 589 (1941)

K11   S. A. Korff and W. E. Ramsey, *Rev. Sci. Inst.* **11,** 267 (1940); *Phys. Rev.* **68,** 53 (1945)

K12   M. Kupferberg, *Rev. Sci. Inst.* **14,** 254 (1943)

K13   J. W. Keuffel, *Rev. Sci. Inst.* **20,** 202 (1949)

K14   P. G. Koontz and T. A. Hall, *Rev. Sci. Inst.* **18,** 643 (1947)

K15   S. A. Korff, *Phys. Rev.* **68,** 53 (1945)

K16   S. A. Korff and A. D. Krumbein, *Phys. Rev.* **76,** 1412 (1949)

K17   A. D. Krumbein, *Rev. Sci. Inst.* **22,** 821 (1951)

K18   L. Koster, *Physica* **10,** 749 (1943)

K19   J. D. Kurbatov and H. E. Mann, *Phys. Rev.* **68,** 40 (1945)

K20   T. P. Kohman, *Phys. Rev.* **72,** 181 (1947)

L1   L. B. Loeb, *Fundamental Processes of Electrical Discharges in Gases*, Wiley, 1939

L2   G. L. Locher, *Phys. Rev.* **55**, 675A (1939)

L3   H. Lifschutz and J. L. Lawson, *Rev. Sci. Inst.* **9**, 83 (1938); **10**, 21 (1939)

L4   W. B. Lewis, *Electrical Counting*, Cambridge, 1942

L5   W. F. Libby, *Phys. Rev.* **55**, 245 (1939)

L6   R. D. Lowde, *Rev. Sci. Inst.* **21**, 835 (1950)

L7   H. Lauterjung and H. Neuert, *Zeits. f. Phys.* **122**, 266 (1944); *Naturwiss.* **34**, 120 (1947)

L8   S. H. Liebson and H. Friedman, *Rev. Sci. Inst.* **19**, 303 (1948)

L9   K. E. Larsson and C. Taylor, *Ark. Fys.* **3**, 131 (1951)

L10 D. H. LaCroisette and J. Yarwood, *J. Sci. Inst.* **28**, 225 (1951)

L11 J. Labeyrie, *J. Phys. Radium* **12**, 569 (1951)

L12 A. Laufer, *Rev. Sci. Inst.* **21**, 244 (1950)

L13 W. R. Loosemore and J. S. Sharpe, *Nature* **167**, 600 (1951)

L14 J. D. Louw and S. M. Naude, *Phys. Rev.* **76**, 571 (1949)

L15 W. F. Libby and D. D. Lee, *Phys. Rev.* **55**, 245 (1939) also W. F. Libby, et al., *Rev. Sci. Inst.* **22**, 225 (1951)

L16 D. A. Lind, *Rev. Sci. Inst.* **21**, 285 (1950)

L17 R. L. Loevinger and M. Berman, *Nucleonics* **9**, No. 1, 72 (1942)

L18 C. Levert and W. L. Scheen, *Physica* **10**, 225 (1943)

M1   C. G. and D. D. Montgomery, *J. Franklin Inst.* **231**, 447 (1941)

M2   R. A. Millikan and H. V. Neher, *Phys. Rev.* **50**, 15 (1936)

M3   C. G. and D. D. Montgomery, *Phys. Rev.* **57**, 1030 (1940)

M4   H. S. W. Massey, *Proc. Camb. Phil. Soc.* **26**, 386 (1930)

M5   C. G. and D. D. Montgomery, *Rev. Sci. Inst.* **11**, 237 (1940)

M6   H. P. Manning and V. J. Young, *Rev. Sci. Inst.* **13**, 234 (1942)

M7   L. Madansky and R. W. Pidd, *Rev. Sci. Inst.* **21**, 407 (1950); *Phys. Rev.* **75**, 1178 (1950)

M8   L. V. McCarty, J. K. Bragg and F. J. Norton, *Science* **112**, 425 (1950)

M9   C. D. Moak and J. T. W. Dabbs, *Phys. Rev.* **75**, 1770 (1949)

M10 W. W. Miller, *Science* **105**, 123 (1947)

M11 C. E. Mandeville and M. V. Scherb, *Phys. Rev.* **73**, 90 (1948)

M13 H. K. Morgenstern, C. L. Cowan and A. L. Hughes, *Phys. Rev.* **74**, 499 (1950)

M14 R. Maze, *J. Phys. Radium* **7**, 164 (1946)

M15 C. E. Mandeville and M. V. Scherb, *Nucleonics* **7**, 34 (1950)

M16 H. Maier-Leibnitz, *Zeits. f. Naturforsch.* **1**, 243 (1946)

M17 C. G. Montgomery and D. D. Montgomery, *Rev. Sci. Inst.*
18, 411 (1947)

M18 C. G. Montgomery, *Tech. Report #2*, Sloane Phys. Lab., Yale
Univ., Oct. 15, 1949

M19 N. Marty, *J. Phys. Radium* **8,** 29 (1947)

M20 C. O. Muelhause and H. Friedman, *Rev. Sci. Inst.* **17,** 506
(1946)

N1 H. V. Neher and W. H. Pickering, *Phys. Rev.* **53,** 316 (1938)

N2 H. V. Neher and W. W. Harper, *Phys. Rev.* **49,** 940 (1936)

N3 H. V. Neher and W. H. Pickering, *Rev. Sci. Inst.* **12,** 140 (1941)

N4 A. Nawijn, *Physica* **9,** 481 (1942); **10,** 513, 531 (1943)

N5 H. Neuert and J. Geerk, *Ann. d. Phys.* **6,** 93 (1950); *Zeits. f.
Naturforsch.* **5,** 231 (1950)

N6 L. D. Novis and M. G. Inghram, *Phys. Rev.* **70,** 772 (1946)

N7 H. E. Newell, *Rev. Sci. Inst.* **19,** 384 (1948); Newell and
E. C. Pressly, *Rev. Sci. Inst.* **20,** 568 (1949)

N8 I. Nonaka and Z. Shimazu, *J. Phys. Soc. Jap.* **5,** 283 (1950)

O1 M. L. E. Oliphant and P. B. Moon, *Proc. Roy. Soc. A* **127,**
388 (1930)

P1 T. P. Pepper, *Rev. Sci. Inst.* **20,** 222 (1949)

P2 R. D. Present, *Phys. Rev.* **72,** 243 (1947)

P3 O. Parkash and P. L. Kapur, *Phys. Rev.* **76,** 569 (1949); *Proc.
Phys. Soc. Lond. A* **63,** 457 (1950)

P4 H. Paetow, *Zeits. f. Phys.* **111,** 770 (1939)

P5 H. Palevesky, R. K. Swank and R. Grenchik, *Rev. Sci. Inst.*
18, 298 (1947)

P6 W. C. Peacock, W. M. Good, A. Kip and S. Brown, *Rev. Sci.
Inst.* **17,** 255, 262 (1946)

P7 R. I. Purbrick, L. T. Cherry, and J. F. Carpenter, *Rev. Sci.
Inst.* **22,** 482 (1951)

Q1 A. A. Quaranta, L. Mezetti, E. Pancini and G. Stoppini, *Nuovo
Cim.* **8,** 618 (1951)

R1 E. Rutherford and H. Geiger, *Proc. Roy. Soc. A* **81,** 141 (1908)

R2 B. Rossi, *Nuovo Cim.* **8,** 49 and 85 (1931); *Zeits. f. Phys.* **68,**
64 (1931); *Proc. Lond. Conf. Nuc. Phys.* (1934); *Acad.
Lencei Atti* **13,** 47 and 600 (1931)

R3 M. E. Rose and S. A. Korff, *Phys. Rev.* **59,** 850 (1941)

R4 M. E. Rose and W. E. Ramsey, *Phys. Rev.* **61,** 198 (1942)

R5   W. E. Ramsey, *Phys. Rev.* **57**, 1022 and 1061 (1940)
R6   G. K. Rollefson and M. Burton, *Photochemistry*, Prentice-Hall (1939)
R7   R. B. Roberts, *Rev. Sci. Inst.* **9**, 98 (1938)
R8   W. E. Ramsey, *Phys. Rev.* **57**, 1061 (1940)
R9   B. Rossi and H. Staub, *Ionization Chambers and Counters*, McGraw-Hill (1949)
R10 B. Rossi and N. Nereson, *LADC* 148
R11 B. Rossi and N. Nereson, *Phys. Rev.* **62**, 417 (1942)
R12 G. D. Rochester and C. B. A. McCusker, *Nature* **156**, 366 (1945)
R13 V. H. Regener, *Rev. Sci. Inst.* **8**, 267 (1947)
R14 C. V. Robinson and R. E. Peterson, *Rev. Sci. Inst.* **19**, 911 (1948)
R15 C. H. Raeth, B. J. Sevold, and C. N. Pederson, *Rev. Sci. Inst.* **22**, 461 (1951)
R16 L. J. Rainwater and C. S. Wu, *Nucleonics* **1**, No. 2, 60 (1947), and **2**, 42 (1948)
R17 A. E. Ruark and F. E. Brammer, *Phys. Rev.* **52**, 322 (1937)

S1   W. D. B. Spatz, *Phys. Rev.* **64**, 236 (1943)
S2   W. F. G. Swann, *J. Franklin Inst.* **216**, 559 (1933); **230**, 281 (1940)
S3   H. G. Stever, *Phys. Rev.* **61**, 38 (1942)
S4   J. A. Simpson, *Phys. Rev.* **662**, 39 (1944)
S5   J. A. Simpson, *Rev. Sci. Inst.* **15**, 119 (1944)
S6   W. D. B. Spatz, Private communication
S7   J. A. Simpson, Private communication
S8   H. K. Skramstad and D. H. Loughridge, *Phys. Rev.* **50**, 677 (1936)
S9   L. I. Schiff and R. D. Evans, *Rev. Sci. Inst.* **7**, 456 (1936)
S10 R. Sherr and R. Peterson, *Rev. Sci. Inst.* **18**, 567 (1947)
S11 E. Segré and C. Wiegand, *Rev. Sci. Inst.* **18**, 86 (1947)
S12 A. Stebler, P. Huber and H. Sichsel, *Helv. Phys. Acta* **22**, 362 (1949)
S13 J. A. Simpson, *Rev. Sci. Inst.* **18**, 884 (1947); **19**, 733 (1948)
S14 C. W. Sherwin, *Rev. Sci. Inst.* **19**, 111 (1948)
S15 L. Shepard, *Rev. Sci. Inst.* **20**, 217 (1949)
S16 J. A. Simpson, *Rev. Sci. Inst.* **21**, 558 (1950)
S17 L. G. Shore, *Rev. Sci. Inst.* **20**, 956 (1949)
S18 H. D. Smythe and E. C. G. Stueckleberg, *Phys. Rev.* **36**, 472 (1930)

S19   H. Saltzman and C. G. Montgomery, *Rev. Sci. Inst.* **21,** 548 (1950)

S20   P. H. Smith, *Rev. Sci. Inst.* **18,** 453 (1949)

S21   M. Suffczynski, *Acta Phys. Polon.* **10,** 270 (1951)

S22   M. H. Shamos and I. Hudes, *Rev. Sci. Inst.* **18,** 586 (1947)

S23   M. V. Scherb, *Phys. Rev.* **73,** 86 (1948)

S24   E. Strajman et al., *Rev. Sci. Inst.* **17,** 232 (1946); *Science* **107,** 71 (1948)

S25   H. Saltis, *Rev. Sci. Inst.* **20,** 353 (1949), and *Ark. Math. Astr. Fys.* **36A,** 17 (1949)

S26   S. M. Skinner, *Phys. Rev.* **48,** 438 (1935)

S27   L. I. Schiff, *Phys. Rev.* **50,** 88 (1936)

T1   M. A. Tuve, *Phys. Rev.* **35,** 651 (1930)

T2   A. Trost, *Zeits. f. Phys.* **105,** 399 (1937)

T3   C. D. Thomas, *Rev. Sci. Inst.* **20,** 147 (1949)

T4   H. Tellez-Plasencia, *J. Phys. Radium* **12,** 89 (1951)

V1   A. G. M. Van Gemert, H. den Hartog and F. A. Muller, *Physica* **9,** 556 (1942)

V2   F. Van Hecke, *Ann. Soc. Sci. Brux.* **60,** 224 (1946)

V3   H. Volz, *Zeits. f. Phys.* **93,** 539 (1935)

W1   S. Werner, *Zeits. f. Phys.* **90,** 384 (1934); **92,** 705 (1934)

W2   M. H. Wilkening and W. R. Kanne, *Phys. Rev.* **62,** 534 (1942)

W3   C. E. Wynn-Williams, *Brit. Pat.* No. 421341

W4   C. E. Wynn-Williams, *Proc. Roy. Soc. A* **136,** 312 (1932)

W5   P. Weisz, *Electronics* **17,** 108 (1944)

W6   R. Wilson, et al., *Rev. Sci. Inst.* **20,** 699 (1950)

W7   D. Willard and C. G. Montgomery, *Rev. Sci. Inst.* **21,** 520 (1950)

W8   P. Weisz, *Phys. Rev.* **74,** 1807 (1948)

W9   P. Weisz and W. P. Kern, *Phys. Rev.* **75,** 899 (1949)

W10   P. Weisz, Private communication

W11   E. Wantuch, *Phys. Rev.* **71,** 646 (1947)

W12   A. Witten, to appear shortly

W13   M. L. Wiedenbeck, *Rev. Sci. Inst.* **17,** 35 (1946)

ADDITIONAL BIBLIOGRAPHY ON COUNTERS NOT SPECIFICALLY REFERRED TO IN THE TEXT

J. S. Allan and T. U. Alvarez, *Rev. Sci. Inst.* **6,** 329 (1936)

H. Aoki, A. Narimatu and M. Scotani, *Proc. Phys-Math. Soc.* Japan **22**, 746–749 (1940)

Y. Beers, *Rev. Sci. Inst.* **13**, 72 (1942)

R. D. Bennett, J. C. Stearns and W. P. Overbeck, *Rev. Sci. Inst.* **4**, 387 (1933)

G. Bernadini, D. Bocciarelli and F. Oppenheimer, *Rev. Sci. Inst.* **7**, 382 (1936)

W. Bothe, *Zeits. f. Phys.* **59**, 1 (1929)

W. C. Bosch, *Rev. Sci. Inst.* **9**, 308 (1938)

F. Burger-Scheidlin, *Ann. Physik* **12**, 283–304 (1932)

A. W. Coven, *Rev. Sci. Inst.* **9**, 188, 230 (1938); **13**, 230 (1942)

J. D. Craggs, *Proc. Lond. Phys. Soc.* **9**, 137 (1942)

J. D. Craggs, *Nature*, **148**, 661 (1941)

J. D. Craggs and J. F. Smee, *Brit. J. Radiol.* **15**, 228 (1942)

S. C. Curran and V. Petrzilka, *Proc. Camb. Phys. Soc.* **35**, 309 (1939)

S. C. Curran and J. E. Strothers, *Proc. Camb. Phil. Soc.* **35**, 654 (1939)

L. F. Curtiss, *Bur. of Stds. J. of Res.* **4**, 5, 115–123, 593, 601–608 (1930)

L. R. Cuykendall, *Rev. Sci. Inst.* **4**, 676 (1933)

W. E. Danforth and W. E. Ramsey, *Phys. Rev.* **49**, 854 (1936)

W. E. Danforth, *Phys. Rev.* **46**, 1026 (1934)

D. DeVault, *Rev. Sci. Inst.* **12**, 83 (1941)

W. U. Dittrich, *Phys.* **41**, 256–269 (1940)

G. F. VonDroste, *Zeits. f. Phys.* **100**, 529 (1936)

R. L. Driscoll, M. W. Hodge and A. Ruark, *Rev. Sci. Inst.* **11**, 241 (1940)

O. S. Duffendack and W. E. Morriss, *Rev. Sci. Inst.* **6**, 243 (1935)

O. S. Duffendack, H. Lipschutz and M. Slawsky, *Phys. Rev.* **52**, 1231 (1937)

J. Dunning and S. M. Skinner, *Rev. Sci. Inst.* **6**, 243 (1935)

J. V. Dunworth, *Rev. Sci. Inst.* **11**, 167 (1940)

A. Eisenstein and N. S. Gingrich, *Rev. Sci. Inst.* **12**, 582 (1941)

A. Eisenstein and N. S. Gingrich, *Phys. Rev.* **61**, 104 and **62**, 296 (1942)

R. D. Evans and R. A. Mugele, *Rev. Sci. Inst.* **7**, 441 (1936)

R. D. Evans and R. L. Alder, *Rev. Sci. Inst.* **10**, 332 (1939)

R. D. Evans and R. E. Meagher, *Rev. Sci. Inst.* **10**, 339 (1939)

N. Feather and J. V. Dunworth, *Proc. Roy. Soc. A* **168**, 566 (1938)

H. Geiger, *Zeits. f. Phys.* **27**, 7 (1924)

J. Giarratana, *Rev. Sci. Inst.* **8**, 390 (1937)

H. Greinacher, *Zeits. f. Phys.* **23**, 371 (1924)

E. Greiner, *Zeits. f. Phys.* **81**, 543 (1933)

R. W. Gurney, *Proc. Roy. Soc. A* **107**, 332 (1925)
C. L. Haines, *Rev. Sci. Inst.* **7**, 411 (1936)
J. Halpern and O. C. Simpson, *Rev. Sci. Inst.* **8**, 172 (1937)
W. E. Hazen, *Phys. Rev.* **63**, 107 (1943)
A. von Hippel, *Zeits. f. Phys.* **97**, 455 (1936)
M. G. Holloway and M. S. Livingston, *Phys. Rev.* **54**, 18 (1936)
D. E. Hull, *Rev. Sci. Inst.* **11**, 404 (1940)
H. Hupperstberger, *Zeits. f. Phys.* **75**, 231 (1932)
R. Jaiger and J. Kluge, *Z. Instrumentchk* **52**, 229–232 (1932)
L. Janossy and R. Ingleby, *J. Sci. Inst.* **19**, 30–31 (1942)
Joneson, *Zeits. f. Phys.* **36**, 6, 426 (1926)
D. L. Jorgensen, *Rev. Sci. Inst.* **10**, 34 (1939)
O. W. Kenrick, *Electronics* **14**, 33–35, 74–76 (1941)
D. W. Kerst, *Rev. Sci. Inst.* **9**, 151 (1938)
W. Kolhorster and E. Weber, *Phys. Zeits.* **42**, 13 (1941)
S. A. Korff, *Phys. Rev.* **56**, 1241 (1939)
W. Kutzner, *Zeits. f. Phys.* **23**, 117 (1924)
L. M. Langer and R. T. Cox, *Rev. Sci. Inst.* **7**, 31 (1936)
D. P. LeGalley, *Rev. Sci. Inst.* **6**, 279 (1935)
W. F. Libby, D. D. Lee and S. Ruben, *Rev. Sci. Inst.* **8**, 38 (1937)
G. L. Locher, *J. Franklin Inst.* **216**, 553–556 (1933)
G. L. Locher and D. P. LeGalley, *Phys. Rev.* **46**, 1047 (1934)
G. L. Locher, *Phys. Rev.* **42**, 525 (1932); **50**, 1099 (1936)
L. B. Loeb, *Phys. Rev.* **48**, 684 (1935)
A. N. May, *Proc. Lond. Phys. Soc.* **51**, 26 (1939)
H. A. C. McKay, *Rev. Sci. Inst.* **12**, 103 (1941)
H. McMaster and M. L. Pool, *Rev. Sci. Inst.* **11**, 196 (1940)
G. Medicus, *Zeits. f. Phys.* **74**, 350 (1932)
G. Medicus, *Zeits. f. Phys.* **103**, 76 (1936)
C. G. Montgomery, D. B. Cowie, W. E. Ramsey and D. D. Montgomery, *Phys. Rev.* **56**, 635 (1939)
C. G. Montgomery, D. D. Montgomery, *J. Franklin Inst.* **229**, 585 (1940)
C. G. and D. D. Montgomery, *Phys. Rev.* **59**, 1045 (1941)
J. C. Mouzon, *Rev. Sci. Inst.* **7**, 467 (1936)
G. J. Neary, *Proc. Roy. Soc.* **175**, 71 (1940)
F. Norling, *Phys. Rev.* **58**, 277 (1940)
H. Paetow, *Zeits. f. Phys.* **111**, 770 (1939)
A. A. Petrankas and D. L. Northrup, *Rev. Sci. Inst.* **11**, 298 (1940)
W. E. Ramsey and M. R. Lipman, *Rev. Sci. Inst.* **6**, 121 (1935)
W. E. Ramsey, *Phys. Rev.* **58**, 1176 (1940)

W. E. Ramsey, E. Hudspeth and W. L. Lees, *Phys. Rev.* **59**, 685 (1941)
W. E. Ramsey and W. L. Lees, *Phys. Rev.* **60**, 411 (1941)
W. E. Ramsey and E. L. Hudspeth, *Phys. Rev.* **61**, 95–96 (1942)
W. E. Ramsey, *Phys. Rev.* **61**, 95–96 (1942)
W. E. Ramsey and W. E. Danforth, *Phys. Rev.* **51**, 1105 (1937)
H. J. Reich, *Rev. Sci. Inst.* **9**, 222 (1938)
A. Roberts, *Phys. Rev.* **57**, 564, 1069 (1940)
A. Roberts, *Rev. Sci. Inst.* **12**, 71 (1941)
G. D. Rochester and L. Janossy, *Phys. Rev.* **63**, 52 (1943)
M. E. Rose and W. E. Ramsey, *Phys. Rev.* **61**, 504–509 (1942)
E. Rutherford and H. Geiger, *Phil. Mag.* **24**, 618 (1912)
M. D. Santos, *Phys. Rev.* **62**, 178–179 (1942)
L. I. Schiff and A. D. Evans, *Rev. Sci. Inst.* **7**, 456 (1936)
J. Schintlmeister and W. Czulius, *Phys. Z.* **41**, 269–271 (1940)
J. E. Schrader, *Phys. Rev.* **6**, 292 (1915)
H. G. Stever, *Phys. Rev.* **59**, 765 (1941)
J. C. Street and R. H. Woodward, *Phys. Rev.* **56**, 1029 (1934)
H. M. Sullivan, *Rev. Sci. Inst.* **11**, 356 (1940)
W. F. Swann and G. L. Locher, *J. Franklin Inst.* **121**, 275 (1936)
R. B. Taft, *Rev. Sci. Inst.* **8**, 508 (1937)
R. B. Taft, *Rev. Sci. Inst.* **11**, 63 (1940)
J. Taylor, *Proc. Camb. Phil. Soc.* **24**, 251 (1928)
A. Trost, *Phys. Z.* **36**, 801 (1935)
J. A. Van Den Akker, *Rev. Sci. Inst.* **1**, 672 (1930)
E. Vickers and C. P. Saylor, *Rev. Sci. Inst.* **10**, 245 (1939)
J. C. Wang, J. F. Marvin and K. W. Stenstrom, *Rev. Sci. Inst.* **13**, 81 (1942)
E. Weber, *Phys. Z.* **41**, 242–256 (1940)
H. C. Webster, *Proc. Camb. Phil. Soc.* **28**, 121–123 (1932)
P. Weisz, *Phys. Rev.* **61**, 392; **62**, 477 (1942)
P. Weisz and W. E. Ramsey, *Rev. Sci. Inst.* **13**, 258–264 (1942)
J. Zeleny, *Phys. Rev.* **24**, 255 (1924)

APPENDIX C

EQUIPMENT AND SUPPLIES

Voltage regulators for stabilizing AC are made by:
Raytheon Mfg. Co., Waltham, Massachusetts
Sola Electric Co., Chicago, Illinois
Copper tubes for counter cylinders are made by:
Improved Seamless Wire Co., 775 Eddy St., Providence, Rhode Island
Glass for counters is manufactured by:
Corning Glass Works, Corning, New York
Metal-to-glass seals are made by:
Stupakoff Laboratories, Pittsburgh, Pennsylvania
Electronic voltage stabilizers are made by:
RCA Manufacturing Co.
Harvey Radio Lab., 444 Concord Ave., Cambridge 38, Massachusetts
Counters, shields and associated apparatus are made by:
Alltools, Ltd., Brentford, Middlesex, England
Anton Electronic Corp., 1226 Flushing Ave., Brooklyn 6, New York
Berkeley Scientific Co., 1908 Alcatraz Ave., Berkeley 3, California
Geophysical Instrument Co., Arlington, Virginia
Herbach & Rademan, 522 Market St., Philadelphia 6, Pennsylvania
Kelley-Koett Instrument Co., 930 York St., Cincinnati 14, Ohio
North American Philips Co., 100 East 42nd St., New York 17, New York
Nuclear Research Corp., 112 South 16th St., Philadelphia 2, Pennsylvania
Radiation Counter Labs., Inc., 1846 West 21st St., Chicago 8, Illinois
Raytheon Mfg. Co., 55 Chapel St., Newtown 58, Massachusetts
Research Equipment & Service, Inc., 6054 Woodlawn Ave., Chicago 37, Illinois

Technical Associates, 3728 San Fernando Rd., Glendale 4, California

Tracerlab, Inc., 130 High St., Boston 10, Massachusetts

Victoreen Co., 5806 Hough Ave., Cleveland 3, Ohio

Electronic circuitry, scalers, power supplies, etc., are made by:

Atomic Instrument Co., 160 Charles St., Boston 14, Massachusetts

Atomlab, Inc., 489 Fifth Ave., New York 17, New York

Beta Electronics Co., 1762 3rd Ave., New York 29, New York

Central Scientific Co., 1700 Irving Park Road, Chicago 13, Illinois

Hewlett Packard Co., 20571 Page Mill Road, Palo Alto, California

Kepco Laboratories, 142–45 Roosevelt Ave., Flushing, L. I., New York

Instrument Development Labs., 817 East 55th St., Chicago, Illinois

Lambda Electronics Co., Corona, L. I., New York

Nuclear Instrument & Chemical Co., 239 West Erie St., Chicago 10, Illinois

Potter Instrument Co., 115 Cutter Mill Road, Great Neck, L. I., New York

Standard Electric Time Co., Springfield 2, Massachusetts

Cathode ray oscilloscopes are manufactured by:

Browning Labs., Winchester, Massachusetts

Allen B. DuMont Co., Passaic, New Jersey

Heiland Research Co., 131 E. Fifth Ave., Denver, Colorado

Radio Corp. of America, Camden, New Jersey

Tektronix Co., 712 E. Hawthorne Blvd., Portland 14, Oregon

Professional glassblowers:

Eck & Krebs, 27–09 40th Ave., Long Island City, New York

Herman Luthner, 200–10 28th Ave., Bayside, L. I., New York

Mechanical impulse registers are made by:

Cyclotron Specialties Co., Moraga 5, California

Streeter-Amet Co., 4101 Ravenswood Ave., Chicago 13, Illinois

Edgerton lamps:

Edgerton, Germhausen & Grier, Inc., 160 Brookline Ave., Boston 15, Massachusetts

Inert gases:

Linde Air Products Co., 30 East 42nd St., New York 17, New York

Radioactive substances:

Canadian Radium & Uranium Corp., 630 Fifth Ave., New York 20, New York

Eldorado Mining & Refining Co., Ltd., P. O. Box 379, Ottawa, Ont., Canada

U. S. Radium Corp., 535 Pearl Street, New York 5, New York

Isotopes, etc.:

Isotopes Division, United States Atomic Energy Commission, Oak Ridge, Tennessee

AUTHOR INDEX

SUBJECT INDEX